BIBLIOGRAPHY OF BASIC TEXTS AND MONOGRAPHS ON STATISTICAL METHODS

1945-1960

BIBLIOGRAPHY OF BASIC TEXTS AND MONOGRAPHS ON STATISTICAL METHODS

1945-1960

WILLIAM R. BUCKLAND

AND

RONALD A. FOX

Published for
The International Statistical Institute

BY

HAFNER PUBLISHING COMPANY

NEW YORK

Published in Great Britain for
The International Statistical Institute by Oliver and Boyd Ltd.
Edinburgh and London, 1963

First published (ISI edition, The Hague) 1951
Second edition 1963

© 1963, The International Statistical Institute

PRINTED IN GREAT BRITAIN BY
OLIVER AND BOYD LTD., EDINBURGH

INTRODUCTION

In 1949 the International Statistical Institute introduced a programme of International Statistical Education. The programme, sponsored by UNESCO and supported financially by this and other organisations, is under the general direction of the Institute's Statistical Education Committee (Chairman: Professor Gertrude M. Cox). One part of the programme is concerned with the preparation of aids to teaching and research, including special bibliographies. The first of these bibliographies, originally published in 1951, now appears in a second edition considerably revised and enlarged. This new edition has been compiled by Ronald A. Fox, Research Associate working in London under the direction of William R. Buckland, a member of the Institute. Although this bibliography is issued in furtherance of the programme of international statistical education, full responsibility for the selection of material rests with the compilers and for this reason their names are inscribed on the title page.

With the rapid growth of statistical literature in book form, some selection was inevitable. Where a balanced set of reviews was available the problem was less difficult but even then it would be quite possible to nominate equivalent entries for some of these chosen. For the more recent books where review material was incomplete or non-existent at the time of going to press, a select list of titles has been given at the end of this edition. This was a more difficult process if only because of the uncertainty that information was complete. However, these entries will come up for review in due course and appropriate arrangements are being made to keep this project on a current basis.

The bibliography now consists of just over 190 entries devoted to basic texts and monographs in the English language on statistical methods and their applications. The items have been selected mainly from the literature of the fifteen years to 1960 but include some earlier works of outstanding importance. No select bibliography can ever hope to meet all tastes, but it is believed that the works included give an all-round coverage of both the theory and the main fields of application for statistical methods. Each work has, at one time or another, been used by the compilers and one of the criteria of selection from a much longer first list was the practical usefulness of a book. It is hoped that the titles included in this bibliography will afford the means for students, teachers and practising statisticians to review their acquaintance with recent and current non-periodical literature in this field.

The general form of each entry is the routine publication details followed by a list of chapter headings and extracts from reviews: appendices are mentioned only where they take the form of additional text. It was decided to omit information on prices in this edition because of the transient nature of such figures. The review extracts have been taken from 20 main statistical and allied journals published in English which include a regular book review section: only four original journals were used in the edition. These journals are listed at the end together with suitably contracted titles. A list is also given of the relevant publishing houses and their addresses. By this means it is hoped that readers will be able to gain a better appreciation of work than is possible from the mere publication details. The extracts from reviews have been selected with a view to showing the general characteristics of a book rather than points of detail. The decision to restrict the coverage of journals was made for purely practical reasons: it has inevitably resulted in some gaps. These can be filled by readers by reference to journals both in other languages and of a more specialised nature according to their particular interests.

The titles have been classified in greater detail than in the first edition and within the thirteen groups as shown on the Contents page the titles are arranged alphabetically by author. Some classification is clearly desirable, and, just as the selection of titles for inclusion will fail to please all, so will some readers have chosen a different basis for classification and allocation of titles. Problems such as these do not admit of a unique solution and it is more important to produce something for use rather than expend time in seeking such a solution. However, the Statistical Education Committee and the compilers would appreciate the views and comments of those who use this Bibliography in order to aid the preparation of future editions or supplements which may become necessary from time to time.

LONDON, S.W. 1
February, 1963

CONTENTS

INTRODUCTION	v
GENERAL INTRODUCTORY TEXTS	
Elementary	1
Intermediate	27
Advanced	41
MATHEMATICAL STATISTICS	
General Texts	61
Special Topics	92
PROBABILITY AND STOCHASTIC PROCESSES	130
SAMPLE SURVEYS: THEORY AND PRACTICE	163
DESIGN OF EXPERIMENTS	190
QUALITY CONTROL AND INSPECTION	210
ECONOMETRICS, TIME SERIES AND INDEX NUMBERS	223
STATISTICAL DECISION AND INFORMATION THEORY	236
DEMOGRAPHY, BIOMETRY AND MEDICAL STATISTICS	248
MISCELLANEOUS APPLICATION OF STATISTICAL METHODS	268
LIST OF JOURNALS CONSULTED FOR REVIEW MATERIAL	285
LIST OF PUBLISHING HOUSES AND ADDRESSES	286
SUPPLEMENTARY LIST OF BOOK TITLES (1960-62)	289
INDEX OF AUTHORS FOR BOOKS IN TEXT	295

GENERAL INTRODUCTORY TEXTS

ELEMENTARY

ALLEN, R. G. D. *STATISTICS FOR ECONOMISTS*
   1957. 3rd Ed., Hutchinson's University Library, vii+216 pp.

Chapter	Contents
1	The Raw Material
2	Sources of Published Statistics
3	Graphs and Diagrams
4	Derived Statistics
5	Frequency Distributions
6	Index Numbers
7	Correlation
8	Time Series
9	Sampling and Significance

Review of 1st Ed.:
Inc. Statist., 1950, **1**, 27.
   " . . . it is clear that this volume will appeal not merely to economists but to a wider field of general readers and to all students instructed in the subject. . . . As often happens with introductory text-books there may be differences of opinion about the manner of exposition and the space devoted to the various branches of the subject. More space might perhaps have been devoted to sampling and a little less to some of the other topics covered. . . . But there can be no difference of opinion about the value of the book as a whole: it is, in these days of inflated prices, an unusually cheap text-book which should prove valuable if not indispensable to every student of statistics."

Reviews of 2nd Ed.:
Econometrica, 1952, **20**, 513.
   " This book presents, at a distinctly introductory level, many of the statistical ideas and methods useful in economics. . . . The

distinct merit of the book is the quality of its exposition which is of the very high order Professor Allen has led us to expect. Explicit examples are worked in most sections; and the device of utilizing, in these examples, data arranged in an appendix of some fourteen tables seems most effective. . . . Apart from the delay in emphasis on the fundamental position of sampling theory in statistics, the very excellence of the treatment of the topics causes the reader to regret that Allen chose to write merely an introduction rather than a more extended volume."

J. R. Statist. Soc. A, 1949, **112**, 338.

" . . . Professor Allen lucidly explains those few and elementary statistical methods an understanding of which is almost indispensable for students of economics, even when they do not specialize in economic statistics . . . almost abolished algebra from his book by using in its place numerical examples and charts wherever possible. In explaining the meaning of a technical term he aims at suggestive and homely phrases that will stick in the memory, rather than at pedantic accuracy. For this reason the book is not altogether suitable for the critical student with some training in mathematical rigour who is prepared to go deeper into the subject . . . [this is not to] imply any serious criticism of the book's excellence for the purpose for which it is intended."

Sankhyā, 1950, **10**, 162.

" This is an elementary but useful book on economic statistics . . . written in a clear and lucid manner and makes interesting reading . . . A short reading list at the end will benefit those who are interested in further study of the subject. . . . "

BOWLEY A. L. *AN ELEMENTARY MANUAL OF STATISTICS* 1951. 7th Ed., Macdonald and Evans, ix+297 pp.

Chapter	Contents
	Part I
1	Nature and Use of Statistics
2	Accuracy and Approximation

3	Averages
4	The Accuracy of Averaging and other Arithmetical Procedures
5	Use of Diagrams
6	Tabulation
7	Sampling
8	Rules for Using Published Statistics
9	Methods of Statistical Analysis

Part II

1	The Population Census
2	Vital Statistics
3	Trade and Transport
4	Prices
5	Production
6	Wages
7	Employment
8	Other Working-Class Statistics
9	Income and Capital
10	Taxes and Rates

J. R. Statist. Soc. A, 1953, **116**, 89.

" Teachers, particularly those in evening institutes or connected with other forms of adult education, will be glad to have this new edition of an old favourite. Its continued influence should do much to spread the idea of the statistical approach to problems of modern society."

BROOKES, B. C. AND DICK, W. F. L. *INTRODUCTION TO STATISTICAL METHOD*
1951. (Reprinted with corrections 1953.) Heinemann, viii + 288 pp.

Chapter	Contents
1	The Representation of Numerical Data
2	Measures of Position
3	Measures of Dispersion
4	Probability

5	The Binomial and Poisson Distributions
6	The Normal Distribution
7	Tests of Significance
8	Regression
9	Correlation
10	Goodness of Fit and Contingency Tables
11	Planning Statistical Experiments

Econ. J., 1952, **62**, 632.

" ... It is not designed for the layman desirous of finding out what statistics can do, but it is intended rather for the serious student of limited mathematical attainments ... [It] ... cannot be described as a very stimulating book but it should prove to be exceedingly useful."

Economica, 1952, **19**, 433.

" They have written a book which can be commended not only for sixth forms at schools, but also for many others needing a first course in statistical techniques.

" ... The text does not deal adequately either with index numbers or with time series, ... and it fails to cover ... curve fitting, interpolation and quality control."

J. R. Statist. Soc. A, 1952, **115**, 139.

" This book ... is primarily intended for use in schools, and deserves particular attention as a pioneer in this field. ...

" The book is particularly rich in examples, especially in the first part. Many of these concern such everyday subjects as motor-car registration numbers and cricket scores, and the students are encouraged to do their own practical work."

Nature, 1952, **169**, 473.

" B. C. Brookes and W. F. L. Dick have succeeded well in a difficult task, though in places they do not emphasise sufficiently the manner in which the interpretation of data must be governed by the source and method of collection. Their first six chapters (which are available separately) provide a course adequate for most of the statistics papers now set for the General Certificate in Education; the remaining five would give a more advanced pupil an excellent foundation for eventual university specialization in statistics, yet without demanding much mathematical knowledge. Much more important than this examination or vocational training, however, is the presentation of statistics as a branch of scientific method that can assist many other school studies. The examples used are especially valuable in showing statistical science at work and in suggesting ' link ' practical exercises connected with both laboratory sciences and everyday affairs."

CONNOR, L. R. AND MORRELL, A. J. H. *STATISTICS IN THEORY AND PRACTICE*
1957. 4th Ed., Pitman, xii+249 pp.

Chapter	Contents
1	Introduction
2	Statistical Data
3	Routine Statistics
4	Special Inquiries
5	Statistical Tables
6	Accuracy and Error
7	Charts
8	Analysis of Time Series
9	Frequency Distributions.
10	Averages
11	Dispersion and Skewness
12	Probability and Some Special Distributions
13	Sampling
14	Regression and Correlation
15	Index Numbers
16	Some Industrial Applications of Statistics
17	Introduction to Published Statistics
18	Demographic Statistics
19	Prices
20	Labour Statistics: 1. Man-power
21	Labour Statistics: 2. Wages, Earnings and Hours of Work
22	Production
23	Overseas Trade
24	Internal Trade
25	National Income and Expenditure

Appendix
1   Punched Card Calculating Machinery and Equipment

Inc. Statist., 1957, **7**, 171.

" This work was originally written by Mr. Connor but has now been revised by Mr. Morrell, who brings to the text a breath of fresh air as he lucidly explains the modern methods of collecting statistical material, whether it be routine statistics so essential to the efficient management of all organisations or *ad hoc* inquiries designed to provide certain information. Mr. Morrell keeps in the forefront that the purpose of statistics is not to satisfy curiosity but to enable correct decisions to be taken. . . .

" Full use has been made of the post-war improvement in official statistics, both in regard to their coverage and their quality. The author concentrates on the economic statistics of prices, earnings, production, overseas and internal trades, and attempts to give some idea of the nature of the problems involved in the construction of indices for these series. . . .

" The book has value, for it fills the need for an easy, up-to-date book on modern methods of collecting statistical material and is a welcome addition to the literature on statistics. Its use to the beginner would have been greatly enhanced had more space been devoted to statistical techniques."

Economica, 1958, **25**, 181.

" The fourth edition of this very good elementary text-book has been thoroughly revised by Mr. Morrell. The revision was long overdue: the ' Practice ' part of the book, which consists of descriptions of published statistical data, has been brought up to date. Now that this part of the book has been completely rewritten, it is again a book to recommend to students. The revision of the ' Theory ' chapters has led to some compression. It seems unfortunate that sections on interpolation (apart from the calculation of the median and quartiles), Pareto and Lorenz curves, contingency and a slight reference to the analysis of variance have been omitted, for these are likely to tempt a student further. Sections on control charts and acceptance sampling have been added."

CROXTON, F. E. *ELEMENTARY STATISTICS WITH APPLICATIONS IN MEDICINE AND THE BIOLOGICAL SCIENCES*
   1959. Dover, vii+376 pp.

Chapter	Contents
1	Introduction; Rates, Ratios and Percentages
2	Tabular and Graphic Presentation of Data
3	The Frequency Distribution
4	Measures of Central Tendency
5	Dispersion, Skewness, and Kurtosis
6	Linear Correlation of Two Variables
7	Non-linear and Multiple Correlation
8	The Normal Curve, the Binomial, and the Poisson Distribution
9	Reliability and Significance of Arithmetic Means
10	Reliability and Significance of Proportions
11	The χ^2 Test
12	Significance Tests for Variances; Analysis of Variance; Tests for Correlation Coefficients and for Measures of Skewness and Kurtosis

J. R. Statist. Soc. A, 1959, **122**, 547.

"This book was first published in 1953 under the title of *Elementary Statistics with Applications in Medicine*. No previous study of statistics is assumed, and only a very modest knowledge of mathematics is expected from the reader. The book is lucidly written and is available at a reasonable price. . . . As might be expected from the title the text is well illustrated with examples drawn from actual survey data . . . the book can be thoroughly recommended; the student will obtain an informed introduction to statistics while the professional statistician will find it a useful source of reference."

CROXTON, F. E. AND COWDEN, D. J. *PRACTICAL BUSINESS STATISTICS*
   1960. 3rd Ed., Prentice-Hall, xx+701 pp.

Chapter	Contents
1	The Nature of Statistical Data

2	The Analysis of Statistical Data
3	Uses of Statistics in Business
4	Misuses of Statistics
5	Selected Topics in Arithmetic
6	Presentation of Data
7	Selected Topics in Algebra
8	Rates, Ratios, and Percentages
9	Logarithmic Scales
10	Sources and Collection of Data
11	Probability and Probability Distributions
12	Statistical Inference
13	Sampling Design
14	Equations and Curves
15	The Frequency Distribution
16	Averages
17	Dispersion
18	Shapes of Frequency Distributions
19	The Normal Probability Distribution
20	Probability Distributions and Quality Control
21	Tests of Hypotheses and Confidence Limits: Arithmetic Mean
22	Tests of Hypotheses and Confidence Limits: Proportions and Standard Deviations
23	Hypotheses Concerning Differences Between Two Samples
24	Fitting a Straight Line
25	Reliability of Regression Estimates
26	The Correlation Coefficient
27	Types of Two-variable Correlation
28	Elements of Linear Trend Fitting
29	Moving Average or Related Series as Trend
30	Seasonal Movements
31	Cycles and Irregular Movements
32	Fundamentals of Index Number Construction
33	Selected Topics in Index Number Construction
34	Polynomial Trends
35	Multiple and Partial Correlation
36	Special Topics in Multiple Correlation
37	Correlation of Time Series and Forecasting

| 38 | Growth Curves |
| 39 | Tests of Homogeneity and Independence |

J. Amer. Statist. Ass., 1961, **56**, 194.

" It is a smorgasbord of statistical techniques, many of use in business and economics and others of only peripheral interest. Its strongest point as a textbook of business or economic statistics is the analysis of time series; in this regard it is better than any of its competitors, to the best of my knowledge. But, although some of the other materials in the book are superb, it has so many serious deficiencies that its overall value as a business statistics textbook is severely compromised."

DAVID, F. N. *A STATISTICAL PRIMER*
1953. Griffin, x+226 pp.

Chapter	Contents
1	Preliminaries
2	Variation
3	Aggregates
4	Aggregates (continued)
5	Measures of Location
6	Measures of Dispersion
7	Methods of Computation
8	Skewness and Kurtosis
9	Probability: Population and Sample
10	Sampling: Normal Population
11	Tests of Significance: the Mean
12	Tests of Significance: the Mean (continued)
13	Tests of Significance: the Mean (continued)
14	Tests of Significance: the Mean (continued)
15	Tests of Significance: the Standard Deviation
16	Tests of Significance: Two Sample Tests
17	Tests of Significance: Ratio of Two Variances
18	Probability: the Binomial Series
19	The Binomial (continued)
20	The Binomial (continued)

21 The Binomial (continued)
22 Poisson's Binomial Limit
23 The Index of Dispersion
24 χ^2 Goodness-of-Fit Test

Biometrika, 1954, **41**, 281.

" This book is intended for the non-mathematical research worker who wishes to learn some statistics, enough to enable him to perform ordinary tests and to design satisfactory experiments without other expert help. . . . Although the emphasis throughout is on elementary principles it is noticeable that there are no half-truths. Exposition is always rigorous with laudable emphasis on basic assumptions. . . . Short tables of the important statistical functions are included so this book can provide the complete armoury required for simple statistical work in the laboratory."

J. R. Statist. Soc. A, 1953, **116**, 325.

" The special feature of Dr. David's primer is the extreme patience with which the most difficult concepts of elementary statistical method are presented. Scientists . . . will welcome the thoroughness with which the arguments are driven home. Similarly, it is very helpful to find examples illustrated by more than one table, showing the state of affairs at successive stages in the calculations. The corollary of this unhurried approach is that the range of topics covered in the book is rather restricted. . . . The book is, in fact accurately described by its title, being intended as an instructor in first principles rather than as a reference book for a wide variety of techniques. As such it is most successful."

FREUND, J. E. AND WILLIAMS, F. J. *MODERN BUSINESS STATISTICS*
1958. Prentice-Hall, xv + 539 pp.

Chapter   *Contents*
1   Introduction
2   Frequency Distributions
3   Measures of Location
4   Measures of Variation

5	Further Descriptions	
6	Probability	
7	Theoretical Distributions	
8	Sampling Distributions	
9	Problems of Estimation	
10	Tests of Hypotheses	
11	Further Tests of Hypotheses	
12	Problems of Sampling	
13	Linear Regression	
14	Correlation	
15	Index Numbers: Basic Concepts	
16	Index Numbers: Theory and Application	
17	Time Series Analysis: Basic Concepts	
18	Time Series Analysis: Secular Trend	
19	Time Series Analysis: Seasonal and Cyclical Variation	

Appendix
- 1 Pictorial Representations
- 2 Quality Control
- 3 Calculations with Rounded Numbers
- 4 The Use of Logarithm and Square Root Tables

Appl. Statist., 1960, **9**, 67.

" This should be a good text-book for a beginner, particularly for one whose mathematics is weak, rusty or non-existent. Each chapter is provided with several sets of exercises and with lists of books for reference or further study. With this book the student should fairly quickly obtain some knowledge of the whole range of statistical methods and their inter-relationships. . . . Throughout the book the text, formulae, tables, diagrams, and charts are presented in an agreeably clear type."

Inc. Statist., 1960, **10**, 145.

" Readers can ignore the word ' Business ' in the title; the book is a straightforward—and very good—text-book of modern statistical theory and methods requiring no mathematics beyond basic algebra. . . . The non-mathematical reader with no previous acquaintance with the book can learn a great deal about the subject. . . . This book can be thoroughly recommended."

J. Amer. Statist. Ass., 1958, **53**, 1032.

" The title of the book represents an insular conception of statistics. The middle word is superfluous and, perhaps, misleading since the principles and methods of statistics are interdisciplinary in nature. . . . The large number of exercises, with answers supplied to the odd-numbered questions, recommend the book to statistics teachers who require problems emphasizing the application of statistical techniques. . . . Most of the subjects are closely reasoned, rigorously treated, and completely detailed. . . . The standard topics are included in the book, so that much ground is covered. The authors accomplished the complete job in fewer pages than is customary in similar texts, a tribute to good organization. . . . Those familiar with statistics texts will find it neither a fresh nor unusual experience since, frankly, it is imitative. There was no attempt at originality in the text's conception hence no subject stands out as particularly noteworthy."

FRYER, H. C. *ELEMENTS OF STATISTICS*
1954. Wiley, viii+262 pp.

Chapter	Contents
1	History and Introduction
2	The Summarisation of Sets of Data Involving One Type of Measurement
3	Elementary Probability
4	The Binomial and Normal Frequency Distributions
5	Sampling From Binomial Populations
6	Introductory Sampling Theory for a Normal Population Involving Only One Variable
7	Linear Regression and Correlation

J. R. Statist. Soc. A, 1954, **117**, 486.

" This work is based on lectures given by Professor Fryer to students with little or no mathematical training and taking their first course in statistics. . . . Given the choice of subject matter and the mathematical level, the book is excellent. The treatment is leisurely, very well illustrated by examples and interesting exercises and the key ideas are carefully and clearly explained. The illustrations are drawn from a wide range of applied fields. . . . The book will be of interest to teachers of elementary statistics. It is suitable for students provided that they are interested primarily in getting a thorough understanding of basic ideas rather than in building up quickly a set of techniques for practical use. It is not suitable as a reference book for the research worker, both because of its limited scope and because methods of computing are not dealt with at all fully."

Appl. Statist., 1955, **4**, 127.

". . . Although its scope is limited to an exposition for non-mathematical students of the simplest types of statistical technique, it is presented with a painstaking and sympathetic thoroughness which would make it an admirable guide to the lone worker. The student's queries are anticipated and answered, and he is given a rich supply of examples, designed to provoke thought as well as to exercise technique. . . . There are one or two minor faults; . . . but considered on the whole, though dear at the price, the book is an excellent introduction to the subject."

HIRSCII, W. Z. *INTRODUCTION TO MODERN STATISTICS* 1957. Macmillan, xiv+429 pp.

Chapter	Contents
1	Introduction
2	Getting Meaning out of a Mass of Data
3	" On the Average "
4	Dispersion
5	Superstition, Hunch and the Laws of Chance
6	Inference
7	Sampling Distribution of Means
8	Estimating Means and Totals
9	Binomial Distribution—Success or Failure, How Likely are They?
10	Estimating Percentages
11	Decisions about Means

12	Decisions about Percentages
13	Index Numbers—Tying Up to the Hitching Post
14	Association Among Quantitative Data—Regression and Correlation Analysis
15	Time Series Analysis—Prophecy Galore
16	Time Series Analysis—Prophecy Galore (continued)
17	Association Among Qualitative Data
18	Decisions by Control Charts
19	The Statistician in the Age of Electronics

Econ. J., 1959, **69**, 152.

" It is well organised, easy to read, with welcome dashes of common sense and humour in the examples. At the elementary level it deals satisfactorily with averages, index numbers and the decomposition of series. At the other extreme it deals—again very satisfactorily—with confidence interval estimation and decision theory. . . . There is no doubt that recent advances in statistical theory have left the middle-aged economist gasping, and it is valuable to have some of these developments distilled into a very readable textbook. But there are other developments in stochastic theory which are more suited to the interests of the general economist. Alas, no one with Professor Hirsch's gifts as a distiller has yet turned to them."

J. Amer. Statist. Ass., 1958, **53**, 751.

" Obviously Hirsch has devoted much effort to make this a book which the typical undergraduate will find easy and enjoyable reading. . . . From the very beginning the book stresses inference and decision making. . . . The treatment of estimation and testing is a model of clear textbook writing. . . . This is not the sort of book which statistical practitioners will buy to keep on their reference shelf. But it is a book which instructors who believe that the elementary statistics text need not be a dull book will wish to look at and try out."

J. R. Statist. Soc. A, 1958, **121**, 109.

" The distinctive feature of the book is its style. The author introduces concepts with an example showing the need for them. . . . Many illustrations are given of the use of statistical methods in business and elsewhere and the exercises at the end of each chapter are framed in terms of practical situations. . . . The text is enlivened by quotations and cartoons. Such light reading is especially likely to appeal to those for whom statistics is a compulsory subsidiary. . . . Unfortunately the text is not always clear and there are a few misprints and errors. . . . For many students, however, these deficiencies will surely be more than compensated by the liveliness and interest of the style of presentation."

McCarthy, P. J. *INTRODUCTION TO STATISTICAL REASONING*
1957. McGraw-Hill, xiii+402 pp.

Chapter	Contents
1	Introduction
2	The Components of a Statistical Investigation
3	The Distribution of a Variable
4	The Location of a Distribution
5	The Spread of a Distribution
6	Simple Random Sampling
7	Experiments with Uncertain Outcomes and Probability
8	The Binomial Probability Model and Statistical Inference
9	Drawing Statistical Inferences from the Arithmetic Mean of a Large Sample
10	Elements of Sample Design
11	χ^2 Procedures for Qualitative Data
12	The Linear Association of Two Quantitative Variables

Appl. Statist., 1958, 7, 130.

" . . . several important topics are conspicuous by their absence, notably small sample procedures based on the t, χ^2 and F distributions, and the analysis of variance. . . . This book then does not add competitively to the range of introductory text-books available in this country, particularly as it covers only a part of any really adequate introductory course on statistics."

J. Amer. Statist. Ass., 1958, 53, 208.

"This introductory book is intended for use in one-semester courses for students who expect to work in the social sciences and have little mathematical preparation.

"The author has had at least three major objectives: (1) to teach the basic concepts of statistical reasoning, (2) to teach the statistical techniques used in many parts of the social sciences, and (3) to provide in an introductory text illustrative material taken from significant investigations in the social sciences."

J. R. Statist. Soc. A, 1958, **121**, 355.

"This book should be useful to beginning students in statistics and particularly to students working on their own. Provision of answers to the exercises would improve matters but the only other criticism would be on the grounds of possibly over-lengthy exposition.

". . . No acquaintance with mathematics is assumed beyond the use of symbols to represent observed variables and the operations of addition, subtraction, multiplication and division.

". . . for the relatively non-mathematically inclined [the book] provides an excellent way of finding the way in which a good deal of statistical reasoning works."

Operat. Res., 1958, **6**, 298.

". . . if this text is a reliable criterion it is evident that the basic, non-mathematical texts are improving. Here is a carefully written book which emphasises the concepts of statistical reasoning rather than attempts to cover a wide variety of techniques. Although the text lacks in mathematical background, many relatively complex concepts, such as power and operating characteristics, are explained rather lucidly through an intuitive approach. Furthermore, the author reviews certain elementary mathematical tools, including the factorial, binomial formula, closed and open intervals, and even the rudiments of symbolic logic."

MOORE, P. G. *PRINCIPLES OF STATISTICAL TECHNIQUES*
1958. Cambridge University Press, viii+239 pp.

Chapter   *Contents*
1   The Scope of Statistics
2   The Collection of Data
3   The Tabulation of Data
4   The Pictorial Representation of Data

5	Frequency Distributions
6	Averages
7	Measures of Dispersion
8	Probability and Sampling
9	The Binomial Theorem
10	Tests of Significance
11	Further Tests of Significance
12	Further Forms of Average
13	Time Series
14	Pairs of Characters

Biometrika, 1959, **46**, 276.

" The author has resisted the temptation to go too deeply into theory, and succeeds in making the book readable, stimulating and beneficial to anyone prepared to carry out the necessary calculations . . . The main asset of the book is the successful use of topics selected from many fields to illustrate principles and techniques. . . . Guidance in the collection and tabulation of data, so rarely given, is nicely handled, and the pitfalls of pictorial representation well illustrated. . . . This book deserves wide use in schools, both for reference and class use, but the cost would appear to be prohibitive for the latter."

Inc. Statist., 1959, **9**, 68.

" Despite its title, ' The Principles of Statistical Techniques ' is an attempt not to examine basic principles but rather—to use the author's own words—to put across the main principles to students who are interested in practical applications. It packs into 230 pages topics ranging from collection of data to the simpler tests of significance, and there are many passages which indicate that no prior knowledge on the reader's part is assumed.

"There are several titles which fulfil this purpose already but the needs and abilities of students vary so considerably that an addition to the list is never unwelcome. Precisely for this reason it comes as a disappointment that Mr. Moore's book, on the basis of its declared aim, must be judged as a failure."

Nature, 1959, **184**, 1523.

" The book is readable from start to finish, and only in Chapters 10 and 11 . . . will more than usual concentration be needed, even

B

if the reader is approaching the subject for the first time. The book will be a valuable addition to every grammar school library."

J. Inst. Actuar., 1959, **85**, 114.

" The treatment throughout is simple, and the mathematics required is elementary. . . . The book is throughout written in a clear and simple style, and contains detailed and illuminating descriptions of the processes involved and the difficulties likely to be encountered in using them. Numerous examples are worked out in the text. . . . There is a large selection of exercises at the end of each chapter, many giving suggestions for practical work, and others purely numerical, but there are no answers provided for these."

MOUNSEY, J. *INTRODUCTION TO STATISTICAL CALCULATIONS*
1952. English Universities Press, 351 pp.

Chapter	Contents
1	Measures of Location—Averages and Partition Values
2	Weighted Averages. Rates. Use of Averages in Connection with the Analysis of Time Series
3	Index Numbers
4	Estimates and Limits of Error
5	Dispersion and Skewness
6	Lines of " Best Fit ". Correlation
7	Calculation of Moments
8	Elementary Problems in Probability
9	Binomial, Poisson and Normal Distributions
10	Significance Tests

Appl. Statist., 1953, **2**, 204.

" As often happens in introductory books, the book is at its best in early sections relating to frequency distributions, index numbers, and moving averages. Here the exercises involve interesting data, often drawn from official sources. The book's quality deteriorates when it comes to deal with more advanced topics such as probability and significance tests. . . . On the whole the exercises are such as to test technique, not understanding, and in the later

sections of the book tend to lack the atmosphere of reality. Even so, Mr. Mounsey will save many a teacher many a headache from hunting for material to illustrate lectures or lessons."
J. R. Statist. Soc. A, 1953, **116**, 331.

" The book deserves the most serious consideration by all who teach statistical methods at the elementary or intermediate levels and by those who, from time to time, have the task of advising students and others upon the bewildering array of current literature in this subject, but it may well prove to be of greater benefit to the teacher than to the student, and it is suggested that a student should be recommended to use it only where it is known that a good text is already available."

Nature, 1954, **173**, 325.

" Mr. J. Mounsey's useful little book contains about six hundred numerical exercises, but is more than a mere collection. His wealth of examples is knit together by introductory text so that the methods of calculation are explained in detail. The book is designed primarily for students in commercial and technical colleges who are preparing for examinations in statistics, and should prove very useful for the purpose. Its scope is about that of the certificate of the Royal Statistical Society—averages, index numbers, estimates of error, dispersion, lines of best fit, moments, elements of probability, binomial, Poisson and normal distributions and significance tests. There are some tables of the usual kind, and answers to the exercises are provided."

NEISWANGER, W. A. *ELEMENTARY STATISTICAL METHODS* 1956. Revised Ed., Macmillan, xx+749 pp.

Chapter	Contents
1	Statistical Methods and Their Use in Economics and Business
2	The Nature and Interpretation of Statistical Results
3	Initiating a Statistical Investigation
4	The Design of Samples
5	Tabular Presentation of Statistical Data

6	Graphic Comparison of Simple Magnitudes
7	Charting Time Series
8	Tabular and Graphic Descriptions of Frequency Distributions
9	Averages
10	Dispersion and Skewness
11	Sampling Error and Statistical Inference:—Arithmetic Means
12	Sampling Error and Statistical Inference:—Proportions—Difference—Small Samples
13	Index Numbers
14	Current Index Numbers and Their Use
15	Analysis of Time Series
16	The Seasonal Variation
17	Cyclical Variation and the Concept of Normal
18	Analysis of Functional Relations
19	Measurement of Correlation

Biometrika, 1957, **44**, 296.

" This is a substantial text-book suitable for use in a one year's course in statistics. It is revised substantially from the 1943 edition when discussing sampling methods and is extended by chapters on sampling errors and statistical inference. . . . The exposition throughout is very clear and within the field chosen most aspects of the subject are treated well and completely. . . . This book if anything errs on the side of giving too much detail. . . . In general this is a good book for students who have the time and are prepared to learn the elements of a subject slowly but methodically, hence getting a good grounding."

J. Amer. Statist. Ass., 1957, **52**, 579.

" Well written and widely adopted, the Neiswanger text now appears in an improved and modernised edition. This fine text has been generally known and highly regarded since its publication in 1943; the revision is both a comprehensive and meticulous job of bringing the volume up to date and perfecting the presentation. . . .

" The new edition is a thoughtful and careful revision in which the style, content, and emphasis of the most readable text in the field have been improved and brought up to date. Compression and clarification of the earlier edition have permitted the addition of a number of new ideas and a completely new chapter on statistical inference, without unduly extending the length of the revised edition. . . .

" One of the most attractive features of the earlier edition was the abundant use of actual statistical examples for which accurate sources were given. In the revised edition these cases have been brought up to date and many new ones added. . . .

" In both the editions the allocation of space seems logical. The first two chapters in each discuss the use of statistical methods in general and the misuse of them in particular. Both are helpful in orienting the student, especially the early introduction of the recurrent theme, allowable error. Thorough treatment is properly given to time series, for the text is designed for the consumer of statistics in the fields of economics and business. Throughout, the emphasis on a verbal as well as a mathematical understanding of statistical concepts helps to orient the nonmathematically trained student in the subject matter. . . .

" In brief it is a pleasure to report that this revision embodies many improvements over an originally very good text."

QUENOUILLE, M. H. *RAPID STATISTICAL CALCULATIONS*
   1959. Griffin, 80 pp.

The book consists of 35 tests grouped into three sections viz.:
A   Methods Involving Mean Level or Scatter of Groups of Observations
B   Methods Comparing Frequencies or Proportions
C   Methods Involving Association

Ann. Hum. Genet., 1960, **24**, 292.

" The author has adopted a clear uniform system of presentation; on the left-hand side of each pair of pages he deals with a particular statistical variable, as mean, standard deviation, median, quartile or other proportion of frequency of distribution, range, tests of significance, analysis of variance, contingency tables and some graphical methods; on the right-hand side of the double page an example is given as an illustration."

Biometrika, 1960, **47**, 488.

" This book is a summary of the tests which are in common statistical practice, and their application to numerical examples. . . . For students and research workers trying to teach themselves statistics it will be found a useful auxiliary to any elementary theoretical textbook of statistical methods."

J. Inst. Actuar., 1960, **86**, 107.

" There are several novel features about this book. The most noticeable is that it has a washable plastic cover—very useful for a book which may well be used under a variety of working conditions. More important, perhaps, is the fact that the title by no means completely describes the contents; beyond the mere directions for calculation, there is an assessment of the value of each method (not restricted to, though including, where appropriate, formal ' Efficiencies ') and references to sources, and also a set of tables. . . . The book slips easily into the pocket, and should be a welcome and widely-used addition to the practising statistician's equipment."

J. R. Statist. Soc. A, 1960, **123**, 336.

" The virtue of this book is that it can be carried readily in the pocket. The binding is sturdy enough to withstand wear and tear and the print is large and easily readable. It serves its purpose admirably and can be recommended to any peripatetic statistician who occasionally finds himself some distance from his computing service."

RHODES, E. C. *ELEMENTARY STATISTICAL METHOD*
1945. Routledge, v + 242 pp.

Chapter	Contents
1	Statistics
2	Statistical Inquiries
3	Assembling Statistical Data
4	Secondary or Derived Statistics
5	Comparison of Averages
6	The Calculation of Averages
7	Graphical Methods

8   The Median and Measures of Dispersion
9   Weighted Sums and Weighted Averages
10 Index Numbers
11 Graphs of Time Series
12 Analysis of Time Series

J. R. Statist. Soc. A, 1934, **97**, 337.
". . . an excellent manual as a first study for students of statistics . . . there is little in the way of technique required by the collector and tabulator of statistical data that does not find a place. . . . The advanced worker will do well to study it carefully to remind himself of all the points that have to be thought of and dealt with before the raw material is in a sufficiently finished state to be amenable to ultra-refined methods, or even to be worth dealing with at all . . up to the point which it professes to reach it is authoritative and comprehensive."

TIPPETT, L. H. C. *STATISTICS*
1956. 2nd Ed., Home University Library, vi+224 pp.

Chapter   Contents
1   Introduction
2   The Raw Material
3   Arranging and Presenting the Material
4   Some Special Tables and Diagrams of Importance
5   " Expressing it in Numbers "
6   Sampling
7   Taking Account of Chance
8   Statistical Laws
9   Statistical Reasoning
10   Statistics in Affairs
11   Statistics and Other Sciences

Biometrika, 1956, **43**, 493.
" This book, already a classic in the ' expositions-for-the-layman ' group has been revised and brought up to date by the author."
J. Amer. Statist. Ass., 1956, **51**, 536.
" According to the preface of this excellent little book, the first

edition of which was published in 1943 and reviewed in this Journal, 1945, **40**, 536:

'This edition has been revised to take care of [recent] developments [in statistics] and to describe things as they are today; and much of the original illustrative material has been replaced by more up-to-date material. The general scope of the book remains unchanged.' "

J. R. Statist. Soc. A, 1956, **119**, 342.

" One welcomes the second edition of this book, which is so different in character from the typical text-book on statistical methods. This is the subject as it is understood by the layman and it is developed continuously through many possible pitfalls from collecting and presenting material, allowing for chance, to the climax of the penultimate chapter called ' Statistics in affairs ' which implies use primarily in economic, adminstrative and industrial fields. The book may be treated as an introduction to the subject, for it will be easily intelligible to the beginner, but to my mind it seems even more suitable for those who have acquired some knowledge of statistical methods and an enthusiasm to apply those methods, perhaps a little indiscriminately."

WALKER, H. M. AND LEV, J. *ELEMENTARY STATISTICAL METHODS*
1958. Revised Ed., Holt, xvi+302 pp.

Chapter	Contents
1	The Role of Statistics
2	Gathering and Recording Data
3	Construction and Use of Tables
4	Graphic Methods
5	Data on a Scaled Variable: Tabulating and Graphing
6	Percentiles
7	Mean and Standard Deviation
8	The Frequency Distribution—A Summary
9	Regression
10	Correlation

11 Circumstances Affecting the Size of Correlation and Regression Coefficients
12 The Normal Distribution
13 Introduction to Statistical Inference
14 Testing Hypotheses
15 Inferences about Proportions
16 Inferences about Correlation Coefficients

J. Amer. Statist. Ass., 1959, **54**, 699.
" Walker and Lev have done it again: this is a fine textbook. . . . One overriding criterion would seem to have dictated the decisions made in writing the book. That is a careful consideration of the problems of ordinary students attempting to learn statistics. Commerical appeal, impressing other statisticians, and the like, are all secondary to the goal of teaching students a great deal of worthwhile statistics as effectively as possible. On every page, it would seem, there are indications of master teachers at work."

WALLIS, W. A. AND ROBERTS, H. V. *STATISTICS: A NEW APPROACH*
1956. Free Press, xxxviii+646 pp.

Chapter   Contents
1 The Field of Statistics
2 Effective Uses of Statistics
3 Misuses of Statistics
4 Basic Ideas
5 Observation and Measurement
6 The Art of Organising Data
7 Averages
8 Variability
9 Association
10 Randomness and Probability
11 Sampling Distributions and the Normal Distribution
12 Statistical Tests and Decision Procedures
13 Further Test Procedures
14 Estimation
15 Design of Investigations

16	Statistical Quality Control
17	Relationships Between Variables
18	Time Series
19	Shortcuts

J. Amer. Statist. Ass., 1956, **51**, 664.

" This book is a general introduction to statistics. It explains the basic ideas with scarcely more than American high-school mathematics, and illustrates their uses in an astonishing variety of interesting and important applications. . . . This is the best book that I have seen for a beginning course to a group of students from varied disciplines. . . . The student who has to learn by himself will find it a pleasure to read."

Appl. Statist., 1957, **6**, 157.

" The claim made in the title of this book that it represents a new approach is quite justified; this is something new in statistical textbooks. It is concerned as much with the ' know-how ' of statistical investigation and inference as with techniques. . . . This book is the mature product of years of experience in the teaching of statistics to students of all kinds. . . . Students will find it stimulating as well as understandable; readers interested in the process of gaining knowledge of the universe, especially the social part of it, will find it interesting and helpful."

Inc. Statist., 1957, **7**, 170.

" The atmosphere of [this book] is designed to create an interest in the subject by an essentially practical approach. . . . The use of examples is indeed lavish: there are over two hundred by way of illustration and a further two hundred for use as ' Do it Yourself ' exercises. . . . The style of type and the layout of this admirable book make for easy reading—in spite of its weight. It can confidently be recommended for all who are or who should be interested in the statistical approach."

J. Inst. Actuar., 1958, **84**, 113.

" Although the book consists of well over 600 pages there is a marked lack of mathematics. . . . It is essentially a practical approach and emphasises the ' common-sense ' interpretation of the subject. . . . One of the most outstanding features is the way in which the book is illustrated with topical examples from every conceivable field."

WILKS, S. S. *ELEMENTARY STATISTICAL ANALYSIS*
1948. Princeton University Press, xi + 284 pp.

Chapter	Contents
1	Introduction
2	Frequency Distributions
3	Sample Mean and Standard Deviation
4	Elementary Probability
5	Probability Distributions
6	The Binomial Distribution
7	The Poisson Distribution
8	The Normal Distribution
9	Elements of Sampling
10	Confidence Limits of Population Parameters
11	Statistical Significance Tests
12	Testing Randomness in Samples
13	Analysis of Pairs of Measurements

J. Amer. Statist. Ass., 1949, **44**, 458.

" Professor Wilks has attempted with the material and arrangement of the new text to follow the recommendation of three distinguished committees on the teaching of statistics regarding the introduction of a basic elementary course available centrally to all students needing an understanding of statistical concepts and techniques common to all fields of application."

INTERMEDIATE

BAILEY, N. T. J. *STATISTICAL METHODS IN BIOLOGY*
1959. English Universities Press, ix + 200 pp.

Chapter	Contents
1	Introduction

2	Variability and Frequency Distributions
3	Estimation, Standard Errors and Confidence Limits
4	The Basic Idea of a Significance Test
5	Simple Significance Tests Based on the Normal Distribution
6	The Use of t-Tests for Small Samples
7	Contingency Tables and χ^2
8	χ^2 Tests of Goodness-of-Fit and Homogeneity
9	The Correlation of Measurements
10	Regression of Analysis
11	Simple Experimental Design and the Analysis of Variance
12	Introduction to Factorial Experiments
13	Random Samples and Random Numbers
14	Partial Correlation and Regression
15	Notes on Computing and Calculating Machines

Appl. Statist., 1960, **9**, 64.

" The book deals with all the standard concepts and methods. . . . A very useful appendix gives a summary of statistical formulae, with a guide indicating for any ordinary type of data the appropriate scheme of calculation and the tables (either in this book or elsewhere) needed for the final interpretation. The explanations throughout the book are lucid and the comments shrewd and serviceable. There are a few minor lapses from this high standard, which are, however, almost inevitable in a first edition. . . . In short, this is just the book for the beginner. It can also be recommended to those who have already learnt to apply statistical methods somewhat mechanically, but wish to understand them better."

Biometrika, 1960, **47**, 489.

" No attempt is made (deliberately) to indicate the derivation of any technique. The method of exposition appears to be modelled on that of R. A. Fisher's ' Statistical Methods for Research Workers ', but it is unlikely that many will be tempted away from that old and tried classic. . . . This book adds one more to the mass of elementary statistical texts which are now on the market. The time is almost ripe for a monograph which will help the student to choose between them."

J. Amer. Statist. Ass., 1961, **56**, 179.

" In 160 pages of text the author lays out an amazingly large variety of statistical techniques. A good heuristic justification ordinarily accompanies each such presentation, as does a worked example. . . . A novel feature of the book is a 30 page section at the end entitled *Summary of Statistical Formulae*. . . . The book is indeed designed to be a cook-book; it is a very good one, since it is thin, lucid, and virtually error-free. . . . It seems to be a book very well suited to two uses. First, it should make a good text for instructing medical students in elementary statistics. Second, it should make a good statistical manual for the laboratory worker in biological science."

J. R. Statist. Soc. A, 1959, **122**, 546.

" The author explains in detail the circumstances for which the various methods are appropriate, in a lucid and idiomatic (indeed, at times almost ' chatty ') style. . . . Little or none of the underlying mathematical theory is included. This approach, adopted to avoid confusing the mathematically inexperienced reader, is legitimate, but seems at times to have been carried to extremes. . . . The principle of least squares estimation is nowhere stated. . . . The general discussion of correlation and regression is excellent, however. . . . The use of large sample methods is stressed, in my opinion too much so. . . . The book is attractively printed and presented, and misprints are few. The price is remarkably low, in view of the number of tables and formulae included."

BERNSTEIN, L. AND WEATHERALL, M. *STATISTICS FOR MEDICAL AND OTHER BIOLOGICAL STUDENTS*
   1952. Livingstone, xii + 180 pp.

Chapter	Contents
1	The Basis of Scientific Method
2	Probability
3	Observed Frequency Distributions
4	Theoretical Frequency Distributions
5	Averages

6 Measures of Scatter
7 Sampling
8 Chance Differences
9 Chance Differences (continued)
10 Regression
11 Correlation
12 Transformations
13 Analysis of Variance
14 Experimental Design
15 Therapeutic Experiments
16 The Interpretation of Observations

Nature, 1953, **171**, 278.
" The authors have rightly concentrated on the logic of statistical methods and their use in medicine. The mathematics involved in the derivation of these methods have either been omitted or reduced to the point where they can be mastered by the use of elementary algebra. The result is very readable, and if the book does not carry the medical student as far along the path as a statistician would like to see him go—or as he must go if he needs to use statistical methods himself—it at least points his feet in the right direction and gives him a useful introduction to the statistical problems he will have to face."

BURINGTON, R. S. AND MAY, D. C. *HANDBOOK OF PROBABILITY AND STATISTICS WITH TABLES*
1953. Handbook Publishers, ix+332 pp.

Chapter *Contents*
1 Introduction
2 Certain Definitions Used in Statistics
3 Frequency Distributions in One Dimension
4 Combinations and Permutations
5 Elementary Probability Theory
6 Probability Distributions in One Dimension
7 Generating and Characteristic Functions
8 Binomial Distribution

9	Poisson Distribution
10	Normal Distribution
11	Probability Distributions in Two or More Dimensions
12	Analysis of Pairs of Measurements, Regression Theory, Time Series
13	Sampling Distributions
14	Statistical Inference, Significance Tests and Confidence Intervals
15	Analysis of Variance
16	Finite Differences Interpolation
17	Sequential Analysis, Sampling Inspection, Quality Control
18	Short Table of Integrals. Some Mathematical Relationships

Biometrika, 1959, **46**, 497.

" This book . . . is intended as a cook-book for users of statistics rather than an instruction text for the embryo statistician. The idea has been to summarise formulae, definitions, theorems etc. commonly met with in elementary statistics and probability theory and to give short tables of the particular functions thus summarised. . . . The exposition is adequate without being inspired."

J. Amer. Statist. Ass., 1956, **51**, 390.

" . . . anyone who wants to make a minimum investment in a library on statistics and probability will find this handbook useful for practical problems. . . . The index is remarkably complete and materially improves the usefulness of the handbook. . . . In the preface, the authors state that their objective was to provide a handbook that readers, without detailed statistical knowledge, could use as a guide and those with statistical training could use as a convenient summary. The first part of the objective has been achieved by including more introductory material than is usual in handbooks. The major limitation, as far as the second part of the objective is concerned lies in the fact that, except in a few cases, the reader is given no help in locating further information on a subject."

CROXTON, F. E. AND COWDEN, D. J. *APPLIED GENERAL STATISTICS*
1955. 2nd Ed., Prentice Hall, xvi+843 pp.

Chapter	Contents
1	Introduction
2	Statistical Data
3	Statistical Tables
4	Graphical Presentation I: Curves using Arithmetic Scales
5	Graphic Presentation II: The Semi-logarithmic or Ratio Chart
6	Graphic Presentation III: Other Types of Charts
7	Rates, Ratios, and Percentages
8	The Frequency Distribution
9	Measures of Central Tendency
10	Dispersion, Skewness, and Kurtosis
11	The Problem of Time Series
12	Analysis of Time Series: Secular Trend I—The Straight Line
13	Analysis of Time Series: Secular Trend II—Non-Linear Trends
14	Analysis of Time Series: Periodic Movements I—Constant Seasonal Patterns
15	Analysis of Time Series: Periodic Movements II—Changing Seasonal Patterns
16	Analysis of Time Series: Cyclical Movements—Adjusting Time Series for Trend, Seasonal, and Irregular Movements
17	Fundamentals in Index Number Construction
18	Index Number Theory and Practice
19	Correlation I: Two-variable Linear Correlation
20	Correlation II: Two-variable Non-linear Correlation
21	Correlation III: Multiple and Partial Correlation
22	Correlation IV: Correlation of Time Series
23	Describing a Frequency Distribution by a Fitted Curve
24	Statistical Significance I: Arithmetic Means
25	Statistical Significance II: Proportions and the Chi-Square Test

26 Statistical Significance III: Variances, Analysis of Variance, Measures of Skewness and Kurtosis, and Correlation Coefficients

J. Amer. Statist. Ass., 1957, **52**, 102.
" This book was first published in 1939, and . . . has attained a very wide acceptance as an introductory textbook.

The title is not quite correct inasmuch as there is a fairly heavy weighting with business and economic data, over two hundred pages devoted to time series and index numbers, plus another chapter given over to the correlation of time series, and some earlier chapters largely devoted to time series charts. Much of the illustrative material throughout is economic.

This is not to detract from the usefulness of the book, but by way of showing for whom it is most useful. The first edition has become one of the most widely used reference books on the shelves of business libraries, and quite properly, for it has served its purpose well. . . .

In this second edition, the Lorenz and Pareto curves are omitted from the chapter on the Frequency Distribution, and the Moving Average no longer appears as a method of describing secular trend. Some re-arrangement appears in some of the other chapters. Of course, the data used are more recent. . . .

Students have experienced difficulty with the following sections: (1) the standard deviation, (2) the calculation of numbers included on p. 220, (3) the adjusting of trend lines in Chapter 12, (4) the concepts of 'explained' and 'unexplained' variation in Chapter 19, and (5) the chapters on statistical inference."

DERMAN, C. AND KLEIN, M. *PROBABILITY AND STATISTICAL INFERENCE FOR ENGINEERS*
1959. Oxford University Press, xii + 144 pp.

Chapter	Contents
1	Preliminaries
2	Elements of Probability Theory
3	Decision Problems

C

J. R. Statist. Soc. A, 1960, **123**, 203.

" This is a book that sets out to teach the principles of statistics and its style is to treat the subject by definitions, examples and exercises, with the absolute minimum of supporting explanation. In this way, a lot of information is condensed into a few pages. . . . The authors have given a modern look to the book with the inclusion of the section of principles of choice, giving an account of Bayes, minimax and admissibility. There is, however, pathetically little on estimation and no mention of least squares or maximum likelihood. This is a strange omission as it is a subject of great practical value to engineers. Despite this criticism I can recommend this book to serious students of statistics whether they be engineers, chemists, physicists or operational research workers, who have the necessary basic mathematical ability and have access to qualified tutorage."

HOEL, P. G. *ELEMENTARY STATISTICS*
1960. Wiley, vii + 261 pp.

Chapter	Contents
1	The Nature of Statistical Methods
2	The Description of Sample Data
3	Probability
4	Theoretical Frequency Distributions
5	Sampling
6	Estimation
7	Testing Hypotheses
8	Correlation
9	Regression
10	The Chi-Square Distribution
11	Nonparametric Tests
12	Analysis of Variance
13	Time Series and Index Numbers

Inc. Statist., 1961, **11**, 64.

" All who have read Professor Hoel's *Introduction to Mathematical Statistics*, and many who have not, will be delighted to see this masterly account of statistical theory at a somewhat lower level. It covers much the same topics as the earlier book, but more simply, being designed for students whose mathematical knowledge extends no further than high school algebra. . . . A model of lucid exposition, which can be strongly recommended to students beginning their studies."

J. Amer. Statist. Ass., 1961, **56**, 411.

" In this reviewer's opinion the book is a welcome addition to the texts already available for use in an introductory course in mathematical statistics. All of the fundamental ideas which ought to be included in such a course are covered in a manner which will be generally acceptable to most mathematical statisticians. Students who have had good previous mathematical training should find this book a valuable text if the material is presented by a competent instructor. . . . The book seems remarkably free of errors and seems to have been carefully written and edited."

KARMEL, P. H. *APPLIED STATISTICS FOR ECONOMISTS*
   1958. Pitman, xi+452 pp.

Chapter *Contents*
1 Introduction
2 Tabular Presentation
3 Collection of Data
4 Graphical Presentation
5 The Frequency Distribution and its Description
6 Sampling and Significance
7 Sample Surveys
8 Quality Control
9 Regression and Correlation
10 Time Series
11 Social Accounts and the Measurement of National Income
12 Price Index Numbers
13 Real National Product and Indexes of Production
14 Demography

J. R. Statist. Soc. A, 1959, **122**, 103.

" As stated in the preface, this text-book may conveniently be divided into two sections. The earlier chapters provide an introduction to statistical theory. This is tailored to the needs of economics students in the topics selected for consideration and at the level of mathematical knowledge assumed. . . . The mathematical knowedge assumed is generally no more than school algebra but ' mathematical formulations are used freely ' and the student whose mathematics is weak will find the book hard going. . . . The second part of the book deals with some topics of applied statistics in economics: social accounts and national income, index numbers of prices and products and demography. It is here that the use of Australian data for illustration becomes a disadvantage for those who have no special interest in them. This is especially true in the chapter on social accounting which follows Australian practice in preference to international (and British) procedure. Apart from this, these chapters provide a useful introduction to these subjects, dealing with many of the theoretical problems involved. Since the book is expressly for economists, the author is able to link his discussion of price index numbers to indifference curve analysis."

MILLS, F. C. *STATISTICAL METHODS*
1956. 3rd Ed., Pitman, xviii + 842 pp.

Chapter	Contents
1	On Statistics and Statistical Methods
2	Aspects of Graphic Presentation
3	The Organization of Statistical Data: Frequency Distributions
4	Some Characteristics of Frequency Distributions: Averages
5	Some Characteristics of Frequency Distributions: Measures of Variation and Skewness
6	Introduction to Statistical Inference and Probability: Binomial and Normal Distributions
7	Statistical Inference: Problems of Estimation
8	Statistical Inference: Tests of Hypotheses
9	The Measurement of Relationship: Linear Correlation

10	The Analysis of Time Series: Secular Trends
11	The Analysis of Time Series: Measurement of Seasonal Fluctuations
12	The Analysis of Time Series: Cyclical Fluctuations
13	Index Numbers of Prices
14	Index Numbers of Production and Productivity
15	Chi-Square and its Uses
16	The Analysis of Variance
17	The Measurement of Relationship: General Approaches to the Study of Regression and Correlation
18	The Measurement of Relationship: Multiple and Partial Correlation
19	Sampling and Sample Surveys

Biometrika, 1956, **43**, 492.

" The presentation is clear and unambiguous without being unusually inspiring . . . as in many other books on the subject, the demand on the reader's acquaintance with elementary algebra varies from chapter to chapter. . . . The perfect text book of elementary statistics still remains to be written, and perhaps it is an impossibility, but the book under review will suit very many students."

J. Amer. Statist. Ass., 1956, **51**, 376.

" Virtually every chapter has been rewritten and modernised for the third edition of this standard introduction to statistics. . . . Mills has been largely successful in his aim of providing a readable textbook of statistical tools with a minimum of proofs and technical discussion. In fact, there are very few statistical techniques not found in this book which the economist requires before he is turned loose on the world. If he is to apply the tools with discrimination, however, he will require a good deal more background in formal probability theory than is available here."

MORONEY, M. J. *FACTS FROM FIGURES*
   1956. 3rd Ed., Penguin, viii+472 pp.

Chapter   *Contents*
   1   Statistics Undesirable

2	The Laws of Chance	
3	The Magic Lantern Technique	
4	On the Average	
5	Scatter	
6	Speeding up Calculations	
7	Fault-Finding—The Binomial Distribution	
8	Goals, Floods, and Horse-kicks—The Poisson Distribution	
9	The Normal Distribution	
10	What Happens when we take Samples	
11	Control Charts	
12	Safety in Sampling	
13	How to be a Good Judge—Tests of Significance	
14	How to be Precise though Vague—Estimation and Confidence Limits	
15	Association, Contingency, and Goodness of Fit—The χ^2 Distribution	
16	Correlation, Cause and Effect	
17	Time Series and Fortune Telling	
18	Ranking Methods	
19	The Analysis of Variation and Co-Variation	
20	Statistics Desirable	

Reviews of 1st Ed.:
Appl. Statist., 1952, **1**, 80.

" The cover describes this book as a ' layman's introduction to statistics . . . with examples drawn from a wide variety of fields '. It seems doubtful, however, if many laymen will find their way unaided unless they are supported in their reading by a very keen interest in statistical methods. . . . Economic, medical and social statisticians reading this book, as I hope they will, can expect to be stabbed into justified annoyance from time to time, but there is a good chance of their gaining by this. A popular text-book which can find space for a simple introduction to discriminant functions, sequential sampling, confounding and replication, as well as most of the more generally known statistical methods, including a treatment of ranking methods which is fully up to date, is well worth much more than the price asked."

Econ. J., 1952, **62**, 632.

" *Facts from Figures* provides ample evidence of having been thrown together in considerable haste. On occasion Mr Moroney explains the theoretical background of statistical application with painstaking clarity, but a few pages later all the good is more than undone by beating the reader about the head with an array of formulae conjured from the air. . . . The author appears almost over-anxious to sell statistics to the public. . . . He is particularly keen to plug the statistics of the factory floor, and only occasionally does he pause to collect enough breath to shout a rude word at civil servants and at economic statisticians. . . . If Mr. Moroney's lack of deep knowledge leads him into trouble, so too does his desire to cover more or less everything in his favourite field. . . . Despite these sharp criticisms, it remains true that many people will derive considerable benefit from reading *Facts from Figures*. If only more people are set on the road to acquire a healthy attitude to figures, a most useful service will have been performed by Mr. Moroney."

Economica, 1953, **20**, 91.

" As a non-mathematical introduction to statistics, the book is generally good and in parts very good indeed. Mr. Moroney's writing is lucid, amusing and stimulating and his book is full of original ideas of presentation and method. . . . My chief criticism is that Mr. Moroney has at times allowed his critical exuberance to go too far. There are genuine criticisms to be made of index numbers and of time series analysis, but Mr. Moroney's aggressive and sweeping comments would discourage the reader from even approaching the subject seriously. . . . This criticism apart, the book will be useful to the many who are engaged on statistical work of a fairly elementary nature and would welcome a knowledge of the subject as a whole. As for the layman, I have little doubt that he will understand only a very small part of this book and, what is more, that only a very small part would be of any interest to him."

Nature, 1952, **169**, 473.

" [The author] states that his intention is ' to take the reader on a conducted tour of the statistician's workshop ' so that ' after watching the craftsman for a while, he may try for himself '. At times Mr. Moroney's enthusiasm may seem to leave the reader machine-minding when he might more profitably admire the view from the window. . . . Nevertheless this enthusiasm has produced a stimulating book, betraying at times the author's prejudices and (by some errors) the speed with which it was written, but encouraging the reader to persevere and presenting difficult ideas with an effective style . . . his book is packed with wise advice on the collection and interpretation of data, all of which is at least as important as the information on analysis."

QUENOUILLE, M. H. *INTRODUCTORY STATISTICS*
1950. Butterworth-Springer, x+248 pp.

Chapter	Contents
1	Presentation of Sets of Measurements
2	Normal Distribution
3	Comparison of Two Sets of Measurements
4	Comparison of Several Sets of Measurements
5	Attributes and Comparison of Proportions
6	Interrelations of Sets of Measurements
7	Concomitant Observations
8	Transformations and Non-Normal Distributions
9	Sampling Methods (for Surveys)

J. Amer. Statist. Ass., 1952, **47**, 94.

" The text consists of nine chapters each divided into two parts. The first part treats the subject matter at an elementary level; the second explores some of the theory and more advanced applications. . . . Despite [a] wealth of material, the book is not entirely successful. It is too condensed for accuracy, elegance, or clarity. . . . Often it fails to crystallize operationally important concepts. To illustrate, there are no useful definitions of population, sample, attribute, variable, random, or estimate. Other concepts are neither adroitly nor efficiently stated."

J. R. Statist. Soc. A, 1951, **114**, 254.

" . . . The book is intended for workers in any of the fields where modern statistical methods are needed. Little mathematical knowledge is presupposed and each chapter is divided into two parts of which the second is more specialized than the first and can be omitted at a first reading. ... The choice of material and balance in its presentation are excellent ... not a mere hash of other books but is a fresh attempt to meet a need still unsatisfied. The particular glory of this book is its splendid profusion of examples."

ADVANCED

BRYANT, E. C. *STATISTICAL ANALYSIS*
1960. McGraw Hill, 303 pp.

Chapter	Contents
1	Introduction
2	Probability
3	Statistical Inference I
4	Statistical Description
5	Statistical Inference II
6	Analysis of Frequencies
7	Simple Linear Regression and Correlation
8	Analysis of Variance and Industrial Experimentation
9	Analysis of Time Series
10	Multiple Regression
11	Sampling
12	Statistical Quality Control
13	Operating-level Problems

J. Amer. Statist. Ass., 1960, **55**, 776.

" This is a basic text dealing with application of statistical methods to managerial decision making. Bryant competently covers the standard topics, and illustrates them with many amusing examples. The following ' bonus ' topics have not previously been covered in a manner that would be suitable for undergraduate instruction: workable computing schemes for multiple regression and correlation, Markov theorem on least squares, analysis of variance theory, and queueing and inventory problems. The strength of the book is in its healthy differentiation between mathematics and statistics on the one hand, description and inference on the other. Bryant shows clearly how statistical theory depends upon mathematics. The more mathematics one knows, the better a statistician one can become. But this does not mean that the two disciplines are identical."

Inc. Statist., 1961, **11**, 62.

" I like the book because it is about methods and meaning rather than mathematics. . . . The explanations are good but it is a pity no answers are given for the numerous exercises. . . . Students for the Association's examinations would find the book worth reading and would like the way Professor Bryant treats the reader as an intelligent person who wants to understand and is prepared to think in order to follow a logically expressed argument.

"The style and treatment are up-to-date. For a book of its size, it manages to get in a good deal of useful material by pruning out traditional dead wood."

DAVIES, O. L. (Editor). *STATISTICAL METHODS IN RESEARCH AND PRODUCTION*
    1957. 3rd Ed., Revised and enlarged, Oliver and Boyd, x+396 pp.

Chapter	Contents
1	Introduction
2	Frequency Distributions
3	Averages and Measures of Dispersion
4	Confidence Limits and Tests of Significance
5	Statistical Tests: Choosing the Number of Observations
6	Analysis of Variance
7	Linear Relationships between Two Variables
8	Multiple and Curvilinear Regression
9	Frequency Data and Contingency Tables
10	Control Charts
11	Sampling and Specifications

Appl. Statist., 1957, **6**, 230.

" . . . the appearance of this book will be welcome to many, for the bringing up to date of a good book needs no justification."

Biometrika, 1957, **44**, 537.

" The book consists mainly of a practical exposition of the logic and application of the more elementary statistical methods. . . . The methods of exposition and the notation are admirably clear. . . . The book may be strongly recommended to anyone, even with very little mathematical knowledge, wishing to apply statistical methods to almost any form of industrial research or production."

Inc. Statist., 1958, **8**, 99.

" The reputation acquired by the first edition will be considerably enhanced by the thorough-going revisions incorporated in this new edition together with much valuable new material—both by way of text and example. . . . Chapter 5 is completely new and may well prove to be the most practically important part of the new material."

J. Inst. Actuar., 1957, **83**, 170.

" An important change is a shift of emphasis to confidence limits as opposed to tests of significance, ' experience having shown the greater practical utility of the former '. If this be interpreted as implying a preference for estimation as opposed to tests of significance, there is a good deal to be said for this point of view. However, many statisticians find confidence limits of rather restricted usefulness in a number of practical situations.

" The revision as a whole has been skilfully carried out and the resulting book should prove of value to anyone concerned with the day-to-day application of statistical methods in industry."

Rev. Int. Statist. Inst., 1957, **25**, 151.

" The book can be highly recommended to all industrial research workers who want to acquire a working knowledge of standard statistical methods without taking the trouble to go into the mathematics of statistics."

DIXON, W. J. AND MASSEY, F J. *INTRODUCTION TO STATISTICAL ANALYSIS*
1957. 2nd Ed., McGraw-Hill, xiii+488 pp.

Chapter	Contents
1	Introduction
2	Distributions
3	Introduction to Measures of Central Value and Dispersion
4	Universe and Sample
5	The Normal Distribution
6	Various Measures of Central Value and Dispersion
7	Statistical Inference
8	The Variance: Estimation and Tests of Hypotheses
9	The Mean: Estimation and Tests of Hypotheses
10	Analysis of Variance
11	Regression and Correlation
12	Analysis of Covariance
13	Enumeration Statistics
14	Probability of Accepting a False Hypothesis
15	Macrostatistics
16	Microstatistics
17	Nonparametric Statistics
18	Sequential Analysis
19	Sensitivity Experiments
20	Probability

Biometrika, 1957, **44**, 539.

" The present writer would agree with Wishart—(*Biometrika*, **39**, 1952)—that ' the book under review compares favourably with others of its kind '. It is, however, somewhat stereotyped and uninspiring."

J. Amer. Statist. Ass., 1957, **52**, 386.

" As its title implies, the emphasis in this book is on statistical techniques. Its strong points are (i) clear exposition of the techniques, with some account of assumptions required and of limitations, and (ii) inclusion both of the older orthodox procedures and of newer methods seldom found in elementary texts. For a well-rounded introductory course in statistics, its chief deficiencies are a scarcity of illustrations of the techniques by applying them to real data, and only a minimal discussion of the initial stages of an investigation—the definition of the problem and the planning and collection of the data."

J. Inst. Actuar., 1957, **83**, 310.

" Subject to certain qualifications . . . this book should prove an excellent text for use by teachers of elementary (and immediately post-elementary) courses in statistical method, and also for those students whose circumstances force them to commence the study of statistics on their own. The main points of excellence of the book are the liberal supply of class exercises, problems and discussion questions, the detailed treatment of each statistical concept, so helpful to the beginner and so often ignored by the expert author . . . and the unusually varied selection of tables provided. The book would have been of even greater value had outline solutions been given for at least some of the problems and exercises; perhaps this will be made good in a third edition. The level of mathematics required from the reader is quite low, though a considerable facility in relatively simple algebraic manipulation would greatly reduce the time taken to master the contents."

FERGUSON, G. A. *STATISTICAL ANALYSIS IN PSYCHOLOGY AND EDUCATION*
    1959. McGraw-Hill, vii + 347 pp.

Chapter	Contents
1	Basic Ideas in Statistics.
2	Frequency Distributions and Their Graphic Representation
3	Averages
4	Measures of Variation, Skewness and Kurtosis
5	Probability and the Binomial Distribution
6	The Normal Curve
7	Correlation
8	Prediction in Relation to Correlation
9	Essential Ideas of Sampling
10	Tests of Significance
11	Chi Square

12	Rank Correlation Methods
13	Other Varieties of Correlation
14	Transformations: Their Nature and Purpose
15	Analysis of Variance: One-way Classification
16	Analysis of Variance: Two-way Classification
17	Selected Non-parametric Tests
18	Errors of Measurement
19	Partial and Multiple Correlation

J. Amer. Statist. Ass., 1961, **56**, 185.

" Ferguson's text is a tightly written yet lucid introduction to contemporary statistical methods. Although aimed primarily at students with minimal mathematical training it maintains the simplicity and directness of more mathematical presentations and avoids the excessive description and language too frequently encountered in less well-written texts. . . .

" The text gains in distinction and quality as it moves from descriptive to inferential considerations. Most impressive is the treatment of the analysis of variance, especially the two-way classification. Here, consideration of the choice of appropriate error terms in fixed, mixed, and random models is particularly clear, while discussion of the problem of unequal numbers or disproportionality in subclasses is straightforward and practical.

" Somewhat unusual is the discussion of statistical transformations. Not only are transformations treated under a single chapter heading but the chapter itself is reserved for a later section of the text. . . .

" The emphasis on educational and psychological measurement is considerably reinforced by an up-to-date and generally lucid discussion of the reliability coefficient and the standard error of measurement. . . .

" An unusual feature in Ferguson's excellent introduction to partial and multiple correlation, at least as far as American texts are concerned, is his discussion of Aitken's method of pivotal condensation rather than Doolittle's approach to the solution of multiple regression equations. . . .

"Introductory statistical texts will continue to appear on the market. If they have any reason for being, it is because of the increased clarity of their presentation and/or their description of more current and less widely known procedures. Ferguson's text fully satisfies these criteria. It is a contribution to the statistical know-how of the behavioral scientist and should enjoy a wide market."

FISHER, R. A. *STATISTICAL METHODS FOR RESEARCH WORKERS*
1954. 12th Ed., Oliver and Boyd, xv+356 pp.

Chapter	Contents
1	Introductory
2	Diagrams
3	Distributions
4	Tests of Goodness of Fit, Independence and Homogeneity; with Table of χ^2
5	Tests of Significance of Means, Differences of Means, and Regression Coefficients
6	The Correlation Coefficient
7	Intraclass Correlations and the Analysis of Variance
8	Further Applications of the Analysis of Variance
9	The Principles of Statistical Estimation

Appl. Statist., 1954, **5**, 68.

" Of its historical value there is no doubt: it was the expression of the impact of a highly original mind on a newly developing science. . . . It is an essential part of the cultural heritage of all statisticians.

" In spite of its shortness a statistician who fully understands its contents would be well equipped even by modern standards. Yet this conciseness is a serious disadvantage to students or research workers making their first acquaintance with statistics. . . ."

J. R. Statist. Soc. A, 1955, **118**, 486.

" The book remains essentially an account of the author's conception of statistical methodology as he formulated it thirty years ago. Its continuing interest comes not only from the enormous influence that it has had but from its presentation of a particular well-defined attitude to the subject. . . . The book is meticulously and forcefully written, in a style that blends obscurity with clarity, vagueness with precision. . . . It seems to me to be much the most interesting book on methods that a student may read to supplement a mathematical text."

GOODMAN, R. *TEACH YOURSELF STATISTICS*
1957. English Universities Press, 239 pp.

Chapter	Contents
1	A First Look Round
2	Frequencies and Probabilities
3	Statistical Models. I: The Binomial Distribution
4	Statistical Models. II: The Poisson Distribution: Statistical Rarity
5	Statistical Models. III: The Normal Distribution
6	More Variates Than One: Bivariate Distributions Regression and Correlation
7	Sample and Population. I: Some Fundamentals of Sampling Theory
8	Sample and Population. II: t, z, and f
9	Analysis of Variance
10	Testing Regression and Correlation
11	Chi-Square and its Uses

Economica, 1958, **25**, 74.
" The merit of this introductory book—and it is a rare one—is that the reader will have very little to un-learn and to re-learn when he has mastered it."

Inc. Statist., 1958, **8**, 146.
" The order of presentation is of interest and the mathematical framework is built up in an orderly way, each step providing the tools required later on, while an excellent set of examples with answers is given at the end of each chapter.
" It is certainly not a book that should be made the centre of the student's work, nor is it recommended for students who are starting their studies with little or no previous knowledge of the subject. . . . The price of the book will make it attractive to the student and

properly studied and treated as a supplementary text it will be well worth its money to the student, especially in the precious hours previous to the examination."

J. Amer. Statist. Ass., 1958, **53**, 1033.

" *Teach Yourself Statistics* provides excellent review reading for those who have at some time studied mathematical statistics. . . . It is not likely to, nor should it, replace any of the several excellent texts now in general use in introductory courses in the mathematics of statistics."

J. Inst. Actuar., 1957, **83**, 314.

" This very concise book covers a great deal of ground in just over 200 small size pages. . . . As a whole this book would be difficult for a student new to the subject to master on his own. It tends to present statistics as a series of mathematical and arithmetical problems. . . . It seems, therefore, that the book would be of most value for a student to have at his elbow while attending a course on statistics. The scope and contents have been carefully chosen and could form the nucleus of a very valuable statistical training."

GOULDEN, C. H. *METHODS OF STATISTICAL ANALYSIS* 1952. 2nd Ed., Wiley, vi+467 pp.

Chapter	Contents
1	Introductory Concepts
2	Variation, Statistics and the Frequency Table
3	Theoretical Frequency Distributions
4	Tests of Significance
5	The Analysis of Variance
6	Linear Regression Analysis
7	Correlation
8	Partial and Multiple Regression and Correlation
9	The Analysis of Covariance
10	Non-linear Regression
11	Basic Experimental Designs

12   Factorial Experiments
13   Incomplete Block Experiments
14   The Treatment of Non-Orthogonal Data
15   Goodness of Fit
16   Tests of Independence
17   The Discriminant Function
18   Probit Analysis
19   Quality Control and Sampling for Inspection and Verification

Appl. Statist., 1954, **3**, 59.
" Throughout, the sections are illustrated by worked examples, and there are exercises at the end of each chapter as well as references to the literature for further reading. The book, improved as it is as the result of many years teaching and advisory experience should enjoy even more popularity than the first edition; if this is not so in this country it will be because the price is almost prohibitive for the student."

J. R. Statist. Soc. A, 1953, **116**, 204.
" Dr. Goulden's book . . . seems certain to amply justify its existence. It is one of the few books in the field which the reviewer has read with ease and enjoyment. . . .
" It is not possible to quarrel much with the choice of topics. There are no faddist inclusions and only one really notable omission . . . he never (even briefly) discusses the criteria of estimation. This seems to be the one serious lacuna in an otherwise first-class book suitable both for study and reference by workers in many fields."

Nature, 1954, **173**, 1159.
" Any scientific worker, whatever his field, who wishes to know the nature and scope of the subject can scarcely do better than begin with this book by C. H. Goulden. Deriving his inspiration from the work of R. A. Fisher, the author runs very lightly over what J. B. S. Haldane once called anti-halientic statistics: he arrives at the analysis of variance in Chapter 4 without having discussed standard errors in large sample theory. Some preliminary reading might therefore be recommended to the beginner before he embarks on the book; but once it has been carried out he can be safely entrusted

to Dr. Goulden's concise and careful treatment. This is quite one of the best introductions to modern statistical methods in experimentation that has yet appeared."

McNemar, Q. *PSYCHOLOGICAL STATISTICS*
1955. 2nd Ed., Wiley, vii+408 pp.

Chapter	Contents
1	Introduction
2	Tabular and Graphic Methods
3	Describing Frequency Distributions
4	Distribution Curves
5	Probability and Hypothesis Testing
6	Inference: Continuous Variables
7	Small Sample or t Technique
8	Correlation: Introduction and Computation
9	Correlation: Interpretations and Assumptions
10	Factors Which Affect the Correlation Coefficient
11	Multiple Correlation
12	Other Correlation Methods
13	Frequency Comparison: Chi-Square
14	Comparison of Variabilities
15	Analysis of Variance: Simple
16	Analysis of Variance: Complex
17	Analysis of Variance: Covariance Method
18	Distribution-free Methods
19	Remarks on Error Reduction

Brit. J. Psychol., 1955, **46**, 231.
". . . the presentation is a little difficult for the mathematically unsophisticated. In addition, some topics (e.g. Discriminant Function, pp. 210-11) are treated so concisely that one is left uncertain both of what the technique is designed to accomplish and of how the actual computation is carried out. . . . Most users of statistics have their favourite text-books; while the present reviewer is unlikely to transfer his allegiance to McNemar, he has already found the book indispensable, and the Appendix contains a particularly handy selection of Tables."

J. Amer. Statist. Ass., 1955, **50**, 1345.

" This reviewer feels strongly that the practitioner of statistical inference must understand much more of his art than he brings to bear on a specific problem; therefore, the ' cookbook ' approach cannot succeed. However, many disagree with this point of view. For these pragmatically-minded individuals, the measure of the cookbook is the quality of the cake produced. This kind of evaluation of books like McNemar's seems impossible to achieve. In the absence of such evaluation, the reviewer can only assert his judgment that McNemar's book is as good as any written in the past two decades for the purpose of putting the sharpest tools of the statistical inference trade in the untrained hands of mature, but mathematically naive, students of the social sciences."

QUENOUILLE, M. H. *ASSOCIATED MEASUREMENTS*
1952. Butterworth, x + 242 pp.

Chapter	Contents
1	Graphical Investigation
2	Graphical Estimation
3	Graphical Testing
4	Linear Association
5	Multiple Association
6	Curvilinear Association
7	Grouping of Observations
8	Uses of the Analysis of Co-variance
9	Large-Scale Investigations
10	Special Problems and Analyses
11	Time Series Analysis
12	Multivariate Analysis

Appl. Statist., 1954, **3**, 61.

" Mr. Quenouille's book is an account of correlation, and its 213 pages of text encompass a wide variety of methods, many otherwise accessible only in journals or difficult text-books. The exposition is lively, rapid, and smooth, helped on by plenty of real-life illustrations and numerical demonstrations. There are a good bibliography and some useful tables. . . . Experienced statisticians will want this book on their shelves since it contains a stimulating and easily read outline of methods old and new. It is not by any means so suitable for beginners who will find that it takes rather a lot of knowledge for granted and who might be led to believe that all the techniques described are generally accepted by statisticians, whereas some are little more than statements of what Mr. Quenouille would do, reasonable though it may be, in the situations described."

Biometrika, 1953, **40**, 471.

" [The book is an] . . . advanced non-mathematical text-book on statistical methods excellently illustrated with examples, mostly biological, which are handled with great skill and with a clear sense of the practical purpose of the statistical analysis. The main fault is an occasional carelessness of writing."

Econometrica, 1961, **29**, 97.

" That the book is a success in explaining the ideas in simple words—almost in layman's language—is unquestionable. As is always true, however, the over-simplification leads, by its very nature to the omission of many points which are of interest in all but elementary experimentation, and gives to the user an over-confidence in the power of these methods. . . . Notwithstanding these defects, I think this book gives an excellent discussion of the essential aspects of regression analysis and a reader of any calibre will benefit by looking at these simple facts which are often not appreciated when one is engaged in untangling the mathematical complexities and in wading through the controversies associated with the methods of regression analysis."

J. Inst. Actuar., 1953, **79**, 122.

" This book deals in a thoroughly practical manner with the modern methods and illustrates them by application to numerous sets of numerical data. . . . The style is condensed and quite an amount of statistical knowledge is assumed. On the other hand, one who has only studied the methods in mathematical form should derive great benefit from the book. He will gain from the examples a greater appreciation of the scope of the methods and of the variety of situations to which they are applicable—methods often rather obscured by mathematical presentation."

J. R. Statist. Soc. A, 1953, **116**, 323.

"*Associated Measurements* is a title that can cover a very wide field, and the author ranges far indeed—from dot diagrams to multivariate analysis—and rapidly. He states that the amount of mathematics has been kept to the minimum necessary to explain the approaches used, and that the non-mathematician should therefore be able to follow the methods given. It is difficult in any textbook to choose and maintain an appropriate level of discussion and, with a field as wide as this, the task is almost impossible if the volume is to be kept to reasonable size; in this case the success is not complete. . . . The bibliography is long and should be useful. In fine, the book serves a good purpose as a connected account of the processes available for the estimation and testing of associations between quantitative methods."

SNEDECOR, G. W. *STATISTICAL METHODS*
1956. 5th Ed., Iowa State College Press, xiii + 534 pp.

Chapter	Contents
1	Sampling of Attributes. Binomial Distribution
2	Sampling from a Normally Distributed Population
3	Sampling from a Normally Distributed Population. Sampling Distributions
4	The Comparison of Two Randomized Groups
5	Short Cuts and Approximations. Less than Fully Efficient and Non-parametric Methods
6	Linear Regression
7	Correlation
8	Large Sample Methods
9	Enumeration Data with More than One Degree of Freedom
10	Two or More Random Samples of Measurement Data. Analysis of Variance
11	Two-Way Experiments. Analysis of Variance

12	Comparisons. Factorial Arrangements of Treatments
13	Covariance
14	Multiple Regression and Covariance
15	Curvilinear Regression
16	Binomial and Poisson Distributions
17	Design and Analysis of Samplings

J. Amer. Statist. Ass., 1957, **52**, 100.

" It is clear that *Statistical Methods*, which was already the best text of its kind, has undergone substantial improvement, and it can therefore be highly recommended to its potential readers."

J. R. Statist. Soc. A, 1957, **120**, 221.

" ' Snedecor ' has been for a long time one of the most popular textbooks for workers in biology and agriculture, and it is still among the best in its field. The fifth edition contains some new material, notably on non-parametric techniques and on multiple tests of significance. . . . The style of the book is leisurely and discursive with liberal use of the first person singular. The abundant worked examples are treated in great detail, and a large number of further examples are provided as exercises. The whole approach is admirably calculated to appeal to the non-mathematician."

STEEL, R. G. D. AND TORRIE, J. H. *PRINCIPLES AND PROCEDURES OF STATISTICS*
1960. McGraw-Hill, xvi+481 pp.

Chapter	Contents
1	Introduction
2	Observations
3	Probability
4	Sampling from a Normal Distribution
5	Comparisons Involving Two Sample Means
6	Principles of Experimental Design
7	Analysis of Variance I: The One-way Classification
8	Analysis of Variance II: Multiway Classifications
9	Linear Regression

	10	Linear Correlation
	11	Analysis of Variance III: Factorial Experiments
	12	Analysis of Variance IV: Split-plot Designs and Analysis
	13	Analysis of Variance V: Unequal Subclass Numbers
	14	Multiple and Partial Regression and Correlation
	15	Analysis of Covariance
	16	Nonlinear Regression
	17	Some Uses of Chi-square
	18	Enumeration Data I: One-way Classifications
	19	Enumeration Data II: Contingency Tables
	20	Some Discrete Distributions
	21	Nonparametric Statistics
	22	Sampling Finite Populations

Biometrika, 1961, **48**, 235.

" This is a ' cook-book ' and a good one for the use of biologists who wish to acquire the elements of biometry. The statistical techniques are presented with the minimum of algebraic manipulation, the procedures to be adopted are clear and the whole is illustrated with many actual illustrations, most of which have the merit, to the reviewer at least, of being fresh material.

" Biologists, no matter from which side of the Atlantic they come, are timorous about algebra and even about algebraic notation, a trepidation which they often cover up with an aggressive disdain for abstract thought. It is difficult to see how Messrs. Steel and Torrie could have used less symbolism than they have, but the average biologist will not find the book easy to read. For those who are forced to apply the techniques set out, understanding will come through hard work. For those who merely want to learn a smattering of a new subject something easier will need to be sought after."

Inc. Statist., 1961, **11**, 170.

" The text has three main aims. Firstly, to present the student with a considerable number of statistical techniques applicable and useful in research. Secondly, to promote disciplined thinking on the part of the student with respect to the conduct of the experiments. Thirdly, to promote disciplined thinking on the part of the student with respect to the analysis of experimental data. The first aim is

certainly achieved. ... The second and third of the authors' aims stand a good chance of being achieved if the reader gives plenty of time to a close study of the text. ...
"A feature throughout the book is the clarity with which the computations are laid out especially in the analysis of variance chapters. Two other merits of the book also deserve mention. First, the authors have made a real effort to be as up-to-date as it is possible to be with a text-book. Many of the latest techniques and tests which have only comparatively recently appeared in the journals are included in the text, with references to original sources. Second, each chapter has an excellent list of references at the end of it; including other text-books, papers in the recognized statistical journals, and articles in some of the less likely journals. The whole approach and layout of the book is strongly reminiscent of the well known *Statistical Methods* by George W. Snedecor. ...."

WALKER, H. M. AND LEV, J. *STATISTICAL INFERENCE* 1953. Holt, xi+510 pp.

Chapter	Contents
1	Inferences Based on Simple Experiments
2	Probability Distributions
3	Inferences Concerning Proportions
4	Chi-Square
5	Populations and Samples on a Continuous Variable
6	Sampling Distributions
7	Inferences Concerning the Mean or the Difference Between Two Means
8	Inferences Concerning Variances and Standard Deviations of Normal Populations
9	Analysis of Variance
10	Linear Regression and Correlation
11	Other Measures of Relationship
12	The Statistics of Measurement
13	Multiple Regression and Correlation
14	Analysis of Variance with Two or More Variables of Classification
15	Analysis of Covariance

16 Percentiles
17 Transformation of Scales
18 Non-parametric Methods

Appl. Statist., 1954, **3**, 206.

"... this is a first-class introduction to practical statistical methods, with a bias in the examples towards applications in the social and educational field.
... it is not only a sound practical text-book ... it approaches the subject from an almost new angle and has a number of unusual features. In all, the book makes the best use of its approach."

Biometrika, 1955, **42**, 541.

"... Despite some defects, however, research students of education and allied fields should find this text invaluable, not only as an instruction manual, but also as a general work of reference in statistical method."

Econometrica, 1955, **23**, 226.

" This is an excellent non-mathematical text on tests of significance intended for those who already have an elementary knowledge of statistics. Although mathematical proofs are not given, basic formulas are presented together with the assumptions on which the formulas rest. The limitations of the analysis are clearly marked and concrete examples illustrate the methods of computation. The examples are generally drawn from the field of education, but the book could be readily used in any intermediate course in statistics.
... In general within the framework of their goal, the authors have done a splendid job."

J. R. Statist. Soc. A, 1954, **117**, 102.

" This is a book on statistical methods for non-mathematicians.
... There are no proofs, though mathematical symbolism is used extensively and carefully explained. The reader is assumed to have done a short course in statistics before, and to be familiar with ideas such as mean, standard deviation and linear regression. ...

" But my main objection to the book is that in its explanation through examples and in its persistent repetition of formulae in slightly varying forms, as though formulae were the magic tools, the essential statistical concepts are obscured."

YULE, G. U. AND KENDALL, M. G. *AN INTRODUCTION TO THE THEORY OF STATISTICS*
1950. 14th Ed., Griffin, xxiv+701 pp.

Chapter	Contents
1	Theory of Attributes: Basic Ideas
2	Association of Attributes
3	Manifold Classification
4	Frequency-Distributions
5	Averages and other Measures of Location
6	Measures of Dispersion
7	Moments and Measures of Skewness and Kurtosis
8	Three Important Theoretical Distributions: the Binomial, the Normal and the Poisson
9	Correlation and Regression
10	Normal Correlation
11	Further Theory of Correlation
12	Partial Correlation
13	Correlation and Regression: Some Practical Problems
14	Miscellaneous Theorems Involving the Correlation Coefficient
15	Simple Curve Fitting
16	Preliminary Notions on Sampling
17	The Sampling of Attributes: Large Samples
18	The Sampling of Variables: Large Samples
19	The Sampling of Variables: Large Samples (continued)
20	The χ^2 Distribution
21	The Sampling of Variables: Small Samples
22	The Analysis of Variance
23	Some Problems of Practical Sampling
24	Interpolation and Graduation
25	Index Numbers
26	Time Series
27	Time Series (2)

Ann. Eugenics, 1951, **16**, 106.

" This new edition represents the second major revision of what has been recognized for some years as a standard introductory text on statistics. While the basic design and material of the book have not been changed, its scope has been widened to cover recent developments in elementary statistical theory, and parts of it have been re-written to bring it into line with the current approach to statistical problems. . . . It is good to find the limitations of the various techniques so explicitly stated."

J. Inst. Actuar., 1951, **77**, 152.

"After nearly forty years 'Yule and Kendall' remains an outstanding standard text-book on elementary statistics . . . . this most recent revision should ensure a continuance of this old favourite in its accustomed place at the centre of English statistical literature."

J. R. Statist. Soc. A, 1950, **113**, 578.

"In its new form it will certainly remain a standard text-book for another generation of statisticians. . . . One of the most valuable features of Yule and Kendall is the use of introductory chapters . . . which survey, with an abundance of illustration, the basic ideas of the subject . . . they give the reader a sense of 'shape' of the material with which he has to deal, and a broad picture of the statistical problems which confront him."

Nature, 1951, **167**, 294.

"The present text, as all previous editions, is designed for those with little mathematical training. As statistical theory becomes increasingly mathematical, it is becoming more and more difficult to give an exposition without calculus. The attempt here is successful, at the price of calling on the reader to accept much without proof. It follows that this is not (and is not intended to be) an introductory text for the mathematician, who will find other books both shorter and more congenial. The book is, in fact, directed to that much larger, and increasing, number of students of statistics who are attempting to reach the standard of statistics as an ancillary subject in many degree courses, or of the certificate of the Royal Statistical Society or the Association of Incorporated Statisticians."

MATHEMATICAL STATISTICS

General Texts

AITKEN, A. C. *STATISTICAL MATHEMATICS*
1957. 8th Ed., Oliver and Boyd, vii+153 pp.

Chapter	Contents
1	Statistics as a Science: Axioms of Probability
2	Probability and Frequency Distributions: Graphical Representation: Calculation of Moments
3	Special Probability Distributions
4	Practical Curve Fitting with Standard Curves
5	Probability and Frequency in Two Variates
6	The Method of Least Squares: Multivariate Correlation: Polynomial and Harmonic Regression
7	Probability Distributions of Statistical Coefficients

J. Inst. Actuar., 1943, **71**, 172.

"The book postulates a maturity of thought which makes it unsuitable for the beginner. Each sentence has been carefully weighed and appraised and Dr. Aitken has succeeded in providing the maximum of information in the minimum of space; like the mathematical text-book, it needs perseverance or an accompanying series of lectures for its full appreciation. . . .

"The book is entirely mathematical in character but occasionally Dr. Aitken works through a numerical example. . . . To the serious student who is prepared to do more than scratch at the surface of a difficult subject, the book is a scholarly, and, in its way, complete, introduction to that "advanced" statistical technique which is so fascinating to its adepts and so irritating to its detractors."

J. R. Statist. Soc., 1940, **103**, 400.

". . . the need for a treatise on Mathematical Statistics as opposed to the existing Method textbooks. . . . With his *Statistical Mathematics* Dr. Aitken has made a first step towards producing such a mathematical treatise. It will be welcome to all those who know, or are prepared to learn, a reasonable amount of mathematics . . . readers of a certain standard of maturity in mathematical reading will no doubt appreciate the book more than beginners. . . .

"The deductive line of approach has been adopted . . . some elementary but important points are fittingly observed. . . . If a criticism may be made, it would concern omissions (due perhaps to lack of space) of important modern small-sample results. . . . These limitations in scope should in no way detract from the value of this admirable little book."

ANDERSON, R. L. AND BANCROFT, T. A. *STATISTICAL THEORY IN RESEARCH*
1952. McGraw Hill, xix+399 pp.

Chapter	Contents
1	Introduction
2	Probability
3	Univariate Parent Population Distributions
4	Properties of Univariate Distribution Functions
5	Bivariate and Multivariate Distributions and Their Properties
6	Derived Sampling Distributions and Orthogonal Linear Functions
7	Derived Sampling Distributions: Normal Parent Population
8	Introduction to Point Estimation and Criteria of "Goodness"
9	Principles of Point Estimation: Maximum Likelihood
10	Interval Estimation
11	Tests of Hypotheses
12	Special Uses of Chi-Square
13	Regression Analysis
14	General Regression Model with Fixed Variates
15	Computational Methods and Methods of Analysis for a General Regression Model
16	Curvilinear Regression: Orthogonal Polynomials

17	Least Squares for Experimental Design Models
18	The Analysis of Designs in Complete Blocks
19	The Analysis of Incomplete-blocks Designs
20	Factorial Experiments
21	The Analysis of Covariance
22	Variance Components: All Random Components Except the Mean
23	Analysis of Data with Both Random and Fixed Effects (Mixed Model)
24	The Recovery of Interblock Information in Incomplete-blocks Design
25	Other Topics Concerning Components of Variance: Summary of Needed Research

Biometrika, 1954, **41**, 283.

" Among the many statistical text-books now pouring from the printing presses of many countries this book written by R. L. Anderson and T. A. Bancroft is outstanding. The authors divide it into two parts; the first which they entitle ' Basic Statistical Theory ' is just what it says. It is a competent exposition of the corpus of statistical theory which we might now term orthodox and consists of material which has been expounded and mis-expounded by many authors.

"The second part entitled 'Analysis of Experimental Models by Least Squares ' is interesting, useful, informative and stimulating. . . . The treatment throughout is unified and mathematical clarity is achieved. What is somewhat surprisingly linked with theoretical clearness is adequate arithmetical exposition of problems allied to theory. The book is to be recommended to all students following a course of analysis of variance and experimental design and to those working statisticians who carry out arithmetical operations every day and who would like to know more of the theoretical background of their operations."

BENNETT, C. A. AND FRANKLIN, N. L. *STATISTICAL ANALYSIS IN CHEMISTRY AND THE CHEMICAL INDUSTRY* 1954. Wiley, xvi+724 pp.

Chapter	Contents
1	Introduction
2	Descriptive Statistics
3	Probability and Statistics
4	Mathematical Machinery
5	Statistical Inference
6	Relationships Between Variables
7	Analysis of Variance
8	The Design of Experiments
9	Analysis of Counted Data
10	Control Charts
11	Some Tests for Randomness

Biometrika, 1955, **42**, 542.

" This book contains a well-written account of statistical techniques, some of which are not readily available elsewhere. . . .

" To those workers in the chemical industry and elsewhere who have been introduced to statistical methods via a ' cookery book ' and who now wish to broaden their knowledge and to learn something more of the basis of these methods, this book is recommended. It will be less useful to those who wish to know how statistics should be used in practice. Some of the examples fail to demonstrate the value of the method discussed, or the sort of circumstances in which it might be used, and instances occur where the statistical analysis confuses rather than clarifies the situation. . . .

" It is very important that the experimenter should be the master and not the slave of statistical methods. In particular, he should not allow himself to be overawed by apparently complicated mathematical machinery. When he feels his problem is not really answered by the application of standard techniques he should try to deal with it from first principles. His solution even if it is somewhat approximate and unorthodox will usually serve him better than the misapplication of a mathematically ' exact ' technique. In helping to instil these first principles this text-book is valuable; the reader should, however, not take too seriously some of the applications which are described."

BROWNLEE, K. A. *STATISTICAL THEORY AND METHODOLOGY IN SCIENCE AND ENGINEERING*
1960. Wiley, xv+570 pp.

Chapter	Contents
1	Mathematical Ideas
2	Statistical Ideas
3	Problems Involving the Use of the Binomial Distribution
4	The Hypergeometric and Poisson Distributions
5	The χ^2 Distribution, the Multinomial Distribution, and Contingency Tables
6	Some Tests of the Hypothesis of Randomness: Control Charts
7	Some Nonparametric Tests
8	The Partitioning of Sums of Squares
9	Tests for Equality of Variances and Means
10	One-Way Analysis of Variance
11	Simple Linear Regression
12	The Bivariate Normal Distribution and the Correlation Coefficient
13	Two-Way Analysis of Variance
14	Three-Way and Four-Way Analysis of Variance
15	Partially Hierarchical Situations
16	Some Simple Experimental Designs
17	Regression on Several Independent Variables
18	The Multiple-Regression Approach to Analysis of Variance
19	Topics in the Design of Experiments

J. R. Statist. Soc. A, 1961, **124**, 573.

" This is a well-thought-out and carefully written book. The author has been at the University of Chicago since 1952 and the book arises out of a course, using only college algebra, designed to give students in the experimental sciences some confidence in the use of statistical methods. This origin is reflected in the style of writing and the manner in which the subject matter is treated. ...

"The style of the book would appeal to all those for whom algebra forms the most natural sequence of development, rather than a geometrical or arithmetical approach. At times the purport of a passage does not quite penetrate the algebra, but the order and logic is impeccable, resulting in a well-balanced and nicely developed text book. However, one is doubtful whether a scientist working on his own would master the contents easily—or be able to use the volume as a work of reference. A study, for example, of the chapters on the fitting of straight lines indicates the need to have a guide, at one's elbow, to assist the practitioner in applying the various techniques to a practical problem. This demonstrates the book's most likely use—and indeed its prime purpose—which is to act as a class text for a one-year course on statistics to those possessing approximately ' A ' level mathematics. The practical problems are not dealt with at sufficient length for other readers to be able to master the subject-matter and apply the techniques with confidence."

BRUNK, H. D. *AN INTRODUCTION TO MATHEMATICAL STATISTICS*
1960. Ginn, x+403 pp.

Chapter	Contents
1	Elementary Probability Spaces
2	General Probability Spaces
3	Random Variables
4	Combined Random Variables
5	The Algebra of Expectations
6	Random Sampling
7	The Law of Large Numbers
8	Estimation of Parameters
9	Central Limit Theorem
10	Confidence Intervals and Tests of Hypotheses
11	Statistical Decision Theory
12	Regression
13	Sampling From a Normal Population

14   Testing Hypotheses
15   Experimental Design and the Analysis of Variance
16   Other Sampling Methods
17   Distribution-Free Methods

J. Amer. Statist. Ass., 1961, **56**, 412.

" This text is intended to serve as an introduction to probability and the fundamental concepts of mathematical statistics for students who have studied the calculus. . . .

" The treatment of the topics covered in the book is in the modern spirit of the axiomatic development of probability theory and the development of the principles of mathematical statistics from the point of view of hypothesis testing and estimation. . . .

" In this reviewer's opinion the book is a welcome addition to the texts already available for use in an introductory course in mathematical statistics. All of the fundamental ideas which ought to be included in such a course are covered in a manner which will be generally acceptable to most mathematical statisticians. Students who have had good previous mathematical training should find this book a valuable text if the material is presented by a competent instructor."

CRAMÉR, H. *MATHEMATICAL METHODS OF STATISTICS*
    1946. Princeton University Press, xvi+575 pp.

Chapter	Contents
1-3	Sets of Points
4-7	Theory of Measurement and Integration in R_1
8-9	Theory of Measurement and Integration in R_n
10-12	Various Questions: Ch. 10—Fourier integrals. Ch. 11—Matrices, determinants and quadratic forms. Ch. 12—Miscellaneous complements.
13-14	Foundations
15-20	Variables and Distributions in R_1
21-24	Variables and Distributions in R_n
25-26	Generalities
27-29	Sampling Distributions
30-31	Tests of Significance, I

32-34 Theory of Estimation
35-37 Tests of Significance, II

Biometrika, 1947, **34**, 374.

" It is a definitive exposition of the theory of mathematical statistics as it existed in 1940 (about) and it is worth while therefore to consider its contents in some detail. . . . As a textbook of mathematical statistics this book will remain unrivalled for many years to come. The mathematical exposition is clear, the development of ideas logical throughout, and the theorems are presented in a very general way. Any student of mathematics who wishes to get a picture of what statistical theory is about will be led inevitably to this book. . . . It only remains to say to the student, ' this is a good book, buy it! ' "

J. Amer. Statist. Ass., 1947, **42**, 174.

" This excellent book will be welcomed by mathematicians who wish to become acquainted with statistical methods, and, even more so, by statisticians who desire a reference book for proofs of the fundamental theorems of statistical theory."

J. Inst. Actuar., 1947, **73**, 169.

" The book . . . is mathematical and will appeal especially to mathematicians interested in the theoretical side of statistics, but it will also be of interest to those statisticians who, though more interested in practical statistical applications, want to appreciate the mathematical background of the subject. . . . If . . . a reader wants something else added he should, to be fair, say what he would exclude and that would indeed be a puzzle. The difficulty of that puzzle is a measure of our gratitude for the book."

FISHER, R. A. *STATISTICAL METHODS AND SCIENTIFIC INFERENCE*
    1956. Oliver and Boyd, viii+175 pp.

Chapter	Contents
1	Foreword
2	The Early Attempts and Their Difficulties
3	Forms of Quantitative Inference

4 Some Misapprehensions About Tests of Significance
5 Some Simple Examples of Inferences Involving Probability and Likelihood
6 The Principles of Estimation

Ann. Hum. Genet., 1957, **22**, 93.

" All statisticians interested in the theory of their subject should buy this book. When they have winnowed the wheat from the chaff in the shape of the principles from the polemics, they will be left with what might be called, in the manner of the seventeenth and eighteenth centuries, the challenge to the problem."

Appl. Statist., 1957, **6**, 226.

" This is definitely a book for the mature statistician, and will undoubtedly join its predecessors, *Statistical Methods for Research Workers* and *The Design of Experiments* as a classic in the literature of statistics. Although it cannot be recommended as a text-book for students, they will find it provocative and interesting reading, and will doubtless be amazed at the intensity of the emotions which can be aroused in arguments on statistical fundamentals."

Biometrika, 1957, **44**, 293.

" This book is welcome in providing an up-to-date and authoritative account of Sir Ronald Fisher's views on statistical inference. Readers new to statistics are, however, advised not to try to read Fisher's book entirely on its own. The issues discussed are fairly technical and sometimes controversial; and this book largely concentrates on the author's original contributions, without always adequate representation of other points of view. The book is in consequence likely to repay study most by those already well acquainted with current statistical methods."

Economica, 1958, **25**, 115.

Under the heading " Statistical Inference " Mr. Alan Stuart of the London School of Economics discusses the philosophy of this book and two others on the same subject.

J. R. Statist. Soc. A, 1957, **120**, 88.

" For many years now there has been a good deal of strenuous controversy about the underlying basis of statistical inference, and the present book—by one of the protagonists in the drama is therefore all the more welcome. It is not of course to be expected that all adherents of inverse probability and followers of the Neyman-Pearson line will immediately be converted to Sir Ronald Fisher's well-known views on the use of fiducial arguments, the frequent inadmissibility of errors of the second kind and the unwise insistence on ' repeated sampling from the same population '. Nevertheless, it is extremely helpful to have these views clearly set out and closely argued within the compass of a single exposition, instead of having, as previously, only a number of papers scattered throughout the literature."

Nature, 1957, **179**, 277.

" *Statistical Methods and Scientific Inference* will not, one suspects, be easy reading even for many of the statisticians at whom, no doubt, it is primarily aimed. The less mathematically minded will find the going still harder. But persistence will be amply repaid by the deeper appreciation which is to be gained of those inductive processes which all experimental science must use, and which Fisher himself has done so much to analyse, clarify and expose for our better understanding."

FRASER, D. A. S. *STATISTICS—AN INTRODUCTION*
1958. Wiley, ix+398 pp.

Chapter	Contents
1	Introduction
2	Simple Probability Distributions
3	Discrete Probability Distributions
4	Continuous Probability Distributions
5	Characteristics of Distributions
6	Sampling from Probability Distributions
7	Sampling from Finite Populations
8	Some Probability Distributions
9	Estimation
10	Hypothesis Testing
11	Confidence Methods

12	Regression Analysis
13	Factorial Designs
14	Some Techniques of Experimental Design
15	Sampling Inspection and Sequential Analysis
16	Nonparametric Methods

Biometrika, 1960, **47**, 211.

" The level of exposition of this book is adequate and it will be found useful by mathematics students wanting to learn something of the mysteries of the statistical craft. . . . The degree of sophistication required is a little more than that for A. M. Mood, *Introduction to the Theory of Statistics*."

J. Inst. Actuar., 1959, **85**, 320.

" This is a sound textbook, in traditional style, which will be an excellent adjunct to university undergraduate teaching. The need of the student for practice in the subject is adequately catered for by an ample provision of problems. . . . Unfortunately no solutions are provided. The book should prove popular with many teachers of statistics . . . and useful to anyone wishing to attain a sound knowledge of basic statistical ideas and techniques at the expense of a reasonable amount of application."

J. R. Statist. Soc. A, 1960, **123**, 201.

" This textbook is for the mathematically-minded student who wants to acquire a thorough training in the basic principles of statistical theory. . . . The author's chosen readers are well served, and the book is likely to prove most useful to them. The style is clear and straightforward, and although at times it may appear repetitive this is likely to be a further advantage to many of its readers. . . . The author builds up the theory carefully and explains it well, giving proofs wherever this is possible without unduly lengthening the text. Each chapter is provided with further references and problems (some theoretical, some numerical) for which a booklet of answers is available on request."

Nature, 1959, **184**, 1008.

" While reading the book one has the impression that among the author's guiding lights has been the wish to introduce students as early as possible to the ways of thinking about statistical problems that are customary among professional research workers. It was particularly good to find a thorough treatment of orthogonal transformations, projections on to sub-spaces and pivotal reductions of the normal equations. Once these basic ideas have been grasped the theory of multiple regression, the analysis of variance and covariance, and much else in statistical theory become straightforward."

HALD, A. *STATISTICAL THEORY WITH ENGINEERING APPLICATIONS*
1952. Wiley, xii+783 pp.

Chapter	Contents
1	Fundamental Calculus of Probabilities
2	Some Fundamental Applications of the Calculus of Probabilities
3	Graphical and Tabular Representation of Observations
4	Definitions and Fundamental Properties of Empirical Distributions
5	Definitions and Fundamental Properties of Theoretical Distributions
6	The Normal Distribution
7	Skew Distributions
8	Some Limit Theorems and Sampling Distributions
9	The Distribution of the Mean
10	The χ^2-Distribution
11	The Distribution of the Variance
12	The Distribution of the Range
13	Statistical Control
14	The Distribution of the Variance Ratio
15	The t-Distribution
16	Analysis of Variance
17	Designs of Sampling Investigations and Experiments
18	Linear Regression Analysis with One Independent Variable
19	The Two-Dimensional Normal Distribution
20	Multi-Dimensional Correlation and Regression
21	The Binomial Distribution

22	The Poisson Distribution
23	The Multinomial Distribution and the χ^2-Test
24	Sequential Analysis
25	The Main Points of a Statistical Analysis

Appl. Statist., 1953, **2**, 203.

" This is not a book for the beginner and the average practising engineer could not refer to a particular section at short notice. On the other hand, given a mathematical training and experience in statistical methods, the reader will find an extremely good coverage in this book which would make a valuable addition to his library. It is a book for the statistician dealing with engineering problems rather than for an engineer dealing with statistical investigations. . . . The book is based on Professor Hald's Danish text-book and in the dozen or so numerical examples from engineering practice only metric units are used, whereby much of their value for British engineers is lost. . . . In a book of nearly 800 pages the absence of misprints is noteworthy. In fact only one was found. The diagrams are clearly the work of a draughtsman and the printing is excellent."

Biometrika, 1953, **40**, 473.

" This book has as its aim the provision, in simple and logical form, of those parts of statistical methods which are of use to the engineer in his daily work. Nevertheless, in its 800 pages, it covers considerably more ground, and that ground in greater detail, than might be expected from this simple aim. The result has been to produce a text-book which derives from first principles and illustrates with practical examples all the common statistical processes. . . . The particular portion of the book that struck the reviewer as one of the best of its kind was the section on the analysis of variance which is developed extremely logically. . . . The technique of the analysis of variance has great value for the engineer and it is rather a pity that the treatment here is not quite as full as in other parts of the book. . . . There is the risk that its length may put off all but the keenest student, particularly if he must find the money to buy it himself."

J. R. Statist. Soc. A, 1953, **116**, 87.

" The claim that the methods given are important to the engineer in his daily work is exaggerated. . . . As a work of instruction, the book is too long and expensive, and there is so much discussion of ancillary topics that the novice will have his attention distracted from important fundamentals. . . . The real value of this book is as a work of reference on the theory of statistics, and as such its value will be considerable. It will doubtless eventually find its way to the bookshelf of almost every industrial statistician; and since most of its contents are of perfectly general application, it will be useful to other statisticians, too. As a source of useful illustrations and elementary mathematical proofs, it will be valuable to the teacher of statistics."

HOEL, P. G. *INTRODUCTION TO MATHEMATICAL STATISTICS*
1954. 2nd Ed., Wiley, xi+331 pp.

Chapter	Contents
1	Introduction
2	Probability
3	Nature of Statistical Methods
4	Empirical Frequency Distributions of One Variable
5	Theoretical Frequency Distributions of One Variable
6	Elementary Sampling Theory for One Variable
7	Correlation and Regression
8	Theoretical Frequency Distributions for Correlation and Regression
9	Testing Goodness of Fit
10	General Principles for Testing Hypotheses and for Estimation
11	Small Sample Distributions
12	Statistical Design in Experiments
13	Nonparametric Methods

Biometrika, 1955, **42**, 271.

" This is a much expanded and revised version of a book that first appeared in 1947. . . . The book is much more self-contained than formerly. . . . Inevitably in a book of this size some things have had to be omitted, for example, time series, equalization of variance and probit analysis. . . . Diagrams are used excellently throughout the book and are well labelled. There are numerous exercises. . . ."

J. R. Statist. Soc. A, 1955, **118**, 103.

" The new edition is about $1\frac{1}{4}$ times as long as the old; as well as the addition of new material there has been rearrangement so that general ideas about significance testing and estimation are introduced at an early stage. . . . The mathematics is restricted to elementary calculus. The development is logical and the style very lucid. . . . My only serious criticism concerns the account of significance tests. . . . Despite this criticism there is no doubt that the book is very valuable and the new edition is to be welcomed."

Inc. Statist., 1955, **5**, 209.

" This book can be warmly recommended to students preparing for the ' Statistical Theory ' paper of the Association's Final Examinations. The author has refrained from giving proofs requiring more advanced mathematics than most students will possess, but the whole book is clear and logical, and there is nothing slipshod about the argument or its presentation."

Nature, 1956, **177**, 813.

" This is one of the best text-books on theoretical statistics at the undergraduate level. The first edition was good, but this second edition has been revised, extended and greatly improved. It is very suitable for first-year students with a knowledge of elementary calculus and some general acquaintance with the scope of statistical method. There are numerous exercises, the answers to which can be obtained separately."

Note:—A set of answers to the exercises in this book is published separately by John Wiley and Sons, Inc.

HOGG, R. V. AND CRAIG, A. T. *INTRODUCTION TO MATHEMATICAL STATISTICS*
   1959. Macmillan, ix + 245 pp.

Chapter   Contents
   1   Distribution of Random Variables

2	Some Special Distributions
3	Introduction to Sampling Theory
4	Transformations of Variables
5	Point Estimation
6	Sufficiency and Stochastic Independence
7	Limiting Distributions
8	Some Distribution-Free Problems
9	Statistical Hypotheses
10	Certain Quadratic Forms
11	Multivariate Distributions

Biometrika, 1961, **48**, 235.

" The authors state that this book is intended for a two-semester course for undergraduate students with some mathematical preparation. They indicate which sections will be found useful if it is desired to cut the course down to one-semester. From the English point of view the students will require little more than advanced level mathematics and the book will certainly be within the compass of the first year general student. . . .

"The mathematical exposition is clear and the seeker for light on the mathematics of statistics will find this book meets his needs admirably."

JOHNSON, N. L. AND TETLEY, H. *STATISTICS: AN INTERMEDIATE TEXTBOOK* (Vol. I)
    1949. Cambridge University Press, xii+294 pp.

Chapter	Contents
1	Essential Features of Statistical Data
2	Descriptive Statistics. First steps
3	Descriptive Statistics. Fundamental Analytical Ideas
4	Descriptive Statistics. Correlation and Linear Regression
5	The Problem of Statistical Inference
6	Probability: Fundamentals
7	Probability: Random Variables
8	Probability: Some Important Distributions
9	Statistical Hypotheses
10	Simple Statistical Tests

Biometrika, 1950, **37**, 453.

" The present volume represents the first part of a two-volume textbook to cover the main statistical requirements of Parts I and II of the new syllabus (of the Institute of Actuaries—England). Although the book has been written primarily for actuarial students, there is every reason for it to have a considerably wider appeal as meeting a requirement not previously filled by existing textbooks. . . . The book is well supplied with examples at the end of each chapter, designed to cover the application of the subjects discussed and also to cover important methods or results which could not be included in the text."

J. Amer. Statist. Ass., 1951, **46**, 258.

" This book should not be confused with the earlier Volume I of *Actuarial Statistics* by Tetley (which was written before the revision of the syllabus) though there are portions of the two books which are similar."

J. Inst. Actuar., 1950, **76**, 175.

" It may be said at once that a long-felt need has been satisfied. There is probably no one existing textbook on statistics that would have satisfied the Institute's requirements by itself, and this addition to the series of Institute textbooks is to be warmly welcomed. Others, too, besides actuaries, will be interested in the presentation of the subject-matter, since there is much demand at the present time for the essentials of statistical methods to be available to a wide class of student. . . . There are exercises at the end of each chapter, the answers, together with notes on the solutions, being given at the end."

J. R. Statist. Soc. A, 1950, **113**, 250.

" The authors have set out to write a textbook, not a manual, and they are pleasantly unselfconscious about it. Their frequency theory of probability is not over-critical, but it is sufficient for their purpose . . . a few words may be allowed concerning the exercises at the end of the chapters. They are on the whole well chosen . . . some however, seem to have been thrown in rather carelessly, for full measure. . . . The present volume augurs well and can unreservedly be recommended to many more readers than actuarial apprentices."

Johnson, N. L. and Tetley, H. *STATISTICS: AN INTERMEDIATE TEXTBOOK* (Vol. II)
1950. Cambridge University Press, xi+318 pp.

Chapter	Contents
11	The Calculus of Distribution Functions
12	Applications of the Calculus of Distribution Functions
13	The Multinomial Distribution and its Applications
14	General Theory of Statistical Tests and Estimation
15	Stratified Populations and the Analysis of Variance
16	Correlation Analysis
17	Curvefitting and Graduation

J. Inst. Actuar., 1951, **77**, 316.

" Viewing the textbook as a whole, the reader is struck by the immense variety of the subject matter which it has been possible to condense into reasonable dimensions, some of it of an advanced order. This is one of the best books on statistics, at the intermediate level, which has ever been published, especially when we consider that for the most part it provides its own proofs and is more than just methodological."

J. R. Statist. Soc. A, 1951, **114**, 253.

" . . . a splendid textbook of those subjects the authors chose to deal with. Their selection of topics shows unmistakable symptoms of adherence to a well-defined ' school ' . . . estimation is treated rather cavalierly: efficiency and consistency, for instance, are not even mentioned. . . . The general reader . . . will gladly note the uncanny skill with which the authors clarify difficulties almost before they are realized . . . this volume may very well rank as a standard work on that part of the subject which it presents."

Nature, 1951, **168**, 486.

" This second volume . . . completes the work. . . . The exercises at the end of each chapter and the end of the volume are numerous and well chosen. . . . The defects of the book—it is perhaps scarcely fair to describe them as such—are inevitable in any attempt to compress statistical theory into a comparatively brief compass at the University Intermediate level. There is only space, for example, for two and a half pages on least-squares estimation, and less than that for maximum likelihood. On the other hand, there are sections on topics which have not yet found their way into standard texts, such as the supplementation of the χ^2 test by tests of changes of sign. Notwithstanding the limited objective of the book, it should also form a useful Intermediate text for non-actuarial students."

KENDALL, M. G. *THE ADVANCED THEORY OF STATISTICS*
(Vol. I)
1948. 4th Ed., Griffin, xii+457 pp.

Chapter	Contents
1	Frequency Distributions
2	Measures of Location and Dispersion
3	Moments and Cumulants
4	Characteristic Functions
5	Standard Distributions (1)
6	Standard Distributions (2)
7	Probability and Likelihood
8	Random Sampling
9	Standard Errors
10	Exact Sampling Distributions
11	Approximations to Sampling Distributions
12	The χ^2 distribution
13	Association and Contingency
14	Product-moment Correlation
15	Partial and Multiple Correlation
16	Rank Correlation

Biometrika, 1945, **33**, 266.
" The work is encyclopaedic . . . Mr. Kendall is here, in the main, content to present us with a picture of statistical theory as he finds it. . . . It is by no means a book to skim through. . . . Anyone who can follow a mathematical argument and who has also at least some small experience of practical statistical problems will find plenty to reward him in a study of Mr. Kendall's book."

J. R. Statist. Soc. A, 1944, **108**, 127.
" It seems to me (the reviewer) that Mr. Kendall's achievement is to have presented for the first time, in admirable form for reference,

the mathematical framework of our theory. Thus, he has provided a book which will be invaluable to the advanced teaching course, since by directing the student to appropriate chapters on theory the teacher will be freer than he has ever been before to tackle the difficult problem of training the mathematician to apply his knowledge soundly in interpreting the numerical data of practical experience. The book will also be welcomed by those of us whose theory has become somewhat rusty and who want to find a clear re-statement in one place of a particular branch of the subject which hitherto it has been necessary to track down in back issues of a number of scientific journals."

KENDALL, M. G. *THE ADVANCED THEORY OF STATISTICS* (Vol. 2)
1951. 3rd Ed., Griffin, vii+521 pp.

Chapter	Contents
17	Estimation: Likelihood
18	Estimation: Miscellaneous Methods
19	Confidence Intervals
20	Fiducial Inference
21	Some Common Tests of Significance
22	Regression
23	The Analysis of Variance (1)
24	The Analysis of Variance (2)
25	The Design of Sampling Inquiries
26	General Theory of Significance-Tests (1)
27	General Theory of Significance-Tests (2)
28	Multivariate Analysis
29	Time Series (1)
30	Time Series (2)

Biometrika, 1948, **35**, 210.

". . . method is rather to let the truth appear—if appear it can—by making an extensive and detailed survey of the whole range covered by modern contributions. . . . Mr. Kendall is content to describe rather than to judge. . . . Looking back after reading through the two volumes of Mr. Kendall's ambitious enterprise, one is forced to the realisation that here we have one of the most remarkable compilations that has ever been attempted by a single writer in any branch of science . . . the many excellences of the work, particularly its freedom from personal animosities and the generosity of its references to the contributions of so many different writers."

J. Amer. Statist. Ass., 1947, **42**, 185.

" The present volume is devoted chiefly to the theory of statistical inference. It gives perhaps a more comprehensive account of the existing theory than other books published so far on this subject . . . the last two chapters are devoted to time series analysis . . . particularly autoregressive schemes and periodogram analysis."

J. R. Statist. Soc. A, 1947, **110**, 144.

" . . . it is now possible for the mathematical statistician who knows the elements of the subject to go through the two volumes in any order he likes and so the complete work takes its place as a quite invaluable reference book. . . . An extremely valuable bibliography is included as an appendix; it covers the subjects dealt with in both volumes. . . ."

KENDALL, M. G. AND STUART, A. *THE ADVANCED THEORY OF STATISTICS* (Vol. I) Distribution Theory
1958. Griffin, xii+433 pp.

Chapter	Contents
1	Frequency Distributions
2	Measures of Location and Dispersion
3	Moments and Cumulants
4	Characteristic Functions
5	Standard Distributions—(1)
6	Standard Distributions—(2)
7	The Calculus of Probabilities
8	Probability and Statistical Inference
9	Random Sampling
10	Standard Errors
11	Exact Sampling Distributions

12 Approximations to Sampling Distributions—(1)
13 Approximations to Sampling Distributions—(2)
14 Order Statistics
15 The Multivariate Normal Distribution and Quadratic Forms
16 Distributions Associated With the Normal

Biometrika, 1959, **46**, 491.

" Broadly speaking, the first 13 chapters of the new volume 1 correspond to the first 11 chapters of the original volume 1 . . . there are additions of entirely new material made necessary by advances in statistical theory and improvements in its techniques. . . . The Exercises left for solution by the reader have been greatly increased in number. . . . This should prove a valuable addition for the serious student."

J. R. Statist. Soc. A, 1959, **122**, 99.

" ' Distribution Theory ' is concerned with the theoretical characterization of empirical distributions and with those methods of manipulating distributions which are needed in the discussion of the sampling fluctuations of statistical quantities. . . . The size of page is slightly smaller, making the book more convenient to handle; the use of a smaller fount for certain notes and examples improves the general appearance of the page; the provision of a larger number of set examples enhances the value to the systematic student; and the inclusion in the text of additional material, embodying results from the statistical literature of the last ten or fifteen years, should prove of assistance to research students."

Nature, 1958, **182**, 1470.

" Although courses of instruction in statistical theory can well be based upon this book, as an aid to which more than 300 exercises (mostly fairly difficult) are included, a majority of statisticians will probably value it and its successors chiefly as an encyclopaedia. Not only are the main lines of development of theory clearly presented, but also the authors embroider their account with mention of many topics of lesser importance: to have these recognised and made more accessible than in past volumes of journals adds greatly to the interest and value of ' Kendall and Stuart ' as a work of reference."

KENNEY, J. F. AND KEEPING, E. S. *MATHEMATICS OF STATISTICS* (Part I)
1954. 3rd Ed., Van Nostrand, 348 pp.

Chapter	Contents
1	Frequency Distributions
2	Graphical Representation
3	The Median and Other Quantiles
4	The Arithmetic Mean and Other Averages
5	Index Numbers
6	Standard Deviation and Other Measures of Dispersion
7	Moments, Skewness and Kurtosis
8	The Normal Curve
9	Probability
10	The Binomial and Poisson Distributions
11	Significance Tests for Binomial Populations
12	Significance of Means and Variances
13	Non-Parametric and Order Statistics
14	Time Series
15	Linear Regression and Correlation
16	Further Topics in Correlation

Review of 1st Ed. by J. F. Kenney, 1939:
J. R. Statist. Soc., 1940, **103**, 401.

"The inductive line of approach has been adopted, and the starting-point is a practical and simple problem: namely, the tabulation of data. Elementary conceptions, such as frequency distributions, graphical representations, averages, and measures of dispersion, are introduced from the need of summarizing data. In this the subject-matter has very much in common with American method text-books. However, great care is taken to explain fully the simple mathematical background of each operation (even such simple matters as the use of the summation sign are taught). As a whole, the text is clear and instructive. There is, however, an unfortunate tendency to state simple relations in terms of formal theorems of mathematical appearance."

KENNEY, J. F. AND KEEPING, E. F. *MATHEMATICS OF STATISTICS* (Part II)
1951. 2nd Ed., Van Nostrand, xiii+429 pp.

Chapter	Contents
1	Probability
2	The Binomial Distribution and the Normal and Poisson Approximations
3	Some Useful Integrals and Functions
4	Distributions of Two or More Variables; Moment-Generating Functions; The Law of Large Numbers
5	The Gamma, Beta, and Chi-Square Distributions; The Pearson and Gram-Charlier Systems of Curves; Curve Fitting
6	Fundamentals of Sampling Theory with Special Reference to the Mean
7	Small or Exact Sampling Theory
8	Linear Regression, Simple Correlation, and Contingency
9	Analysis of Variance and Covariance
10	Matrix Algebra and the Method of Least Squares
11	Curvilinear Regression; Multiple and Partial Correlation
12	Further Considerations on Statistical Inference

J. Amer. Statist. Ass., 1952, **47**, 686.

" The topics covered include probability, distribution theory, the laws of large numbers, large and small sample theory, regression (linear and curvilinear), correlation (simple and multiple), analysis of variance and covariance, and, finally, a chapter on statistical inference. A large number of sub-topics are covered under each of these main headings so that in some respects the book is encyclopædic. . . .

" The mathematics in this book is carefully done. Where proofs are omitted, this is stated, and no attempt at pseudo-rigor is presented. . . .

" Much of the new material in the book and many of the new problems are statistical rather, than mathematical, in content. It may be noted that the title of this book emphasizes that it is a mathematics text. However, it will be advocated for and used by those interested in teaching or learning mathematical statistics. For such people, this book is not, in the opinion of the reviewer, a suitable text. The important conceptual bases of mathematical statistics have been relegated to the final chapter, where limitations of space alone make an adequate treatment impossible. The concepts of Type 1 and Type 2 error and the Neyman-Pearson theory of testing hypotheses are covered in a few brief pages of this final chapter (although Type 1 error is mentioned briefly and vaguely on two earlier occasions). A chapter is devoted to least squares, but the Markov theorem, which forms the foundation stone of the technique, is dismissed in part of a sentence and not even mentioned by name. . . .

" The lack of a conceptual basis to the book to a large extent makes it a collection of results rather than an integrated theory. . . .

" While in the reviewer's opinion the text fails from a statistical point of view, it is probably the best available at its level for those whose interest is primarily in mathematical techniques. Moreover, because of its inclusiveness with respect to many of the topics covered, it should prove a useful reference text in any mathematical statistics course."

MOOD, A. M. *INTRODUCTION TO THE THEORY OF STATISTICS*
1950. McGraw-Hill, xiii+443 pp.

Chapter	Contents
1	Introduction
2	Probability and Combinatorial Methods
3	Discrete Distributions
4	Distributions for Continuous Variates
5	Expected Values and Moments
6	Special Continuous Distributions
7	Sampling
8	Point Estimation
9	The Multivariate Normal Distribution
10	Sampling Distributions
11	Interval Estimation
12	Tests of Hypotheses

13	Regression and Linear Hypotheses
14	Experimental Designs and the Analysis of Variance
15	Sequential Tests of Hypotheses
16	Distribution-Free Methods

J. Inst. Actuar., 1951, **77**, 328.

" This book is a pleasure to read, for the clear and lucid way in which it is written, for the value and interest of its contents, and for the attractive manner in which the printer has set out the material given to him. . . . It is difficult to conceive that any student with reasonable mathematical ability could fail to derive considerable profit from a study of this book. He will never be ' talked down to ', nor will he find the arguments over his head, though there are some few sections which appear to have been condensed without sufficient regard for the troubles of the novice . . . the reviewer would recommend a special study of the numerous problems provided (about 30-40 per chapter). Here will be found encouragement, in the many very easy questions and interest in some of the more difficult."

PARADINE, C. G. AND RIVETT, B. H. P. *STATISTICAL METHODS FOR TECHNOLOGISTS*
1960. English Universities Press. viii + 288 pp.

Chapter	Contents
1	Introductory
2	Frequency Distributions. Statistical Parameters
3	Probability. The Binomial Distribution
4	Poisson's Distribution. The Normal Distribution
5	Sum of Squares of Normal Variates. Goodness of Fit
6	Small Samples. Student's *t*. Variance Ratio
7	Quality Control
8	Sampling Inspection Schemes
9	Theory of Errors
10	The Method of Least Squares
11	Correlation
12	The Analysis of Variance
13	The Principle of Maximum Likelihood. Probit Analysis

Review of 1st Ed., 1953:
J. R. Statist. Soc. A, 1954, **117**, 107.
" Mr. Paradine and Mr. Rivett have written an introduction to statistical methods and theory for engineers and technologists. The balance of theory and methodology is typical of books on applied mathematics for engineers: proofs are given in full when they involve only elementary algebra and calculus, some proofs requiring more advanced mathematics are given but may be omitted without disturbing the continuity of the book, while topics requiring elaborate mathematical treatment are discussed without proof. There are many worked examples in the text and an excellent collection of exercises for the student. . . .

" The general plan of the book is good, it is well written and it is designed to meet a real need for a moderately mathematical account of modern statistical ideas. Unfortunately, however, there are a number of details which are open to criticism. . . .

" Despite these points, the book can be recommended, particularly to students. To work through the book doing a fair proportion of the exercises would be a very good introduction to statistics."

RAO, C. R. *ADVANCED STATISTICAL METHODS IN BIO-METRIC RESEARCH*
1952. Wiley, xvii + 390 pp.

Chapter	Contents
1	Algebra of Vectors and Matrices
2	Theory of Distributions
3	The Theory of Linear Estimation and Tests of Hypotheses
4	The General Theory of Estimation and the Method of Maximum Likelihood
5	Large Sample Tests of Hypotheses with Applications to Problems of Estimation
6	Tests of Homogeneity of Variances and Correlations
7	Tests of Significance in Multivariate Analysis
8	Statistical Inference Applied to Classificatory Problems
9	The Concept of Distance and the Problem of Group Constellations

Biometrika, 1954, **41**, 283.

" Dr. Rao has confined himself for illustrative purposes to the field of biometry and in particular to the field of anthropometry, but he has actually written a text-book of statistics which is interesting and to a certain extent novel in exposition."

J. R. Statist. Soc. A, 1953, **116**, 86.

" Perhaps the most stimulating feature of the book is the command which the author has over the statistical methods, and the apparent ease with which he is able to handle large quantities of data and subject them to analysis.

"It is a pity that with such excellent material at his disposal the exposition should be so unsatisfactory. The reviewer gets the impression that the book has been much too hastily written: not nearly enough care has been devoted to the relationship between the parts, and details of the discussion are often confusing.

"This book is not likely to be very valuable for students in view of the weaknesses in style, but research workers with some knowledge of the methods discussed and the patience to follow Rao's terse remarks will benefit from the ideas he introduces."

Appl. Statist., 1953, **2**, 202.

" Professor Rao's book is . . . essentially a book on mathematical statistics and requires a knowledge of mathematics at least up to university degree standard for its understanding. The book is therefore intended for the serious student of statistics and for the professional statistician. The development of the subject is quite general and not limited to the field of biometric research except in the examples used to illustrate the methods.

" The mathematical treatment is severely algebraic, and the use of vector and matrix algebra in particular have considerably simplified the presentation; this results in elegance and a saving of space, and in a surprising amount of information being presented in a book of no more than normal size. It is unquestionably a good book and ranks with the other leading books on mathematical statistics."

TIPPETT, L. H. C. *THE METHODS OF STATISTICS*
  1952. 4th Revised Ed., Williams and Norgate, 395 pp.

Chapter	Contents
1	Frequency Distributions and Measures
2	Distributions Derived From the Theory of Probability
3	Inference From Random Samples
4	Errors in Large Samples
5	Small Samples
6	A Simple Analysis of Variance
7	A Further Analysis of Variance
8	Correlation and Association
9	Sampling Errors in Simple Correlation Analysis
10	Multiple and Partial Regression and Correlation
11	Non-linear Regression
12	Problems of Practical Application

Appl. Statist., 1953, **2**, 72.

" This is a revised edition of the book written in 1931, especially for experimenters, ' to expound Fisher's methods in comparatively simple terms '. . . . In the present edition the rewriting of several of the chapters, the division of others, and the addition of a chart to correspond with each statistical table account for over one hundred new pages. . . . The new pages deal among other things with time series, ranking methods, sampling, fitting orthogonal polynomials, transformations of variates, and discriminant functions. It is disappointing to find so little under the heading Principles of Experimental Arrangement; pertinent material appears, however, in other sections and the bibliography is extensive. Probit analysis deserves more than the passing mention it gets. The book is well produced."

WEATHERBURN, C. E. *A FIRST COURSE IN MATHEMATICAL STATISTICS*
  1949. 2nd Ed., Cambridge University Press, xv+271 pp.

Chapter	Contents
1	Frequency Distributions

2	Probability and Probability Distributions
3	Some Standard Distributions
4	Bivariate Distributions, Regression and Correlation
5	Further Correlation Theory. Curved Regression Lines
6	Theory of Simple Sampling
7	Standard Errors of Statistics
8	Beta and Gamma Distributions
9	Chi-square and Some Applications
10	Further Tests of Significance. Small Samples
11	Analysis of Variance and Covariance
12	Multivariate Distributions. Partial and Multiple Correlations

Biometrika, 1947, **34**, 373.

" An outstanding feature of the present statistical time is the number of text-books which are being written, each one from a slightly different point of view. . . . Professor Weatherburn has taken a rather formal mathematical exposition . . . recommend this book to students who have obtained some idea of the aims and objectives of statistical theory and who are desirous of learning the development of the mathematical technique as well as its application."

J. Amer Statist. Ass., 1947, **42**, 345.

" . . . treatment of non-linear regression is brief. He gives the least squares solution for a parabolic regression and indicates that some non linear expressions may be linearized by transformation. He does not indicate that such linearization will not give the least squares fit to the original equation unless suitable weighting is used. . . . There is no adequate discussion of the principles on which methods of estimation and tests of significance should be chosen. . . . The reviewer's general conclusion is that both Weatherburn's and Hoel's books should be on the shelves available to students but that most teachers will probably find that neither is completely satisfactory. . . ."

J. R. Statist. Soc. A, 1946, **109**, 506.

" A very good idea of what the subject is about generally, and of how it is dealt with by modern exponents can be had from this book by anyone who has a moderate mathematical knowledge. . . . An innovation is the introduction of the Gamma and Beta distributions. . . . This is an attractive way of approaching distributional theory. . . . The only major criticism the reviewer has is that the author should have gone further than he did."

WILKS, S. S. *MATHEMATICAL STATISTICS*
    1946. Princeton University Press, xi+284 pp.

Chapter	Contents
1	Introduction
2	Distribution Functions
3	Some Special Distributions
4	Sampling Theory
5	Sampling from a Normal Population
6	On the Theory of Statistical Estimation
7	Tests of Statistical Hypotheses
8	Normal Regression Theory
9	Applications of Normal Regression Theory to Analysis of Variance Problems
10	On Combinatorial Statistical Theory
11	An Introduction to Multivariate Statistical Analysis

J. Inst. Actuar., 1945, **72**, 295.

" Prior to Wilks's book under review, no text-book on mathematical statistics had given prominence to the theories of estimation and tests of statistical hypotheses which are so fundamental to the important present-day applications of mathematical probability. . . . Wilks's book, in fact, is based on a series of lectures delivered at Princeton to graduate and advanced undergraduate students of mathematics. . . . There are no numerical illustrations: the work is a mathematical treatment of statistical problems."

J. R. Statist. Soc. A, 1943, **106**, 279.

" However, from the title the general reader might be entitled to expect a comprehensive treatment. . . . The reader must be prepared to grapple by himself . . . for such ideas as stochastic convergence and the law of large numbers . . . an interesting chapter on combinatorial statistical theory with some useful recent results in the theory of runs, is incomplete when the reader has to go back to some of the original papers for assistance in the numerical use of these results. . . .

"The rest of (this) last chapter on multivariate analysis is valuable in its presentation of comparatively recent results in canonical variate theory. . . .

"This book will be useful to the professional mathematical statistician also to mathematically-minded students provided that they are not solely reliant on it; it is not recommended to the amateur nor to the student who is more interested in method than in theory."

Special Topics

ACTON, F. S. *ANALYSIS OF STRAIGHT LINE DATA*
1959. Wiley, xiii+267 pp.

Chapter	Contents
1	The Choice of a Model
2	The Classical Model: x Known without Error; Variance of y Constant
3	Regression with Several Values of y for Each Known x
4	Samples from Bivariate Normal Populations
5	Regression with both x and y in Error
6	Several Lines; the Analysis of Variance
7	The Exposure of Curvature: Orthogonal Polynomials
8	The Use of Transformations
9	The Rejection of Unwanted Data
10	Cumulative Data: The Fading Line

Appl. Statist., 1960, **9**, 130.

"I liked the start of Acton's book and thought that it showed a realistic approach, but I fear that the loss of enchantment with the later material, experienced by the author, afflicted me at an earlier stage. Chapter 2, dealing with classical regression analysis with

x free from error, struck me as somewhat laboured and cluttered up with inessentials . . . . Acton gives a good deal of information concerning linear regression, but the reader needs to have a certain amount of patience to sift the really useful material from that of incidental interest. For a book of its length and subject, I thought it had too few down-to-earth practical examples."

Biometrika, 1960, **47**, 486.

" The author says that his book, grown from a small pamphlet, is a discussion of techniques that have been proved both pertinent and useful. Some of the classical approaches are excluded, however, on the ground that ' they encourage an unthinking mechanical solution to the problem of straight-line data fitting '. . . . There is an appendix of useful tables—some from formerly unpublished material of Prof. Tukey—the usual index, a list of forty-two quoted references and an Additional Bibliography of annotated references not quoted in the text. . . . This book may not be suitable for students or the recently qualified statistician, but the general body of practising statisticians will do well to note and use this book as a reference point for statistical expertise on its chosen topic."

J. Amer. Statist. Ass., 1961, **56**, 414.

" This book was written to explore the analysis of experimental data that can be described in terms of linear relationships. . . . Apparently the author feels that the experimenter's primary interest is in functional relationships and not prediction. . . . Although the reader will find it hard to follow many of the procedures presented in this book, he will be adequately rewarded if he takes to heart some of Dr. Acton's keen observations on the analysis of data."

J. R. Statist. Soc. A, 1960, **123**, 70.

" The subject of the analysis of experimental data from the viewpoint of fitting linear relationships is one that is of concern to most experimenters and all statisticians. It still requires a good deal of delving into the statistical literature to satisfy one's statistical conscience on various practical problems in this field. In general, textbooks do not meet the case, so that there has long been the need for a monograph on this important subject. Now we have such a book, it is fortunate that it is a very good one.

" The main emphasis is on showing how the nature of the experiment, and the type of information to be extracted from it, influences the choice of statistical model and the resulting method of analysis. . . . The author's treatment is scholarly but always enlivened with humour and experimental common sense. . . . It is to be hoped that all statisticians and some experimenters will add this book to their library."

AITCHISON, J. AND BROWN, J. A. C. *THE LOGNORMAL DISTRIBUTION*
1957. Cambridge University Press, xviii+176 pp.

Chapter	Contents
1	Introduction
2	General Properties of Lognormal Distributions
3	The Genesis of Lognormal Distributions
4	Artificial Lognormal Samples and Tests of Lognormality
5	Estimation Problems: I
6	Estimation Problems: II
7	The Lognormal Distribution and Probit Analysis
8	Comparisons of Lognormal Populations
9	Truncated and Censored Distributions and the Treatment of Zero Observations
10	Examples of Lognormal Distributions
11	The Distribution of Incomes
12	Applications of Lognormal Theory in the Analysis of Consumers' Behaviour
13	Computation Problems

J. R. Statist. Soc. A, 1957, **120**, 481.

" The comprehensive account of the lognormal distribution given in this book will be valuable to all statisticians. Econometricians will find in addition suggestions for promising lines of further research."

J. Amer. Statist. Ass., 1958, **53**, 219.

" Perhaps the most valuable part of the book is the applications of the lognormal distribution to economic problems. . . . The most novel part of the book is probably the pages dealing with the application of the lognormal distribution to consumer's behaviour. The discussion centers around the Engel Curve.

" It is a great merit that, in addition to the literature in English, works in Dutch, French, Italian and German have been considered also (in the bibliography)."

Appl. Statist., 1957, **6**, 228.

" The authors are to be commended on the skill with which they have collected together and summarised in a systematic way the previous work, both on the theory of the lognormal distribution and on its practical applications. In addition, they have made useful and interesting contributions of their own on both the theory and the applications."

Inc. Statist., 1958, **8**, 145.

" Besides being of great value to any statistician who is called upon to make anything more than slight use of the lognormal distribution, this publication may well serve to encourage further attempts to consolidate the existing literature of statistical science."

Rev. Int. Statist. Inst., 1957, **25**, 154.

" All statisticians will want to have this book available for its comprehensive treatment of a special topic. Its extensive bibliography and general historical and developmental discussions illustrating the many fields in which lognormality has arisen will prove of wide interest. The account of estimation methods is not likely to be superseded for a long time and together with the Appendix Tables will be frequently used by applied statisticians. The more strictly economic sections have a narrower appeal, but the future may demonstrate their influence on the development of econometric techniques."

Econ. J., 1957, **67**, 713.

" While the book is certainly of high calibre and a very welcome addition to our fund of knowledge, it is not without its faults. The authors apparently go astray in the matter of maximum likelihood estimation. . . . Their exposition could have been much simplified on this score. . . .

"These minor faults are all on matters of detail that can easily be rectified and should not draw one's attention away from the obvious merits of this fine contribution."

ANDERSON, T. W. *AN INTRODUCTION TO MULTIVARIATE STATISTICAL ANALYSIS*
1958. Wiley, xii+374 pp.

Chapter	Contents
1	Introduction
2	The Multivariate Normal Distribution
3	Estimation of the Mean Vector and the Covariance Matrix
4	The Distributions and Uses of Sample Correlation Coefficients
5	The General T-statistic
6	Classification of Observations
7	The Distribution of the Sample Covariance Matrix and the Sample Generalized Variance
8	Testing the General Linear Hypothesis; Analysis of Variance
9	Testing Independence of Sets of Variates
10	Testing Hypotheses of Equality of Covariance Matrices and Equality of Mean Vectors and Covariance Matrices
11	Principal Components
12	Canonical Correlations and Canonical Variables
13	The Distribution of Certain Characteristic Roots and Vectors that do not Depend on Parameters
14	A Review of Some Other Work in Multivariate Analysis

Biometrika, 1958, **45**, 594.

" Undoubtedly Prof. Anderson's book will long remain the standard textbook and work of reference for multivariate theory based on the normal distribution. If such a beautifully written and beautifully printed book can have any fault—of being ever so slightly too smooth—what a good fault. . . ."

J. R. Statist. Soc. A, 1958, **121**, 482.

" The present text-book is a solid and competent attempt at

SPECIAL TOPICS 97

systematizing the subject, with special reference to the needs of undergraduate or immediate post-graduate students. Although applications still occupy a definitely minor position, the impression is gained that the author really has done his best, in present circumstances, at any rate, to show the way to apply as many of the techniques as he can.

" Matrices are used throughout the book, and the bold type used lends a falsely formidable appearance to the text. But provided the intending reader is not intimidated by cumbersome appearances, he will find he is reading a text of considerable lucidity and power.

" This book does provide a really effective student's text-book in what is practically a fresh field for such books, but it is a field which will probably still remain a highly specialized one for many years. This may account for the exceptionally high price, which is justified by the quality of the book, but which may well have an unfortunate effect on its sales."

Operat. Res., 1958, **6**, 454.

" The prerequisites for an understanding of this text are a knowledge of the usual theory of univariate statistics and matrix algebra, as well as maturity in mathematics. . . . For those individuals who have the mathematical background, Anderson's book presents in an organised and systematic manner the extensively developed multivariate methods based on the normal distribution."

Inc. Statist., 1959, **9**, 67.

" Provided the reader will do his part, and study the book with ' traditional ' thoroughness, he will gain a clear idea of the content and aims of modern multivariate analysis. The author has carried out his task of welding together results from widely scattered original papers into a coherent whole with an efficiency which disguises the really hard work which must lie behind this volume. The text is not unreasonably difficult to comprehend, provided the reader can tackle straightforward matrix theory and fairly simple manipulative mathematics. There are collections of exercises (but no solutions) at the end of each chapter."

Nature, 1958, **182**, 1183.

" Prof. Anderson's book is intended for the advanced college
G

student, and has—among other desirable text-book features—a clear and thorough manner of exposition, examples in the text, and an ample supply of problems (but no model solutions). . . . Careful study of this book should leave few gaps to be filled—apart from those created by the present flow of papers on this subject."

DEMING, W. E. *STATISTICAL ADJUSTMENT OF DATA* 1943. Wiley, x+261 pp.

Chapter	Contents
1	On the Meaning of Adjustment
2	Simple Illustration of Curve Fitting
3	Propagation of Error
4	The General Problem in Least Squares
5	Geometric Conditions
6	Systematic Computation for Geometric Conditions
7	Adjusting Sample Frequencies to Expected Marginal Totals
8	Curve Fitting in More Complicated Circumstances
9	Systematic Computation for Fitting Curves by Least Squares
10	Exercises in Fitting Various Functions
11	Examples of Curve Fitting

J. Amer. Statist. Ass., 1945, **40**, 380.

" In this book a great many types of problems are considered under the general principle of least squares. . . .

" This book has a number of distinctive features. . . . The use of Lagrange multipliers. . . . The saving of time and effort made possible . . . by the use of approximate values of parameters. . . . The technical discussions are liberally supplemented with bits of good practical advice . . . since original articles in this field are not readily accessible the many well-chosen references and historical notes are especially helpful. . . ."

DuBois, P. H. *MULTIVARIATE CORRELATION ANALYSIS*
  1957. Harper, xv+202 pp.

  Chapter   Contents
  1   The Nature of Multiple R
  2           $R_{(0, 1, 2, \ldots n)}$ By Reduction of Criterion Variance
  3   Beta Coefficients and Regression Equations
  4   Checking Procedures
  5   Selecting a Reduced Number of Predictors
  6   The Abbreviated Solution
  7   Partial Correlation
  8   Variations of the Correlation of Residuals
  9   Multiple R with Several Criteria
  10   Some Properties of the Variance-Covariance Matrix
  11   Factor Analysis in Terms of Reference Variates
  12   Factor Analysis in Terms of Defined Components
  13   Some Mathematical Considerations
  14   Inference and Prediction in Multivariate Correlation
  15   Multivariate Analysis in Social Science Research

Biometrika, 1959, **46**, 268.

" The prime purpose of the present book written for non-mathematicians is to set out systematic methods of calculating Yule-type partial and multiple correlations. Its subsidiary purpose is to give a brief account of, and to relate to correlation analysis, the methods of factor analysis developed by Spearman and Thurstone. It is regrettable that scarcely any mention is made of orthodox modern statistics, and the distinction between population and sample is almost completely ignored. . . . although the book will no doubt be of value to psychological research workers it is not likely to be very helpful to statisticians in other fields."

Rev. Int. Statist. Inst., 1958, **26**, 141.

" Chapter 1 opens with the statement that ' a coefficient of multiple correlation indicates the degree of relationship between 2 (and only 2) variables ': an observation which is probably worth making somewhere in the text. Rubbing it in right at the beginning does not do justice to the concept of multiple correlation. Of course, the purpose of the volume is not for explaining the concepts but for providing details of formulae and computations of coefficients like the multiple, partial and part correlation and regression, and of simple cases of factor analysis. The data chosen for illustrations are often ' fictitious selected for ease in arithmetical operations '."

EZEKIEL, M. AND FOX, K. A. *METHODS OF CORRELATION AND REGRESSION ANALYSIS*
   1959. Wiley, xv + 548 pp.

(Previously published under the title " Methods of Correlation Analysis " by M. Ezekiel).

Chapter	Contents
1	Measuring the Variability of a Statistical Series
2	Judging the Reliability of Statistical Results
3	The Relation Between Two Variables and the Idea of Function
4	Determining the Way One Variable Changes when Another Changes: (1) By the Use of Averages
5	Determining the Way One Variable Changes when Another Changes: (2) According to the Straight-Line Function
6	Determining the Way One Variable Changes when Another Changes: (3) For Curvilinear Functions
7	Measuring Accuracy of Estimate and Degree of Correlation
8	Practical Methods for Working Out Two-Variable Correlation and Regression Problems
9	Three Measures of Correlation and Regression—the Meaning and Use of Each
10	Determining Multiple Linear Regressions: (1) By Successive Elimination
11	Determining Multiple Regressions: (2) By Fitting a Linear Regression Equation
12	Measuring Accuracy of Estimate and Degree of Correlation for Linear Multiple Regressions
13	Practical Methods for Working Out Multivariable Correlation and Regression Problems
14	Determining Multiple Curvilinear Regressions by Algebraic and Graphic Methods

15	Measuring Accuracy of Estimate and Degree of Correlation for Curvilinear Multiple Regressions
16	Short-cut Graphic Methods of Determining Net Regression Lines and Curves
17	The Sampling Significance of Correlation and Regression Measures
18	Influence of Selection of Sample and Accuracy of Observation on Correlation and Regression Results
19	Estimating the Reliability of an Individual Forecast
20	The Use of Error Formulas with Time Series
21	Measuring the Relation Between One Variable and Two or More Others Operating Jointly
22	Measuring the Way a Dependant Variable Changes with Changes in a Qualitative Independent Variable
23	Cross-Classification and the Analysis of Variance
24	Fitting Systems of Two or More Simultaneous Equations
25	Types of Problem to which Correlation and Regression Analysis Have Been Applied
26	Steps in Research Work, and the Place of Statistical Analysis

Biometrika, 1960, **47**, 487.

" In this third edition the material has been brought up to date by emphasizing regression rather than correlation and by the addition of a new chapter on fitting systems of two or more simultaneous equations. There is also fuller treatment of the analysis of variance. As in previous editions the book sets out how to apply techniques. It is a useful ancillary tool for any research worker who is faced with the problem of studying the relationships between two or more variables."

J. R. Statist. Soc. A, 1960, **123**, 337.

" The amount of mathematical knowledge required is not very great. . . . The style at the beginning is indeed rather reminiscent of school algebra. . . . The authors are extremely practical in their outlook and every technique is illustrated with an appropriate example, the latter being carefully discussed in general terms before any complicated algebra or arithmetic is attempted. . . . Most of the examples are drawn from economics, agriculture, and animal husbandry. Industrial applications are poorly represented. . . . Despite its length some common correlation problems are omitted, or only discussed extremely briefly. . . . Undoubtedly the great majority of practical regression techniques are available within the compass of this volume, but one is left with the impression that the material could have been equally well presented in many fewer pages."

J. Amer. Statist. Ass., 1961, **56**, 192.

". . . the book retains its basic excellence and is significantly improved in this third edition. . . . A text which does an extremely thorough job of presenting the technique and rationale of least squares and free hand graphic methods of regression analysis, especially with respect to curvilinear regressions. . . . The authors are not afraid to express their views on controversial issues. . . . I did not feel that their positions were unreasonable, nor were their presentations of the issues unfair. . . . The most attractive single feature of the text to me was the repeated expression of the role of theory as a guide to empirical research, especially the emphasis on the necessity of logical bases for variables included in regressions and for the forms of the regression equations that one fitted."

FINNEY, D. J. *PROBIT ANALYSIS*
    1952. 2nd Ed., Cambridge University Press, xiv+318 pp.

Chapter	Contents
1	Introductory
2	Quantal Responses and the Dosage-Response Curve
3	The Estimation of the Median Effective Dose
4	The Maximum Likelihood Solution
5	The Comparison of Effectiveness
6	Adjustments for Natural Mortality
7	Factorial Experiments
8	The Toxic Action of Mixtures of Poisons
9	Miscellaneous Problems
10	Graded Responses
11	Recent Developments

Biometrika, 1953, **40**, 473.

" A second edition of Finney's *Probit Analysis* is very welcome. . . . Few changes have been made in the original material, but a substantial new chapter on Recent Developments has been added, and some of the tabular matter is new. . . . Alternatives to probit analysis are still rather inadequately treated (as the author himself points out), but this has been remedied by the very full discussion in the later book. . . . *Probit Analysis* remains an essential book for the many biologists and statisticians who work with sigmoid curves."

J. Inst. Actuar., 1952, **78**, 388.

" Dr Finney gives a description of the methods of probit analysis with clear instructions and examples of the numerical calculations, together with tables of the necessary functions. Formulae are given, usually without proof, together with sufficient of the theory behind them to enable the methods to be applied with understanding. A good knowledge of statistical theory would be required of the reader who wished to derive the methods and formulae given. . . . the changes that have been made in the second edition . . . consist principally of rewriting four paragraphs and Appendix II (Mathematical Basis of the Probit Method), and the addition of a new chapter on recent developments."

J. R. Statist. Soc. A, 1952, **115**, 436.

" Dr. Finney's admirable text-book has lost its youthful slimness and assumed something of a middle-age spread. This is due partly to the use of thicker paper in the new edition, and partly to an important new chapter on recent developments of the subject. . . . In addition to this completely new section, Dr. Finney has made some other alterations from the first edition. In particular he has suggested a slightly different method of solution of the maximum likelihood equations when natural mortality is taken into account, which enables the computations to follow the routine for multiple regression. . . . This book will continue to be the standard work of reference for all who are interested in the analysis of quantal response data."

FRASER, D. A. S. *NONPARAMETRIC METHODS IN STATISTICS*
1957. Wiley, x+299 pp.

Chapter	Contents
1	The Sample Space
2	Statistical Inference
3	Nonparametric Problems
4	The Estimation of Real Parameters and Tolerance Regions
5	The Theory of Hypothesis Testing
6	Limiting Distributions
7	Large Sample Properties of Tests

Biometrika, 1958, **45**, 591.
" This book is likely to be of considerable value to theoretical statisticians who are familiar with the advanced text-book by Cramér or that by Kendall or, preferably with both. . . . There is a fair number of trivial misprints . . . and a very large number of problems for solution. . . . The index is inadequate for a book likely to be of value as a reference source. . . ."

Econometrica, 1959, **27**, 536.
" The book is written in a very clear and accurate manner. The author has contributed much to the subject by his own papers. . . . Unfortunately there are many misprints and errata too numerous to be listed here. An objection must be expressed concerning the choice of the literature quoted. In general only American literature is cited. . . . Nevertheless, the book is a welcome and important enrichment of the mathematical-statistical literature."

J. Amer. Statist. Ass., 1957, **52**, 384.
" The reviewer believes that the book is of sufficient merit to demand a place on every mathematical statistician's book shelf. It is clearly presented and well indexed as a reference book (especially the first part), while at the same time containing sufficient examples, motivation, and problems for a text-book (especially the second part). On the other hand the book does *not* reduce the need for a more extensive and detailed coverage of the theories of estimation and hypothesis testing. . . . Neither does it cover comprehensively the field of non-parametric statistics."

J. R. Statist. Soc. A, 1957, **120**, 481.

" Certainly the most curious, not to say ridiculous, feature of the book is its title. 125 pages (being chapters one and two) are devoted to a general account of mathematical statistics without specific attention to non-parametric ideas. Furthermore the book is throughout concerned with theory: methods receive little or no attention. The first two words of the title are therefore misleading: a clumsier, but more adequate, title would be ' The Theory of Mathematical Statistics, with special reference to Nonparametric Theory ' . . . In points of detail Fraser's book suffers from a high number of misprints, some obscurities of expression . . . and some errors. But I would strongly recommend the book to the attention of mathematical statisticians in this country, despite these defects because, especially in the first two chapters, it presents a development which will probably be strange to them but will certainly repay study."

GUMBEL, E. J. *STATISTICS OF EXTREMES*
1958. Columbia University Press, xx+375 pp.

Chapter	Contents
1	Aims and Tools
2	Order Statistics and Their Exceedancies
3	Exact Distribution of Extremes
4	Analytical Study of Extremes
5	The First Asymptotic Distribution
6	Uses of the First Asymptote
7	The Second and Third Asymptotes
8	The Range

Biometrika, 1960, **47**, 209.

" Anyone who is interested in extreme values will have to read this treatise in order to find out what has been done. In the limited field of mathematical statistics which this book delineates it is encyclopaedic and can be unhesitatingly and unreservedly recommended."

J. Amer. Statist. Ass., 1960, **55**, 383.

" *Statistics of Extremes* is the definitive work to date on this important subject. It is a complete treatise on the subject, bringing together many fundamental studies by scientists working in different fields and in many countries. . . . The book contains many detailed examples of the use of extreme values in such diverse fields as flood control, dam, bridge, reservoir, and hydroelectric plant construction, mortality tables, metal fatigue and building codes. . . . The book will be of 'extreme value' to statistically minded people who are interested in the theory of extremes."

J. R. Statist. Soc. A, 1959, **122**, 243.

" The book is intended for statisticians and statistically-minded scientists and engineers, and the author states that he has tried to write on an elementary level and to use graphical procedures in place of complicated calculations. The first objective has been achieved, in that an undue standard of rigour and generality has not been imposed; the book is definitely on statistics rather than on abstract probability theory. As for the graphs, there are about one hundred of these, nearly all illustrating theoretical relationships rather than practical data. . . . Many will feel that the effort of unravelling the meaning of some of these is not worth while. . . . One of the most useful features of the book is a closely-printed 22-page bibliography of works in the pure and applied field. There are also 'exercises' and 'problems', the latter being more difficult questions, some of which could serve as research projects."

Nature, 1959, **184**, 754.

" Prof. Gumbel has for many years been a leading authority on the subject and his book is likely to become a standard work . . . the book . . . collects and elaborates previous work hitherto widely scattered in the statistical literature and contains many tables and graphs of functions occurring in the theory. There is an excellent bibliography containing references to both theoretical and applied work."

KENDALL, M. G. *RANK CORRELATION METHODS* 1955. 2nd Ed., Griffin, vii + 196 pp.

Chapter	Contents
1	The Measurement of Rank Correlation

Chapter	
2	Introduction to the General Theory of Rank Correlation
3	Tied Ranks
4	Tests of Significance
5	Proof of the Results of Chapter 4
6	The Problem of m Rankings
7	Proof of the Results of Chapter 6
8	Partial Rank Correlation
9	Ranks and Variate Values
10	Proof of the Results of Chapter 9
11	Paired Comparisons
12	Proof of the Results of Chapter 11
13	Some Further Applications

Biometrika, 1957, **44**, 298.

" This is a revised and much enlarged second edition of a book which first summarised the theory of rank correlation. In its new form the book brings up to date the theory of ranking and may be considered indispensable for the research worker in both the theoretical and practical fields."

J. R. Statist. Soc. A, 1956, **119**, 90.

" This is the second edition of a book which although published only in 1948 has established itself in statistical literature. The first edition, written by one who has contributed more than anyone else to this particular branch of statistics, was welcomed as filling a long-felt want. The second edition consists of a revision of the first with some new material interpolated; the original plan of the text is left unchanged. . . . The changes are not of sufficient magnitude to require those statisticians who possess a copy of the first edition also to buy the second. . . . Either in its first edition or in its present form the book is still indispensable to those statisticians interested in rank correlation methods."

KENDALL, M. G. *A COURSE IN MULTIVARIATE ANALYSIS*
   1957. Griffin, 185 pp.

Chapter	Contents
1	Introduction

2	Component Analysis
3	Factor Analysis
4	Functional Analysis
5	Canonical Analysis
6	Some Problems of Sampling
7	Notes on The History of Multivariate Analysis
8	Tests on Homogeneity
9	Discriminatory Analysis

Biometrika, 1958, **45**, 594.

" The author says in the Preface: . . . ' I have tried to expound the essential concepts and techniques and have limited the mathematical treatment as much as possible.' . . . Prof. Kendall has achieved his aim with the skill that one would expect from. . . . All the main concepts and methods are illustrated by examples drawn from the literature—over twenty of them. These examples, with critical discussion are the main strength of the book."

J. R. Statist. Soc. A, 1958, **121**, 480.

" Statisticians must count themselves fortunate that one so skilled in exposition and of so encyclopaedic a grasp as Professor Kendall has taken on the task of guiding them through the techniques of Canonical Analysis, Component Analysis . . . etc. . . . The sometimes extremely subtle differences between models are carefully dissected with full numerical illustration, and many obscurities are clarified. . . . We may hope that perhaps the most important contribution of this book will be to stimulate an enlightened and vigorous assault on the outstanding problems. . . . The reader will be well advised to follow up the list of further reading recommended by Professor Kendall and perhaps to embark on a preliminary course of Chapter 28 of his *Advanced Statistics*, Vol. II, or the latter chapters of Wilks (1943)."

J. Amer. Statist. Ass., 1958, **53**, 753.

" One remarkable feature of Kendall's *Course* is its mode of presentation. . . . The ' classical ' system of teaching multivariate analysis . . . has been abandoned in favour of a functional approach. . . . From the applied statistician's point of view, this presentation is certainly helpful. . . . On the whole we must concede that Kendall's *Course* is a valuable contribution in that it proposes a new approach to the teaching of multivariate analysis."

Operat. Res. Quart., 1958, **9**, 63.

" Altogether, this book may be recommended as an excellent introduction to the theory of multivariate analysis, at least for readers who possess the ' considerable body of prerequisite knowledge ' referred to in the preface—this includes ' matrix algebra, 3-dimensional co-ordinate geometry, beta functions, and statistical theory up to the theory of correlation and regression, the bivariate normal surface and tests of significance based on normal theory '."

J. Inst. Actuar., 1958, **84**, 112.

" While a full understanding of the subject matter requires quite a wide knowledge of mathematics, the text is so arranged that the methods can be adequately understood by students with a grasp of the more common statistical techniques and arguments. The ample provision of worked-out numerical examples considerably helps this aspect of the book, and is a very welcome feature."

LEHMANN, E. L. *TESTING STATISTICAL HYPOTHESES*
   1959. Wiley, xiii+369 pp.

Chapter	Contents
1	The General Decision Problem
2	The Probability Background
3	Uniformly Most Powerful Tests
4	Unbiasedness: Theory and First Applications
5	Unbiasedness: Applications to Normal Distributions: Confidence Intervals
6	Invariance
7	Linear Hypotheses
8	The Minimax Principle

Biometrika, 1960, **47**, 210.

" The whole field of testing statistical hypotheses is not covered in this volume; the main concern being the two decision problem as it presents itself after the experiment has been set up. Other areas not fully explored are essentially the chi-square and likelihood ratio tests. . . . Throughout use is made of numerous examples to illustrate and emphasize, and each chapter is concluded with an extensive set of classified problems. Worthy of mention also are the references which are printed in such a way that they give a good guide to the related literature . . . both the teacher and the student in the field will find the book a most useful one."

Inc. Statist., 1960, **10**, 98.

" This book is an excellent publication for the professional mathematical statistician. He will find here a thorough treatment of most of the basic tools and, more important, of the basic concepts used in his work. This treatment is in the spirit of those developments of the Neyman-Pearson approach to statistical problems initiated by Wald and associated with the term ' decision functions ' . . . the author uses mathematics freely and with consummate skill, always making it plain that they are used as means to ends—never, however intrinsically interesting, as ends in themselves."

J. R. Statist. Soc. A, 1960, **123**, 200.

" This is a remarkable book, the product of years of research and also (as the reader will soon perceive) of profound reflection. . . . One of the reasons why this book is likely to have the wide influence it deserves is that the author does not attempt too much: very little of the book deals with large sample theory. Another is that although the treatment is rigorous and formal, statisticians of the English school . . . will find it easily penetrable. Thirdly, the exposition is almost entirely on Neyman-Pearson, rather than decision-theoretic, lines. . . . There is an excellent set of high-level exercises and a really good index to support a text which positively glides along, always perfectly controlled. No professional mathematical statistician should be without this book; no teacher of statistical theory can afford to be."

J. Amer. Statist. Ass., 1961, **56**, 163.

" Almost anyone interested in mathematical statistics will find many things he ought to know but doesn't about even the most familiar statistical problems in the course of this impeccable, detailed, mathematically rigorous treatment of ' optimum ' properties of significance tests and related confidence procedures . . . never before has the theory of significance tests initiated by Neyman and Pearson been so thoroughly explored and so definitely treated. . . . Lehmann has given us a definitive and beautiful mathematical treatment of an important part of the leading theory of statistics. As such it will be invaluable to statisticians of all philosophies."

LUKACS, E. *CHARACTERISTIC FUNCTIONS*
 1960. Griffin, 216 pp.

Chapter	Contents
1	Introduction
2	Preliminary Study of Characteristic Functions
3	Fundamental Properties of Characteristic Functions
4	Criteria for Characteristic Functions
5	Factorization Problems—Infinitely Divisible Characteristic Functions
6	Factorization Problems—General Theorems from the Arithmetic of Distribution Functions
7	Analytic Characteristic Functions
8	Factorization of Analytic Characteristic Functions
9	Mixtures of Distribution Functions and Transformations of Characteristic Functions

J. R. Statist. Soc. A, 1960, **123**, 484.

" This is an admirable and invaluable book and puts us all very much in the author's debt. The first four chapters (77 pages) cover the classical results (the uniqueness, inversion and continuity theorems; Bochner's theorem on positive-definite functions; Polya's theorem about convex characteristic functions, etc.). Chapters 5 to 8 (121 pages), which form the heart of the book, are all concerned in one way or another with factorization problems. The author gives an extremely thorough account of infinitely divisible c.f.'s, indecomposable c.f.'s, stable c.f.'s, and the special factorization properties of analytic c.f.'s. . . .

" These chapters of the book should be compulsory reading for any students beginning research in the theory of dams (unless they do so with the praiseworthy object of abolishing independent inputs—and hence infinite divisibility—from the subject). . . .

"The student viewing this book as an introduction to research may initially be appalled by the amount which is known—and which might well have been unknowable. But he need not be too distressed; the subject is really still wide open. Lukacs has very little to say about c.f.'s of distributions supported by $(0, \infty)$, and these Laplace-Stieltjes transforms have a largely unexplored theory of their own which is of great importance in applied stochastic process problems (where the random variables, usually times, have a way of being non-negative). The work of Lindley and W. L. Smith has shown the importance in queueing theory of random variables which can be represented as the difference of two independent non-negative random variables. How can one recognize the c.f. of such an object? Very little is known about the c.f.'s of vector variables, and still less about c. functionals. Finally one can frame teasing questions about absolutely continuous laws; for example, can $(\sin t)/t$ be factored into two c.f.'s each of which belongs to an absolutely continuous distribution?"

Inc. Statist., 1960, **10**, 147.

"The book under review will be of interest to research workers in and students of analytical probability theory and to those theoretical statisticians whose work in part borders on pure mathematics. There is nothing in the book of direct concern to applied statisticians. The mathematical equipment necessary to read the book is the theory of functions rather beyond that usually contained in an Honours Degree course in mathematics at a British university. For the class of readers indicated at the start of the review, this book is likely to be very useful. The first part of the book is a valuable collection of standard results, the second is in effect an extended essay on the application of the classical theory of functions to probability problems, and contains many elegant results . . . whose proofs have not previously been readily available. The mathematical statistician whose taste . . . is for classical function theory rather than for modern abstract mathematics is likely to find this a most enjoyable, as well as rewarding book."

PLACKETT, R. L. *PRINCIPLES OF REGRESSION ANALYSIS*
1960. Oxford University Press, ix+174 pp.

Chapter	Contents
1	Linear Equations
2	Quadratic Forms in Normal Variables
3	Least Squares
4	Linear Hypotheses
5	Departures from Standard Test Conditions
6	Polynomial Regression
7	Stationary Error Processes
8	Symmetrical Factorial Experiments
9	Randomization

J. Amer. Statist. Ass., 1961, **56**, 418.

" Rigorous proofs are given of all the basic results, with sketches of the proof for some of the more recent and complex developments. The level of exposition is high, though the reader needs a firm grasp of matrix and determinantal theory and (to a lesser extent) of contour integration, since results from these areas are used freely. At the end of each chapter there is a good selection of mathematical exercises, many of them embodying results in the research literature. ... It is a book about mathematics for young mathematicians, rather than about statistics for young statisticians. As a possible text for a course on regression leading to a Ph.D. in Statistics the book would require much supplementation to explain why the topics and results are important to statisticians, to give the students training in the difficult business of applying the results to statistical problems and to introduce aspects of regression theory omitted by the author. As a reference for extra reading during such a course the book is highly welcome, since it brings together in a lucid and compact form much of the recent theoretical work on regression."

J. R. Statist. Soc. A, 1961, **124**, 251.

" The book is not about regression methods in the narrow sense but concerns the general application of the method of least squares to observational data in all those situations where expected values may be described by linear functions of population parameters. In the earlier chapters the properties of multivariate normal distributions are discussed together with the related theory of the distributions of linear and quadratic forms in normal variables. The special distributions arising in the classical theory of least squares are then obtained. The treatment here is designed primarily for mathematicians, brevity of expression being attained by the use of matrix notation. . . . Mr. Plackett . . . has now given us a book that should notably help the recruitment of students to statistical science. . . . the standard of production and printing is what one usually obtains from the Oxford Press . . . the price is one which most students should be able to afford."

QUENOUILLE, M. H. *THE ANALYSIS OF MULTIPLE TIME SERIES*
1957. Griffin, 105 pp.

Chapter	Contents
1	Introduction
2	Specification
3	Identification
4	Preliminary Investigation
5	Practical Complications
6	Estimation
7	Significance and Goodness-of-Fit Tests
8	Practical Examples: U.S. hog Series

Biometrika, 1959, **46**, 267.

" Mr. Quenouille's book is remarkable in that much of what it contains is new work developed over a relatively short period. The author is concerned with an extension to stationary multiple series of the correlation properties, which are well known in the case of single series and also makes a start with the associated inference problems, confining himself almost entirely to large sample theory. . . .

" It is unfair perhaps to criticize a book which explores so much new ground, but it is necessary to draw attention to the fact that it should not be read uncritically. . . .

" A general point which may occur to other readers is that the approach to time-series which is pursued in this monograph is entirely empirical—this is no doubt related to the author's interest in particular subject-matter fields where no other approach seems possible. . . .

" However, these criticisms in no way detract from the overall excellence of this monograph, an outstanding feature of which is the very elegant use of matrix methods. It is not difficult to predict that it will become a standard book worthy of serious study for years to come."

J. Amer. Statist. Ass., 1961, **56**, 419.

" This book reports some research and ideas of the author concerning multivariate time series. . . . In most of the study the statistical model assumed is a stochastic difference equation . . . some attention is paid to a model of a finite moving average . . . and occasionally reference is made to a combination of these models in which the disturbance of the stochastic difference equation is a moving average. These are all special cases of a stationary vector stochastic process. . . . Unfortunately, this book has serious drawbacks that limit its value; it is hard to understand, inaccurate, and sometimes in outright error. . . . In spite of all its shortcomings, the book will be of interest to mathematical statisticians doing research on these finite-parameter models for stationary vector processes, for it contains a number of interesting ideas."

Nature, 1958, **182**, 1183.

" The essential qualities of the . . . [book] . . . are: . . . a readable book, repaying the effort of understanding the rather unusual notation; coverage of subject rather uneven, but not unduly so for a fresh subject."

Operat. Res. Quart., 1957, **8**, 220.

" The problems considered are concerned with the specification of the generation of interdependent time-series and with their correlation properties. The effects of sampling variations, incorrect specification and estimation of parameters are studied.

" Two valuable features of the book are an interesting description of the application of some theoretical methods discussed, and an up-to-date and select list of references."

QUENOUILLE, M. H. *THE FUNDAMENTALS OF STATISTICAL REASONING*
1958. Griffin, 169 pp.

Chapter	Contents
1	Probability Theory
2	Specification and Derivation of Distributions
3	Properties of Estimators
4	Testing of Hypotheses
5	Selection of Hypotheses
6	Limits of Estimation
7	Selection of Significance Tests

Biometrika, 1959, **46**, 268.

" ' The practical man seeking a step-by-step explanation of how to carry out statistical calculations will not find it here. Nor will the mathematician find proofs of the formulae involved in deriving such procedures. If either should, however, be interested in the foundations of statistics, in the principles rather than the proofs or practices, this monograph is aimed at him '. (From the author's preface) . . . After this introduction, the present reviewer was somewhat disappointed to find that the first two parts have been devoted to an exposition of the *mathematical* concepts used in statistical theory. . . . There is very little discussion of the relation of these concepts to statistical practice in the real world. . . . A great improvement is apparent in the final part. . . . Professional statisticians . . . will be stimulated by this final part, and plain mathematicians may be intrigued; but Mr. Quenouille's practical men are likely still to require convincing that the theory outlined has any relevance to their problems."

Inc. Statist., 1959, **9**, 66.

" As regards content and approach, this monograph can well be described as a useful addition to the statistical literature, but unfortunately it suffers from one marked defect. The author has evidently reaped little benefit from earlier criticism . . . and is still to be censured on the grounds of careless writing. The present work contains loose or meaningless phrases and statements, which make the argument difficult to follow and may even lead to definite misunderstanding. In addition, the misprints are too numerous to be comfortable."

Nature, 1959, **184**, 217.
" . . . Few subjects are in greater need of careful choice of every word, yet all too often the writing here is ambiguous or lacking in clarity. . . . The second half of the book is of a different order of difficulty and of much greater interest. . . . Mr. Quenouille has a gift for devising the illuminating example."

Operat. Res. Quart., 1959, **10**, 73.
" The necessarily condensed treatment of a book of this size makes it unsuitable for readers who do not already possess a working knowledge of the methods of statistics. Given this background there is much of interest, although the presentation of inductive principles is exclusively in terms of fiducial probability. The full discussion of the power of a test of significance should prove a useful corrective to the tendency to regard the control of Type I errors as the only purpose of such tests. Many readers will find the numerous concrete examples, often discussed in numerical terms, preferable to the entirely abstract approach so often encountered in modern statistical writing."

ROBINSON, E. A. *AN INTRODUCTION TO INFINITELY MANY VARIATES*
   1959. Griffin, 132 pp.

Chapter	Contents
1	Metric and Measure
2	Probability
3	The General Limit Theorem
4	Hilbert Space
5	Linear Operators
6	Spectral Representation
7	Stationary Processes

Inc. Statist., 1961, **11**, 173.
" This is intended as a text for undergraduate courses in mathematical statistics and probability theory. It would hardly be of use

except with classes of particularly bright and receptive mathematicians. Even then the statistical motivation is scant, and would certainly need to be supplemented by the lecturer.

"The book is based on the philosophy that an undergraduate should be exposed to advanced techniques early in his statistical training and its object is to extend undergraduate work, usually confined to the finite case, to cover treatment of an infinite number of random variates. As such, it is concerned with probability theory, limit theorems and stationary stochastic processes. . . .

"The type of reader to whom this book would appeal would be a mathematician with an interest in the abstract unification of statistical methods. The practising statistician not primarily concerned with time series would find the relevance to his subject at best tenuous."

J. Amer. Statist. Ass., 1961, **56**, 465.

" The author of the book under review feels that the limit theorems of probability theory (other than the Law of Large Numbers and the Central Limit Theorem) and the Hilbert space structure of stationary time series deserves a place in the basic programme of instruction of students of statistics. He has written a short, but fact-filled and well-written, book with the aim of giving ' a concise presentation of probability theory, limit theorems, and stationary stochastic processes '. . . . So that overall unity would not be lost in details and lengthy description, many of the proofs and applications are either outlined or left as exercises. Throughout the book the student is encouraged to go to the references, which is the key toward making him research minded."

J. R. Statist. Soc. A, 1960, **123**, 485.

" The book is virtually an exposition of two particular examples of an ' infinite problem ' (limit laws for sums of independent random variables, and the spectral theory of stationary processes) and of the requisite background material. Thus, after quoting some definitions and results from the theories of measure and of metric spaces, the author sketches an introduction to probability, which although in the main elementary, is in the spirit of Kolmogorov's Foundations. He then quotes a number of properties of characteristic functions, and continues with a fairly self-contained treatment of infinitely divisible distributions, the Khintchine-Bawly general limit theorem for sums of independent variates, and the now classical conditions for normal and Poisson convergence. There follow three chapters on Hilbert space, linear operators, and spectral representations in Hilbert space. This theory is then applied to give fairly detailed treatment of stationary processes: spectral theory, an ergodic theorem, the Wold decomposition, prediction. After this concentrated diet a concluding list of 136 exercises provides a welcome aid to digestion: in fact, the exercises are well chosen to illustrate the point of the theory. . . .

" The only serious criticism I have to make is that the book might have served its avowed purpose better had it been less ambitious: if instead of ranging so far the author had given more attention to the detailed comparison of analogous finite and infinite problems which alone can clarify the special features of the infinite case. There is no doubt, however, that Dr. Robinson has achieved a *tour de force* in covering this wide field with an account that is at once brief, lucid and informative, and that many will find his work useful both as a quick introduction and as a rapid reference."

Roy, S. N. *SOME ASPECTS OF MULTIVARIATE ANALYSIS* 1957. Wiley, and Indian Statistical Institute, viii+214 pp.

Chapter	Contents
1	Notation, Preliminaries and General Objectives
2	A Class of Tests Including in Particular the Type I and II Tests
3	The Multivariate Normal Population
4	Random Samples from P-variate Normal Populations
5	Statement of the Specific Problems to be Discussed
6	Tests for the Null Hypothesis
7	Reduction of Some Distribution Problems and Some Actual Distributions
8	On the C. D. F. of the Largest and/or the Smallest Root
9	Operating Characteristics and Lower Bounds on the Power Functions of the Test Regions

10 The Monotonic Character of the Lower Bounds on the Power Functions
11 Other Monotonic Lower Bounds on Power Functions
12 Least Squares and Univariate Analysis of Variance and Covariance with Multivariate Extensions
13 Some Univariate and Bivariate Confidence Bounds
14 Multivariate Confidence Bounds
15 Some Non-parametric Generalizations of Analysis of Variance and Multivariate Analysis

Biometrika, 1958, **45**, 594.

" Prof. Roy begins by enunciating a principle of test construction somewhat different from the usual likelihood ratio method. (Anyone who can be saying something interesting about tests by as soon as page 6 of his book deserves applause.) With this he chooses test criteria for a number of standard normal-theory null hypotheses. The criteria can be expressed in terms of the characteristic roots of a determinantal equation—sometimes the largest root, sometimes both largest and smallest roots. Associated with each test are measures of departure from the null hypothesis, based on a concept of distance; in terms of these the author obtains bounds for the operating characteristics of the tests. He is then able to achieve his main objective, namely, to derive by inversion confidence bounds for these measures of departure from the null hypothesis. There is also a final chapter concerned with the analysis of categorical data (contingency tables). Work is evidently still in progress, and there are various references to further results to be presented in another monograph or in a second edition of this one. The book will interest many whose concern is theoretical research in statistics."

J. Amer. Statist. Ass., 1958, **53**, 1034.

" This monograph primarily deals with samples from multivariate normal populations, although there is one chapter which deals with data categorized into contingency tables. . . . The monograph is admittedly not adequate for the needs of a possible user of statistics, but should interest advanced students and research workers. . . . The format, typography, editing, exposition, and proof-reading of this monograph are all unfortunately poor and tend to distract and annoy the reader. There is no index. . . . Despite its defects, this

monograph will find a useful place in the library of the advanced student or research worker in mathematical statistics."
Nature, 1958, **182**, 1183.
" Prof. Roy's book describes a number of special topics in multivariate analysis to which he has applied some original ideas on the construction of tests and confidence intervals. This book is really a rather loosely connected series of monographs, technically of a rather advanced nature, requiring a good deal of previous reading for full appreciation, but yielding rewards in stimulation and interest."
Operat. Res., 1958, **6**, 454.
" The book . . . is concerned with those particular developments in multivariate analysis that have been of special interest to the author. There is no attempt to cover the entire field of multivariate analysis. The major emphasis is on obtaining confidence bounds on certain parametric functions. Except in the last chapter, the author is concerned exclusively with normal variates. . . . The reviewer feels that every operations-research analyst should have some comprehension of the topic. However, Roy's book will be of little interest to such analysts unless they are also advanced students of theoretical statistics."

SAVAGE, L. J. *THE FOUNDATIONS OF STATISTICS*
1954. Wiley, xv+294 pp.

Chapter	Contents
1	Introduction
2	Preliminary Considerations on Decision in the Face of Uncertainty
3	Personal Probability
4	Critical Comments on Personal Probability
5	Utility
6	Observation
7	Partition Problems
8	Statistics Proper

9	Introduction to the Minimax Theory
10	A Personalistic Reinterpretation of the Minimax Theory
11	The Parallelism Between the Minimax Theory and the Theory of Two-Person Games
12	The Mathematics of Minimax Problems
13	Objections to the Minimax Rules
14	The Minimax Theory Applied to Observations
15	Point Estimation
16	Testing
17	Interval Estimation and Related Topics

J. Amer. Statist. Ass., 1956, **51**, 657.

" Of any new book it is natural to ask two questions: (1) What is the point of it; where does it fit in? (2) How well does it succeed in doing what might reasonably be expected of it? In the present case neither question is quite simple to answer. As to the first, the book does not really come under the heading of Statistical Methodology, but rather under that of Scientific Reasoning. A sufficiently developed theory of scientific reasoning would be the ground from which statistical methods intended for practical use could be properly evaluated. Savage has made a fine contribution to this study, one which should assist statistical theorists and philosophers for many years to come. At first the title of the book may seem a little misleading—until one reflects that anyone interest in the foundations of statistics will certainly need to read it. As for how well the book succeeds in its task, the answer must be ' excellently as far as it goes '. . . . To sum up, if there is any serious flaw in Savage's argument, it is one of excessive definiteness at the outset. Savage's theory of decisions is adequate for the discussion of many, but not all, problems in statistical methodology. Questions of goodness of fit of a scientific theory to observations are outside its scope."

J. R. Statist. Soc. A, 1955, **118**, 245.

" The first hundred pages of the book are devoted to the construction and discussion of what the reviewer would call a theory of rational behaviour, i.e. a theory of probability and utility. Probabilities and utilities are introduced simultaneously, following F. P. Ramsey, but with far more attention to detail. The effect is to define the subjective probabilities and utilities for a man in terms of his preferences between acts. The principle of rational behaviour, the recommendation to maximise the mathematical expectation of utilities, is proved by making only the most convincing assumptions. . . . The theory contains a theory of probability agreeing with that of Ramsey, B. de Finetti and B. O. Koopman, in short a theory of (subjective) degrees of belief. This theory, again, includes the ordinary orthodox theory of probabilities of say Kolmogoroff, but not with the frequentist interpretation, which the non-frequentists think is not operationally expressible except in terms of a non-frequentist theory. Incidentally Savage was originally a frequentist, but has changed his views.

"Statistics proper, discussed in the second half of the book, is defined as 'the art of dealing with vagueness and with interpersonal differences in decision situations'. The discussion is largely centred on the minimax rule and the ' group minimax rule '. These two rules are respectively attempts to achieve the two aims of statistics proper, just mentioned. . . . Throughout the book ' key references ' are given, enabling the reader to enter the front lines of research. For example, although there is no discussion of fiducial probability, seventeen references are given. The text contains 288 references to other writers, and the Bibliography contains 172 items of which 142 are dated 1940 or later.

"The writing is nearly always lucid, but the book as a whole is difficult to read, largely because of the conciseness of the style. As the author says in the Preface ' Serious reading of mathematics is best done sitting bolt upright on a hard chair at a desk. . . . In this book . . . when exercises are indicated, it is absolutely essential that they be read, and nearly essential that they be worked, because they constitute part of the exposition . . .' This then is a book for the practical philosopher rather than the arm chair philosopher."

Nature, 1956, **177**, 679.

"My main objection to this book concerns its title. The first half deals with theories of probability in their subjective and objective aspects; the second half defines ' statistics proper ' as ' the art of dealing with vagueness and with interpersonal difference in decision processes '. Some of the words in this definition, perhaps, provide avenues of escape; but . . . it is fair to construe [the author's] attitude as one which takes statistics to be a theory of decision. This view is not shared by many British statisticians, who rightly insist, first, on the fact that statistical inference is only part of statistics and, second, on the fact that decisions are only part of statistical inference.

"As a contributor to the foundations of the theory of decisions, Prof. Savage's book is, however, welcome and stimulating."

SCHEFFÉ, H. *THE ANALYSIS OF VARIANCE*
1959. Wiley, xvi+477 pp.

Chapter	Contents
1	Point Estimation
2	Construction of Confidence Ellipsoids and Tests in the General Case under Normal Theory
3	The One-Way Layout. Multiple Comparison
4	The Complete Two-, Three-, and Higher-Way Layouts. Partitioning a Sum of Squares.
5	Some Incomplete Layouts: Latin Squares, Incomplete Blocks, and Nested Designs
6	The Analysis of Covariance
7	Random-Effects Models
8	Mixed Models
9	Randomization Models
10	The Effects of Departures from the Underlying Assumptions

J. Inst. Actuar., 1960, **86**, 230.

" The present book will provide a final answer to all those who excuse the use of the ' recipe ' books on the grounds that ' nothing else is available '. Here is a book giving a thorough treatment of most of the basic ideas, and much of the subsequently elaborated superstructure of analysis of variance as understood by a well-trained mathematical statistician. The demands on the mathematical equipment of the reader are severe, but not excessively so.
. . . The lack of numerical illustrations is partially compensated by the provision of numerical data in problems at the end of chapters; there is also the usual collection of statistical tables. . . .

Appendices provide the necessary background of knowledge of mathematics in an efficient manner: a competent teacher, guided by the content of these appendices would be even better of course. The book is rounded off by a comprehensive bibliography and good subject and author indexes."

J. R. Statist. Soc. A, 1960, **123**, 482.
" The first adjective that comes to mind to describe this book is professional. The author has mastery of his subject and its literature, and clearly has taken great care over the organization of the book, over the details of the writing, and over the provision of illustrative examples and exercises. The mathematical analysis is carried out with much attention to detail and to the need to provide results of sufficient generality to cover a wide range of special cases. The main tools are vector and matrix algebra; appendices set out the principal mathematical results used in the book. While the flavour of the book is mathematical, I did not feel that any mathematical complications had been introduced for their own sake. . . . A specially praiseworthy aspect of the book is the care taken to explain why the various linear models are put in the form they are. . . . There are two notable omissions. One is the absence of an account of 'missing-value' and related formulae. The other, and more serious, is the omission of the split-plot layout. . . . Altogether this is a most important book, deserving to be widely read. Statisticians working in fields where analysis of variance is used extensively are likely to find the book extremely valuable in consolidating their knowledge of the theoretical side of the subject. The work is intended also as a text for students; it seems to me right, however, that students should have first a mathematically more elementary and intuitive introduction to the subject."

TSCHUPROW, A. A. *PRINCIPLES OF THE MATHEMATICAL THEORY OF CORRELATION*
1939. Hodge, x+194 pp. (First published in German in 1925)

Chapter	Contents
1	The modern ' Mathematical ' Theory of Correlation and the methods of ' Non-mathematicians '

2   Subject matter and problems of Statistical Correlations. Causal Relation and Correlation
3   Stochastic Connection and Functional Relationship between variable magnitudes
4   The a priori Joint Frequency-Distribution and the Related System of Parameters
5   The Empirical material and the Coefficients which summarise it
6   Estimate of *a priori* Coefficients on the Basis of Empirical material
7   Stochastic Supposition of the Measurements of Correlation
8   Object and Value of Correlation Measurement

Biometrika, 1940, **31**, 396.

" . . . It will be of interest to many people in that it is a complete survey of correlation theory and its underlying principles. . . . Although the application of this theory to practical problems is perhaps a little out of date, it still forms a necessary background which the student must acquire, and of which a proper understanding will always be essential.

" The book as a whole shows an astonishing ' patchiness ' in writing. . . . Taken as a whole, this book is a worthy contribution to correlation literature, and it is surprising that no translation has been published until this date. It certainly should be read by all who attempt to gain an understanding of statistical theory."

J. R. Statist. Soc. A, 1939, **102**, 451.

" . . . approaches this translation . . . with some doubts whether it may be rather out of date. Such doubts are groundless. Notwithstanding the advances of recent years Professor Tschuprow's tract remains . . . a notable contribution to the literature of correlation, and may still be read with profit. . . . The greater part of the book is concerned with the logic of correlation analysis, the connection between causal relation and correlation and the nature of stochastic dependence. . . .

" The difficulty about coefficients of correlation is to interpret them. On this aspect the book is incomplete. . . . A further chapter on the logic of partial correlation analysis would add greatly to the value of the book. . . ."

WALD, A. *SEQUENTIAL ANALYSIS*
1947. Wiley, xii+212 pp.

Chapter	Contents
1	Elements of the Current Theory of Testing Statistical Hypotheses
2	Sequential Test of a Statistical Hypothesis: General Discussion
3	The Sequential Probability Ratio Test for Testing a Simple Hypothesis H_0 Against a Single Alternative H_1
4	Outline of a Theory of Sequential Tests of Simple and Composite Hypotheses Against a Set of Alternatives
5	Testing the Mean of a Binomial Distribution (Acceptance Inspection of a Lot where each Unit is Classified into One of Two Categories)
6	Testing the Difference between the Means of two Binomial Distributions (Double Dichotomies)
7	Testing that the Mean of a Normal Distribution with Known Standard Deviation Falls Short of a Given Value
8	Testing that the Standard Deviation of a Normal Distribution Does Not Exceed a Given Value
9	Testing that the Mean of a Normal Distribution with Known Variance is Equal to a Specified Value
10	The Choice of a Hypothesis from a Set of Mutually Exclusive Hypotheses (Multi-valued) Decision
11	The Problem of Sequential Estimation

J. Amer. Statist. Ass., 1947, **42**, 658.
". . . Sequential analysis in a sense is the natural result of the coming of age of statistical methods in scientific investigation . . . sequential analysis marks the entry of statistical considerations into the very process of experimentation itself.
". . . the full impact of the book will be best felt by those with a little more familiarity with mathematical ideas . . . for the more

mathematical reader, the exposition has a clarity and a unity which make it exceedingly attractive . . . a most stimulating number of unsolved questions are raised."

Note:—This review is extremely detailed and treats of many fundamental points in connection with the subject-matter.

Sankhyā, 1948, **8**, 390.

" In the Neyman-Pearson's theory of testing hypotheses the basic principle is to choose, for a sample of given size, a critical region which effects the ' best ' control over the two kinds of errors involved in such tests. There are, however, situations where one can vary the sample size as well to one's advantage to arrive at a decision.—In these types of problem, sequential tests have been evolved which, apart from controlling the two kinds of errors, economise to a large measure the average amount of sampling necessary to come to a conclusion. . . ."

WILLIAMS, E. J. *REGRESSION ANALYSIS*
 1959. Wiley, ix+214 pp.

Chapter	Contents
1	Introduction
2	Linear Regression
3	Multiple and Polynomial Regression
4	Regression Equations Requiring Iterative Calculation
5	Choice Among Regression Formulas
6	Estimation from the Regression Equation
7	The Analysis of Covariance
8	The Treatment of Heterogeneous Data
9	Simultaneous Regression Equations
10	Discriminant Functions
11	Functional Relations

Appl. Statist., 1960, **9**, 130.

" . . . there were many . . . examples and the book impressed me as having come to grips with quite a variety of interesting experimental situations. This variety results in a fairly concentrated expository style; at times it is not easy reading. As the author states in the preface, some familiarity with statistical methods is assumed. I should be inclined to regard the simpler sections as a text book and, after a preliminary skimming, to regard the more difficult sections as a reference book to be pondered over when need arises."

J. Amer. Statist. Ass., 1960, **55**, 616.

" This book offers the practical statistician a compendium of the classical techniques associated with regression analysis. The author has included references from recent literature, but the point of view is that which existed before the advent of statistical decision theory. The book is full of good numerical examples which also serve to illustrate the way in which departures from the usual simple models arise in practice. In particular there are good examples of such topics as estimation from non-linear equations, estimation of zeros of a fitted curve, etc. A great many of the examples are taken from the field of forestry."

PROBABILITY AND STOCHASTIC PROCESSES

ARLEY, N. AND BUCH, K. R. *INTRODUCTION TO THE THEORY OF PROBABILITY AND STATISTICS* 1950. Wiley, xi+236 pp.

Chapter	Contents
1	The Concept of Probability
2	The Foundations of the Theory of Probability
3	Elementary Theorems
4	Random Variables and Distribution Functions
5	Mean Value and Dispersion
6	Mean Value and Dispersion of Sums, Products and Other Functions
7	The Normal Distribution
8	Limit Theorems
9	The Relation of the Theory of Probability to Experience and its Practical Importance
10	Application of the Theory of Probability to Statistics
11	Application of the Theory of Probability to the Theory of Errors
12	Application of the Theory of Probability to the Theory of Adjustment

J. Amer. Statist. Ass., 1950, **45**, 459.

" One of the brightest features of the book is the large number of interesting problems, e.g. special distributions drawn mainly from the field of physics. . . .

" It is difficult to find a suitable place for this book . . . among the literature of the field of probability and statistics. It is a good deal too technical for the mathematician, while, on the other hand, it can hardly be called sufficiently comprehensive for a course in the mathematical theory of probability and statistics."

J. R. Statist. Soc. A, 1950, **113**, 412.

" This is an introduction to the theory of statistics which was originally published in Danish. . . . The mode of approach to statistical problems largely reflects the authors' interest in physical science and for a person of such interests this book provides a clear, accurate, and useful introduction. The biologically minded mathematician would, however, require to supplement it by other reading, for example, on the design of experiments. . . . The translation is good and the mathematical treatment clear and accurate."

Nature, 1951, **168**, 217.

" When a physicist and a pure mathematician join forces, the outcome is sure to be interesting; in this case it is a highly individual book which should do good work in familiarizing students of the natural sciences with the ideas notations and techniques of the modern theory of probability. Its excellence as an introductory textbook for physicists may be illustrated by mentioning that Poisson's distribution makes its first appearance in connexion with the Poisson process. No attempt is made to burden the book with proofs of the central-limit and allied major theorems; but their substance is sufficiently indicated, and the reader is given an accurate and clear picture of what can be expected from the mathematical theory. He will, if serious in his intentions, find this a very useful introduction to a detailed study of the more comprehensive work by Feller. As a textbook on statistics as opposed to probability theory, I found the book much less satisfactory, and it is perhaps a pity that a third collaborator was not found to prepare the ' Fisherian' chapters."

BARTLETT, M. S. *AN INTRODUCTION TO STOCHASTIC PROCESSES*
1955. Cambridge University Press, ix+312 pp.

Chapter	Contents
1	General Introduction
2	Random Sequences
3	Processes in Continuous Time
4	Miscellaneous Statistical Applications
5	Limiting Stochastic Operations

6 Stationary Processes
7 Prediction and Communication Theory
8 The Statistical Analysis of Stochastic Processes
9 Correlation and Analysis of Time Series

Biometrika, 1955, **42**, 539.

" This book is the best which has yet been produced on this specialised topic. It is lucidly written by someone who clearly sees the statistical implications of the abstract theory and may be read without undue difficulty by any student who has two years of university mathematical training behind him. It will undoubtedly be found indispensable by anyone wishing to learn something of a subject which has engaged the attention of nearly all probabilists in the past decade."

J. R. Statist. Soc. A, 1955, **118**, 484.

" Professor Bartlett has addressed himself primarily to applied mathematicians and statisticians who wish to aquaint themselves with a broad range of available techniques and to be given some indication of the underlying mathematical theory . . . [He] has managed to incorporate a wide range of theory and applications in a single book of moderate size. . . . There can be no doubt that the book is a substantial contribution to the development of the subject."

J. Amer. Statist. Ass., 1956, **51**, 383.

" The book under review . . . is is entirely without precedent in completeness and variety. . . . Anyone who has a specific problem in the application of stochastic processes will turn to it for specific ideas and references. . . . In two respects, though, I am disappointed in the book. First, I had hoped to find more emphasis on the qualitative behaviour of stochastic processes; and, second, the writing seems trying and difficult."

Appl. Statist., 1956, **5**, 70.

" Professor Bartlett's book meets an important need in presenting a general treatment of the subject, showing the essential unity of the mathematical concepts and methods which pervade all these applications. . . . The standard of mathematical attainment required in the reader is high, though by no means so high as by

Professor Doob in his recent book; an honours degree in mathematics would be about right."

Rev. Int. Statist. Inst., 1955, **23**, 125.
" The title ' Introduction ' must not be taken to indicate an elementary text. The exposition is rather a broad yet penetrating orientation which displays the many types of process, the richness of their applications, the diversity of mathematical methods in play, and the rapid development of theoretical and applied work.
. . . The author's firm grasp of the subject is manifest in the bibliography which is broad in scope with carefully selected references and emphasises pioneer contributions."

Inc. Statist., 1956, **6**, 161.
" The subject of stochastic processes is . . . not an easy one. It . . . follows that Professor Bartlett's allotted task of providing a useful and readable exposition of the subject for statisticians and other potential users of these techniques was itself one of considerable difficulty. He has succeeded in doing just that."

BHARUCHA-REID, A. T. *ELEMENTS OF THE THEORY OF MARKOV PROCESSES AND THEIR APPLICATIONS*
1960. McGraw-Hill, xi+468 pp.

Chapter	Contents
	Part I
	Theory
1	Processes Discrete in Space and Time
2	Processes Discrete in Space and Continuous in Time
3	Processes Continuous in Space and Time
	Part II
	Applications
4	Applications in Biology
5	Applications in Physics: Theory of Cascade Processes
6	Applications in Physics: Additional Applications
7	Applications in Astronomy and Astrophysics

  8 Applications in Chemistry
  9 Applications in Operations Research: The Theory of Queues

Inc. Statist., 1961, **11**, 126.

" Without any doubt, this is one of the most interesting books which has been written about probability theory since the pioneer works of Feller and Bartlett. . . .

" Inevitably, it will be bought by a wide range of people with a wide spectrum of interests. In the writer's opinion, the type of person who is likely to benefit most from its reading is the specialist in probability theory whose interest lies with mathematical techniques rather than the individual who is genuinely interested in applications. . . .

" Judged as a book for mathematicians, this work will be of immense value—the author is to be praised for an extremely comprehensive survey of a wide number of fields and for the carefully compiled set of references which will provide useful following up material for the condensed accounts given in many parts."

BIZLEY, M. T. L. *PROBABILITY*
  1957. Cambridge University Press, viii+230 pp.

Chapter	Contents
1	Fundamental Principles
2	Rules of Combination of Principles
3	The Theorems of Waring and Bayes
4	Repeated Trials: Expectation
5	Indirect Methods
6	Runs
7	Continuous Variables
	Appendix

Biometrika, 1958, **45**, 593.

" The book is apparently a course-book designed to cover a specific syllabus and this vitiates its appeal to the general reader, since the topics covered are selective rather than encyclopaedic. On the other hand, it faces the limited mathematical attainments of its intended readers with ingenuity and the problems are, considering this limitation, surprisingly representative. Sometimes the ingenuity is more restrictive however: for instance it would be hard to derive the normal distribution plausibly or instructively from a situation couched in terms of classical geometrical probabilities.

" A more serious criticism of the logical development of the book arises when the first chapter, on the nature of probability, and the appendix, on theories of probability are considered. The author's own opinions are not clear . . . he gives an ear more or less impartially to the different schools of thought without having adequate space to deal with the contradictions between them."

J. Inst. Actuar., 1957, **83**, 310.

" This addition to the series of textbooks published under the authority of the Institute and Faculty has fully maintained, to say the least, the standard set by those already published, and that is a very high standard indeed. Two things in particular stand out. First, a probability textbook depends largely for its success on its worked examples; those given by Bizley are always appropriate to the context, instructive and fully and clearly worked out. Secondly, it is a real pleasure to read this book if only to appreciate the clarity, simplicity and elegance with which the author has expressed himself."

J. R. Statist. Soc. A, 1957, **120**, 182.

" The book is, in fact, a primer setting out, with the utmost clarity, the various methods that can be used in the solution of problems in probability and the circumstances in which each is likely to be appropriate. A number of these methods and the results derived from them do not appear to have been given in any previous textbook. . . . The student who has mastered this work will have acquired both a thorough grounding in the principles of probability and a knowledge of how best to attempt the solution of a variety of practical problems."

Nature, 1957, **180**, 1270.

"This book, designed to meet the requirements of actuarial students, is concerned solely with classical probability theory, although the importance of relating this to statistics is emphasized. The development is elementary, but sound within the limits of an acknowledged incompleteness of discussion of the fundamental nature of probability. The general account of alternative definitions of probability is indeed good, and the subsequent presentation of standard theory of combinations of probability is excellent . . . more use might have been made of actuarial problems and of applications of probability to science and industry."

CRAMÉR, H. *THE ELEMENTS OF PROBABILITY THEORY*
1955. Wiley, 281 pp.

Chapter	Contents
1	Historical Introduction
2	Definition of Mathematical Probability
3	Elementary Rules of Calculation Probability
4	Some Applications of the Fundamental Theorems
5	Variables and Distributions in One Dimension
6	The Binomial and Related Distributions
7	The Normal Distribution
8	Further Continuous Distributions
9	Variables and Distributions in Two Dimensions
10	Variables and Distributions and Distributions in More Than Two Dimensions
11	Introduction (to Applications)
12	Descriptive Treatment of a Statistical Material
13	Sampling Distributions
14	Problems of Statistical Inference
15	The Test
16	Some Further Applications

J. R. Statist. Soc. A, 1955, **118**, 486.

" This book provides a sound introductory course in probability theory. . . . The book is excellently printed but the price is rather high considering its size and the class of reader—mainly undergraduates—for whom it is designed."

J. Amer. Statist. Ass., 1956, **51**, 165.

" Within . . . (the) . . . limitations set by the author it is hard to see how a better book could have been written. Cramér's

clarity and conciseness of expression should serve as an ideal for writers of other text-books. The many examples given illustrate and extend, in a masterful way, the theory presented."
J. Inst. Actuar., 1956, **82**, 160.

". . . this is a valuable book from the point of view of an actuarial student for two reasons. In the first place it is written at just about the correct mathematical level for the student to be able to follow and yet be stimulated by it. Secondly, the book makes a conscious and successful attempt to bridge a difficult gap and link together probability theory and the practical side of statistical analysis. . . . The style is lucid and the whole work is liberally sprinkled with examples to drive home the points made."

DAVID, F. N. *PROBABILITY THEORY FOR STATISTICAL METHODS*
1949. Cambridge University Press, ix+230 pp.

Chapter	Contents
1	Fundamental Ideas
2	Preliminary Definitions and Theorems
3	The Binomial Theorem in Probability
4	Evaluation of Binomial Probabilities
5	Replacement of the Binomial Series by the Normal Curve
6	Poisson's Limit for Binomial Probabilities. The Negative Binomial
7	Probabilities *a posteriori*. Confidence Limits
8	Simple Genetical Applications
9	Multinomial Theorem and Simple Combinational Analysis
10	Random Variables. Elementary Laws and Theorems
11	Moments of Sampling Distributions
12	Random Variables. Inequalities. Laws of Large Numbers. Lexis Theory
13	Simple Estimation. Markoff Theorem on Least Squares
14	Further Applications of the Markoff Theorem
15	Characteristic Functions. Elementary Theorems

16 Characteristic Functions. Moments and Cumulants. Liapounoff's Theorem
17 Characteristic Functions. Converse Theorems

Annals of Eugenics, 1949, **15**, 93.

" Dr. David tends to go back to Laplace for some of her theory, revising it along the lines developed by Neyman and Pearson. That is to say, she tries to base every argument on the conception of a set of equally probable arrangements. This approach is particularly well suited for the treatment of elementary genetics, though if she ever tries to tackle lineage estimation she will find it a rather narrow foundation. The treatment is rigorous, except that, as the author does not use point set theory, most of her theorems are only completely proved for discontinuous probability distributions. It leads inevitably to the ' unbiased estimate ' as the ideal to be aimed at."

Biometrika, 1949, **36**, 469.

" This book deals with the simpler parts of probability theory in so far as they are relevant to common statistical techniques . . . it will be found useful by all who are interested in statistical methods, as it gathers together a number of useful results which otherwise are very much scattered throughout the literature."

J. Amer. Statist. Ass., 1949, **44**, 567.

" . . . emphasize that this book is based on a carefully organised set of lectures. The imprints of Karl Pearson and Jerzy Neyman are plain to see . . . it should be helpful supplementary reading for both students and teachers. . . ."

J. Inst. Actuar., 1961, **75**, 262.

" As might be expected from one so well versed in statistical theory and applications and from the stated object of the book, namely, to ' prove in elementary mathematical language those propositions and theorems of the calculus of probability which have been found useful for students of elementary statistics ', David writes throughout in a manner calculated to appeal to statisticians. Her account of the methods available for evaluating numerically the sum of a number of binomial terms is unusual, but all the more welcome in a text on probability theory. . . . [the

book] provides an excellent treatment of its subject-matter disguised under a 'probability' title . . . a compendium of probability theorems for reference by the practising statistician."
Sankhyā, 1950, **10**, 140.
". . . the book covers a wide range of topics . . . the deviations of the various properties of . . . important distributions are well presented. The chapter on the evaluation of binomial probabilities is especially interesting. . . . Chapter VIII is an added attraction to the book. . . . Chapter XV, XVI and XVII . . . treatment is not comprehensive but the topics covered there serve as a good introduction to some advanced portions of mathematical statistics. . . ."

Doob, J. L. *STOCHASTIC PROCESSES*
1953. Wiley, vii + 654 pp.

Chapter	Contents
1	Introduction and Probability Background
2	Definition of a Stochastic Process—Principal Classes
3	Processes With Mutually Independent Random Variables
4	Processes With Mutually Uncorrelated or Orthogonal Random Variables
5	Markov Processes—Discrete Parameter
6	Markov Processes—Continuous Parameter
7	Martingales
8	Processes With Independent Increments
9	Processes With Orthogonal Increments
10	Stationary Processes—Discrete Parameter
11	Stationary Processes—Continuous Parameter
12	Linear Least Squares Prediction—Stationary (Wide Sense) Processes

Biometrika, 1954, **41**, 284.
". . . What Prof. Doob has really written is a text-book covering the mathematical development of probability theory, the emphasis being on stochastic processes. . . . The book will be of little use

to anyone who has not been trained in modern methods of mathematical analysis; it will be no use at all to the non-mathematician seeking for applications. For the mathematical statistician seeking to make rigorous his knowledge of probability theory and wishing to learn up to the boundary of present day research it will be indispensable. It is definitely a specialist's book, which is obviously what the author intended, and within the limited field it will be without rival for years to come."

J. R. Statist. Soc., 1953, **116**, 454.

" The student of the mathematical theory of stochastic processes is well served by this book. It is very useful to have such an able presentation of material which has previously been accessible only in journals and often in a foreign language. The mathematical treatment is masterly and the extent astonishing, even if it only shows how ignorant one was. The major defect is explained by the author in his preface: ' it stresses most those parts which appeal most to me '. The result of this attitude is a lack of purpose. In chapter after chapter a new type of process is introduced and very skilfully investigated; largely because the mathematics is beautiful? This is a book of mathematically interesting theorems, not a book of solutions to problems. . . . Thus without some other material the book is rather uninteresting unless mathematical manipulation for its own sake exerts enough of an appeal. . . . Here then is a book which every person interested in stochastic processes and with the necessary mathematical ability will find indispensable. He will also find it difficult but very worth persevering with and understanding."

J. Inst. Actuar., 1954, **80**, 135.

" The book is intended to be a mathematical treatise. . . . the author . . . is concerned solely with the theoretical development of the subject. . . . For those with sufficient time the study of Professor Doob's work will prove richly rewarding, even if some will find his strictly mathematical outlook unhelpful and even perhaps annoying. It is a book the real worth of which can only be assessed after a considerable passage of time, but it will undoubtedly have a profound effect on the future direction of research in the field of stochastic processes."

Nature, 1954, **173**, 935.
"This text is important for at least two reasons. It meets a long-felt need for a systematic account of a subject which has grown rapidly during the last 20-30 years; and it is an account in English of a subject which has developed largely outside the English-speaking world. . . . The reader who is not a specialist in measure theory will find the going heavy in places, but he may be consoled by the fact that there is a supplement on measure theory. . . . It is perhaps worth emphasizing that the present work is mathematical rather than applied in character, in the sense that mathematical formulation and method take precedence over the details of applications."

DYNKIN, E. B. *THEORY OF MARKOV PROCESSES*
1960. Pergamon, ix+210 pp.

Chapter	Contents
1	Introduction
2	Markov Processes
3	Subprocesses
4	The Construction of Markov Processes with Given Transition Functions
5	Strictly Markov Processes
6	Conditions for Boundedness and Continuity of a Markov Process

Nature, 1961, **191**, 321.
"This important and highly original work is devoted to a study of the foundations of theory of Markov processes. It is written for the professional probabilist and has little to offer to the non-expert, although any mathematician concerned with the teaching of measure theory will find it worth his while reading Chapter 1. . . . This chapter also contains a careful account of conditional probabilities, some information about the new concept of ' topological measurable spaces ', and the best extension yet of the Daniell-Kolmogorov theorem on the construction of probability measures on function-space. The remainder of the book presents the first

thorough formulation of theory of Markov processes, starting with a whole collection of measures corresponding to all possible initial instants and all possible initial states, and allowing (as is now found convenient) the termination of the process at a random instant. The difficult theory around the concept of a ' strict ' Markov process is set out in great detail."

FELLER, W. *AN INTRODUCTION TO PROBABILITY THEORY AND ITS APPLICATIONS.* Vol. I. 1957. 2nd Ed., Wiley, xv+461 pp.

Chapter	Contents
1	The Sample Space
2	Elements of Combinatorial Analysis
3	Fluctuations in Coin Tossing and Random Walks
4	Combination of Events
5	Conditional Probability. Stochastic Independence
6	The Binomial and the Poisson Distributions
7	The Normal Approximation to the Binomial Distribution
8	Unlimited Sequences of Bernoulli Trials
9	Random Variables; Expectation
10	Laws of Large Numbers
11	Integral Valued Variables. Generating Functions
12	Compound Distributions. Branching Processes
13	Recurrent Events. The Renewal Equation
14	Random Walk and Ruin Problems
15	Markov Chains
16	Algebraic Treatment of Finite Markov Chains
17	The Simplest Time-Dependent Stochastic Processes

Biometrika, 1958, **45**, 287.

" This is the second edition of a book which was first issued in 1950. . . . The major difference from the first edition appears to be the insertion of Chapter III . . . where the random walk occurs a little earlier than originally. During the seven years since this book was issued it has rapidly established itself as a classic in probability theory connected with the discrete variable."

J. Inst. Actuar., 1958, **84**, 232.

" Examination reveals that Professor Feller has accomplished the seemingly impossible task of bettering his own masterpiece by means of an increase in scope, and a more thorough concatenation of related topics, rather than by any amelioration of the existing detail. The changes have been made so deftly that the author has nowhere disturbed the continuity, or marred the beauty, of the unfolding pattern of his work; rather has his practised hand blended it anew into yet more attractive form. Those who admired the first edition—and they surely include all its readers—may be unreservedly advised to read the second; high though their hopes may run, they will assuredly be delighted."

J. R. Statist. Soc. A, 1958, **121**, 355.

" The first edition of this outstanding book appeared in 1950 and it is now firmly established both as an introductory text-book and as a reference work on more advanced topics. For the second edition Professor Feller has put in a new chapter, carried out extensive minor revision, and added a considerable number of further exercises."

Nature, 1958, **182**, 489.

" The theory of probability is developed with a degree of rigour which should satisfy the pure mathematician. But there are also applications to practical situations, including the estimation of the size of an animal population, the distribution of misprints in a book, or of raisins in a cake, or of flaws in a material; and the exposition is made the more colourful by reference to card games, birthdays and the spread of rumours."

Operat. Res., 1958, **6**, 636.

" It does not take long to discover a definite streamlining in most chapters. In addition, the elements of queuing theory have been woven into the context throughout the book and serve as a unifying thread. . . . The general streamlining has done nothing to spoil the readability of the book, but on the contrary has improved it."

GRENANDER, U. AND ROSENBLATT, M. *STATISTICAL ANALYSIS OF STATIONARY TIME SERIES*
1957. Wiley, 300 pp.

Chapter	Contents
1	Stationary Stochastic Processes and their Representations
2	Statistical Questions when the Spectrum is known (Least Squares Theory)
3	Statistical Analysis of Parametric Models
4	Estimation of the Spectrum
5	Applications
6	Distribution of Spectral Estimates
7	Problems in Linear Estimation
8	Assorted Problems

Biometrika, 1958, **45**, 283.

" The authors of this work have done statisticians a service in bringing together for the first time the diversity of applications of time-series analysis in the physical sciences, especially in electrical engineering . . . it is to be hoped that it will be widely read."

Econometrica, 1959, **27**, 139.

" In several papers the authors have made important contributions to the theory of statistical inference in stationary time series. The present monograph sums up and brings further results, the most original and central ones being the non-parametric estimation of spectral density (Chapter 6) and the asymptotic properties of least squares estimates of regression coefficients (Chapter 7). . . . As a theoretical exposition of its subject the text is more modern and covers more ground than any other yet in existence."

J. Amer. Statist. Ass., 1958, **53**, 221.

" A large proportion of the Grenander-Rosenblatt work is devoted to proofs and a good command of mathematical analysis is required of the reader. . . . One of the major shortcomings of the book is its unevenness of presentation. The technical demands it makes on the reader vary widely. . . . Statisticians and scientists will find the statements of the theorems interesting and useful in getting some ideas about variability in this area. The book contains a very fine collection of problems at the end. The student will find much to challenge him and test his skill."

J. R. Statist. Soc. A, 1957, **120**, 353.

" The present monograph . . . will be a valuable reference book for some of the most important research contributions, including many from the authors themselves. It might, however, be remarked that the book is more a research monograph than a comprehensive treatise and should not be regarded in the latter sense, not only because the authors have tended to concentrate on problems of spectral analysis in which they are interested, but because the subject is one in which further development is not yet over, so that further results and procedures have appeared after this book, which has been somewhat late in appearing in print, was written. . . . Mathematical statisticians should find most of the material of value; econometricians much less, because spectral analysis is not so useful with time-series of rather limited length."

Nature, 1958, **181**, 1495.

" The statistical problems which arise in the analysis of time series are truly formidable and in several ways require techniques which are not familiar to many statisticians. It is accordingly very useful to have this unified treatment of the spectral approach. The authors, noting that existing literature is characterised by a certain lack of precision, have devoted a good deal of space to rigorous mathematical proofs. This it must be admitted makes the book rather difficult reading; but then it is a difficult subject, and one applauds their willingness to make assumptions which would be restrictive to a mathematician seeking complete generality but are no limitation so far as concerns practical applications."

HANNAN, E. J. *TIME SERIES ANALYSIS*
    1960. Methuen, vii+152 pp.

Chapter   *Contents*
  1   The Spectral Theory of Discrete Stochastic Processes
  2   Estimation of the Correlogram and of the Parameter of Finite Parameter Schemes
  3   Estimation of the Spectral Density and Distribution Functions

K

| 4 | Hypothesis Testing and Confidence Intervals |
| 5 | Processes Containing a Deterministic Component |

J. R. Statist. Soc. A, 1961, **124**, 252.

" In this relatively short monograph, the second in the Methuen series on Probability Theory and Statistics, Professor Hannan has managed to cover most of the important topics in time-series analysis with a degree of thoroughness and detail which many would have thought impossible in a book of this size. There is no doubt that it will prove of immense value in the teaching of the subject at postgraduate level to statisticians with a reasonable degree of competence in mathematics. . . .

The calibre of the mathematical development is of an exceptionally high standard throughout and a particularly pleasing feature is the recognition that results expressed in terms of the spectrum rather than the a.c.f. are neater in form and much easier to interpret. Perhaps one may be permitted to make two minor criticisms from a practical point of view. Firstly, it may be a little unfortunate, but inevitable in a book of this size, that the examples seem to have been used only as numerical illustrations rather than to show the reader what is capable of being achieved by time-series analysis; for example, confidence intervals are given for the fitted parameters of a second-order autoregression to the lynx data (p. 51) when the fit itself is rather bad. Secondly, it would seem to the writer that undue emphasis has been placed on hypothesis testing since the hypotheses themselves are so vague. It might even be argued that the attaching of confidence intervals to individual spectra is a fairly academic problem if the two halves of the same series or further experiments produce quite different spectral shapes. These criticisms are not valid, however, for a text book on mathematical statistics and in this respect Professor Hannan deserves to be congratulated on having done an excellent job."

KEMENY, J. G. AND SNELL, J. L. *FINITE MARKOV CHAINS* 1960. Van Nostrand, viii+210 pp.

Chapter	Contents
1	Prerequisites

2	Basic Concepts of Markov Chains
3	Absorbing Markov Chains
4	Regular Markov Chains
5	Ergodic Markov Chains
6	Further Results
7	Applications of Markov Chains

J. Amer. Statist. Ass., 1961, **56**, 182.

" As the title suggests this book is concerned with the theory and applications of finite Markov chains. The authors intend their book to be useful as a textbook in an undergraduate course in probability as well as useful as a reference book for workers in fields outside mathematics.

According to the authors the book contains a ' new approach ' to finite Markov chains. This new approach presumably simplifies the treatment so that a minimum of mathematical background is needed. Briefly, this approach is that of defining a number of so-called ' fundamental matrices ' in terms of which interesting information about the Markov chains can be derived.

" The best part of the book is Chapter VII. The theory developed previously is applied to a number of well-chosen probability models. These include the random walk and applications to sports, genetics, learning theory, mobility theory, and economics. The authors are concerned with three aspects of each example: the assumptions inherent in the model, its mathematical analysis, and the interpretation of the mathematical results. Except for one example, (mobility theory), too little attention is paid to the first of these aspects. On the other hand, the mathematical analysis and interpretation is handled very well."

KERRICH, J. E. *AN EXPERIMENTAL INTRODUCTION TO THE THEORY OF PROBABILITY*
    1946. Munksgaard, 98 pp.

    5 Sections—no chapter headings, but a page to page detailed table of contents is given

J. Amer. Statist. Ass., 1949, **44**, 147.

" Various results from these experiments are recorded in tabular and graphical form. Data are analysed both in the large and in sub-sequences with respect to various ratios. . . . The analysis leads to a body of ideas. . . . Thus the author arrives at the tools of pure mathematics. . . . In the reviewer's opinion, the author has admirably achieved his objective as stated in the Foreword. . . . And his hope is well founded when he says that students of these pages will never have to reject any of the ideas given here, no matter how much they may refine them as their knowledge of the subject grows."

J. R. Statist. Soc.A, 1947, **110**, 74.

" All those who have been introduced to the foundation of the theory of probability must have tried . . . to envisage what it looked like exactly when ratios were computed step by step from an actual experiment. Lack of time might have prevented us from passing to a real experiment from an imaginary one. The author had ample time nor did he apparently suffer from impatience. As a British subject he was . . . interned by the Danish authorities . . . and we we can well imagine the soothing effect of spinning a coin . . . or drawing two balls out of four while the time scale seems to stretch to infinity. . . .

" The author has succeeded in writing a very instructive and easily readable book. . . ."

Kolmogorov, A. N.   *FOUNDATIONS OF THE THEORY OF PROBABILITY*
   1956. Chelsea Publishing Company, 84 pp.

Chapter	Contents
1	Elementary Theory of Probability
2	Infinite Probability Fields
3	Random Variables
4	Mathematical Expectations
5	Conditional Probabilities and Mathematical Expectations
6	Independence; the Law of Large Numbers

Review of 1st English Edition, 1950.
J. Inst. Actuar., 1951, **77**, 332.

" The epithet classic is nowadays used so freely that it seldom conveys to the reader the connotation of universally admitted excellence which it really implies. It can, however, be applied in its strict sense to Kolmogorov's *Grundbegriffe*—to use the spelling and abbreviated title which is familiar to students of probability theory everywhere. The booklet was written in Moscow in 1933 and published in Germany the same year, and was the first comprehensive development of axiomatic probability calculus in terms of completely additive set theory. Members wishing to study this work will no longer suffer the double handicap of a foreign language and the possibly unfamiliar processes of a generalized Lebesgue measure theory. The former has been eliminated by a new American translation. The latter remains no mean hurdle for most of us and may relegate Kolmogorov's *Foundations* to a respected but inviolate place on our bookshelves."

Biometrika, 1957, **44**, 298.
" This is the second edition of the translation of the original German monograph . . . by the world's leading probabilist. It is a book from which nearly all our modern ideas may be deemed to have sprung. In this . . . edition there are no alterations."

LINDGREN, B. W. AND MCELRATH, G. W. *INTRODUCTION TO PROBABILITY AND STATISTICS*
 1959. Macmillan, vii + 277 pp.

Chapter	Contents
1	Simple Probability Models
2	Random Variables and Distribution Functions
3	Discrete Distributions
4	Continuous Distributions
5	Sums of Random Variables
6	Sampling
7	Presentation and Description of Data
8	Testing Statistical Hypotheses
9	Testing and Estimating Location
10	Estimating and Testing Variability
11	Comparison of Two Populations
12	Some Further Topics

J. Amer. Statist. Ass., 1961, **56**, 187.

" This text provides an introduction to the basic notions and concepts of mathematical statistics and probability theory. Calculus is a required prerequisite, with here and there some knowledge of what may be found in courses in advanced calculus needed. . . . The appendices are followed by answers to all the exercises, except for the review problems at the end of each chapter.

"Overall, it may be concluded that a very good job was done. The first chapter while sketchy is still adequate. It would perhaps be preferable to have a rearrangement of Chapters 2, 3, and 4. Chapter 3 could quite nicely take off from the first chapter as a generalisation of the idea of solving individual probability problems and then move to the notion of a probability function. Chapter 4 could then follow with the idea of a density function. After this has been disposed of, the cumulative distribution function would provide a nice completion of the topic. . . . The rest of the text from Chapter 5 on is very nice indeed. There is a distinct modern flavor which is evidenced by the topics covered, for example the Kolmogoroff-Smirnov statistic, but yet full attention has been given to the important fundamental ideas contained in the central limit theorem and the Neyman-Pearson lemma. All the ideas are clearly set forth and the number and kind of illustrative examples are excellent."

LOEVE, M. *PROBABILITY THEORY*
1960. 2nd Ed., Van Nostrand, xvi+685 pp.

Chapter   *Contents*
Introductory Part: Elementary Probability Theory

Part I

Notions of Measure Theory
1   Sets, Spaces and Measures
2   Measurable Functions and Integration

Part II

General Concepts and Tools of Probability Theory
3   Probability Concepts

4	Distribution Functions and Characteristic Functions

Part III
Independence

5	Sums of Independent Random Variables
6	Central Limit Problems

Part IV
Dependence

7	Conditioning
8	From Independence to Dependence
9	Ergodic Theorems
10	Second Order Properties

Part V
Elements of Random Analysis

11	Foundations; Martingales and Decomposability
12	Markov Processes

Nature, 1961, **192**, 7.

" The first edition of this book appeared in 1955 and went a long way to fill a serious gap in the mathematical literature. The new edition, revised in detail and longer by two chapters, comes a little nearer to closing the gap and is still the only (and an excellent) approximation to a comprehensive text-book on mathematical probability. . . . There is, a valuable synthesis of the recent work by Feller, Dynkin and others on diffusion theory."

MORAN, P. A. P. *THE THEORY OF STORAGE*
   1959. Methuen, 111 pp.

Chapter	Contents
1	General Introduction
2	Inventories
3	Dams—Discrete Time
4	Dams—Continuous Time
5	' Monte Carlo ' and other Statistical Methods
6	The Programming of Storage Systems

J. Inst. Actuar., 1960, **86**, 104.

" This small monograph is a handy compendium of recent work on that part of the Theory of Queues having particular relevance to storage problems. . . . The lack of provision of sufficient numerical results to give the reader some general idea of the real nature of the problems is the most notable defect of the book. On the credit side, there is a remarkably clear and concise description of the various types of problem to which storage theory can be applied, and of the methods used to attack these problems. . . . Despite some unevenness in the relative amounts of detail accorded to different topics, and the lack of numerical illustration, this book should be a worth-while purchase for persons wishing to possess a good knowledge of one of the most fruitful fields of statistical research in recent years. Provided they are not intimidated by some of the names . . . appearing in chapter 1, they will find the mathematics in the rest of the book well under control, and serving its proper purpose of clarifying the argument."

J. R. Statist. Soc. A, 1960, **123**, 485.

" In the main the book is concerned with the mathematical treatment of the operating behaviour of systems in their aspect of stochastic processes, and it will be of more interest to theoreticians than to, say, operational research workers. Although, of course, the type of application is of prime importance in operational research, the emphasis in the latter field is on the design of optimal systems rather than on mathematical analysis of stochastic behaviour. . . . For the beginning postgraduate student, this little book provides a good short introduction, together with a brief bibliography, to a rewarding field of research."

MORSE, P. M. *QUEUES, INVENTORIES AND MAINTENANCE*
    1958. Wiley, ix+202 pp.

Chapter   *Contents*
   1   Representation in Terms of Probabilities
   2   Probabilistic Description of Arrivals and Service Times
   3   Single Exponential Channel

4   Multiple Exponential Channels
5   Simulation of Non-Exponential Distributions
6   General Considerations, Transient Solutions
7   Single Channel, Infinite Queues
8   Multiple Channels, Infinite Queues
9   Queue Discipline and Priorities
10   Problems of Inventory Control
11   Maintenance of Equipment

Biometrika, 1959, **46**, 496.

" [the author's] aim is modest: ' The present volume does not pretend to be an exhaustive treatise on queuing theory. Its purpose is primarily expository, to present enough of the concepts, to define some of the terms and to illustrate a few of the analytic techniques ' . . . and within this framework he is very successful . . . he has written a book which will be useful particularly to the practical man who wants to describe real situations and useful also to the mathematician coming fresh to queuing theory who wants to know what it is about without being overwhelmed by rigour."

J. Amer. Statist. Ass., 1958, **53**, 761.

" The book is directed primarily toward the operation researcher and much of the discussion is justifiably motivated by practical considerations. . . . The book is very well organized and focuses quickly on interesting applications. Unfortunately, the high frequency of misprints makes difficult reading. Nevertheless, this book is an invaluable compilation of distribution theory for the characteristics of a large number of useful queuing models. Insights, applications, and interpretations of the theoretical queuing results related to operational problems of waiting time, maintenance, and inventory will serve for many years to come as the reference for all future studies of this kind."

J. R. Statist. Soc. A, 1958, **121**, 356.

" Professor Morse has written an excellent introduction to the theory of queues, applying a single mathematical technique to a wide variety of systems. The general implications of each result are clearly discussed and the behaviour of the main formulae is illustrated graphically. . . . The central ideas of input, queue discipline etc. are illustrated by brief, rather idealized, examples, but there is no attempt to discuss real applications in detail ... much recent work on queuing theory is not dealt with. In fact, the author's aim, as set out in his Preface, is not to give a comprehensive account of the subject, but rather to present a simple technique which can be used by the operational research worker to set up and solve his own special problems."

Operat. Res. Quart., 1958, **9**, 325.

" Professor Morse has produced an excellent introduction which, while intended to be expository, will allow the reader to make use of the techniques. . . . Throughout the work Professor Morse avoids straying from the practical path; sample problems are related to realistic problems in industry. . . . This is not a book for the mathematically immature; some background in statistics and calculus is essential, as it should be for a comprehensive review of an important subject for operations research workers. A glossary of symbols is provided which allows the volume to be used for reference purposes. The book also includes seven tables of great value to those using queuing theory in real problems."

NEYMAN, J. *FIRST COURSE IN PROBABILITY AND STATISTICS*
1950. Holt, ix+350 pp.

Chapter	Contents
1	Introduction: Scope of the Theory of Probability and Statistics
2	Probability
3	Probabilistic Problems in Genetics
4	Random Variables and Frequency Distributions
5	Elements of the Theory of Testing Statistical Hypotheses

Ann. Eugen., 1952, **16**, 382.

" The whole emphasis of the book is on the use of probability and its simpler properties, and they are carefully and lucidly explained throughout. But there is very little statistical theory in the usual sense of the word. . . . In short, this is a book for the student who wishes to grasp the fundamental ideas clearly, but it has very little direct bearing on the kinds of statistical problem most commonly met with in practice. . . . The value of the book is greatly increased by a large number of entertaining examples and exercises. It is well written, well arranged and well printed. It is a useful and unconventional addition to the literature.

Biometrika, 1951, **38**, 261.

" It is particularly interesting to have set out in simple form what may be termed Professor Neyman's philosophy of statistical thought. The characteristic feature of his contribution to statistics during the past 25 years has lain in his conviction that the more empirical British and American approach to mathematical statistics needed strengthening by a closer and more sure integration with the theory of probability."

J. R. Statist. Soc. A, 1950, **113**, 578.

" This book is intended as an introductory course in probability and statistics for students who are encountering the subject for the first time and have little mathematics beyond elementary algebra. The first chapter is intended to introduce the reader to the concept of statistics as a theory which provides rules of inductive behaviour. . . . The last and most important chapter is devoted to the theory of statistical tests. . . . No statistician can fail to benefit by a careful study of this section. This chapter also contains a discussion of the lambda principle of constructing tests, industrial sampling and capture-recapture sampling methods."

PARZEN, E. *MODERN PROBABILITY THEORY AND ITS APPLICATIONS*
   1960. Wiley, xv+464 pp.

Chapter	Contents
1	Probability Theory as the Study of Mathematical Models of Random Phenomena
2	Basic Probability Theory
3	Independence and Dependence
4	Numerical-Valued Random Phenomena

5	Mean and Variance of a Probability Law
6	Normal, Poisson, and Related Probability Laws
7	Random Variables
8	Expectation of a Random Variable
9	Sums of Independent Random Variables
10	Sequences of Random Variables

Appl. Statist., 1961, **10**, 63.

". . . It is written as a text book for a course in probability that can be adapted to the needs of students with diverse interests and backgrounds. I think it is possible that a student working under supervision would find it quite useful: it contains a good deal of information and is well supplied with exercises of various kinds, some of them being ' theoretical exercises ' in which the student is made to do some of the theoretical work himself. I should be less happy in recommending this book to a private student, as I feel that the arguments sometimes lack cohesion at vital points."

Inc. Statist., 1960, **10**, 141.

". . . the intending reader should be aware that the word ' modern ' in the title must be understood to mean ' currently accepted ', or ' fashionable ' and not ' advanced ' or ' recently developed '. . . . This book is in fact a remarkably thorough compendium of established probability theory, embellished with numerous examples of applications. Also remarkable is the unusually slow rate of development. . . . So painstaking and exhaustive is the development, indeed, that the book is ideally suited to students working without the benefit of formal tuition."

J. Amer. Statist. Ass., 1961, **56**, 413.

" The book is written with considerable care, with the exception of a rather mysterious definition of random phenomena and random events given in Chapter 1. . . . There are a number of illustrative examples which present a remarkable variety of applications of probability. The book also has interesting exercises, both theoretical and applied, at the end of each section. The reviewer would have wished that the author had done more to give the flavor of stochastic processes. This would be more in the spirit of modern probability theory. Parzen's book is apt to be compared with Feller's Introduction to Probability Theory and its Applications, and hence some remarks on this comparison might be made. Both books strive for completeness but in quite a different way. Parzen attempts to give as much as possible of the foundations of probability theory without using measure theory. He treats, therefore, both the discrete and continuous experiments. He keeps the level of difficulty fairly uniform. Feller restricts himself to discrete experiments and gives a very complete discussion. So complete that his book has served both as a text and a standard reference for this part of probability theory. The completeness causes the level of difficulty to be quite uneven. Feller's book has been responsible for much of the rapid growth of probability theory in the past decade. It has itself, perhaps, created the need for a somewhat more comprehensive treatment of the foundations of probability theory at the undergraduate level. Parzen's book provides this treatment."

J. R. Statist. Soc. A, 1961, 435.

". . . a text book has been needed for a one year undergraduate course covering in addition some of the ideas associated with more general sample spaces. Professor Parzen's book satisfies this need and is most welcome. . . . The last two chapters stand apart from the rest of the book in the level of mathematical technique required. They contain a detailed and rigorous treatment of the properties of characteristic functions and their application to the law of large numbers and the central limit theorem. . . . There are a large number of excellent examples and exercises."

RIORDAN, J. *AN INTRODUCTION TO COMBINATORIAL ANALYSIS*
1958. Wiley, xi+244 pp.

Chapter	Contents
1	Permutations and Combinations
2	Generating Functions
3	The Principle of Inclusion and Exclusion
4	The Cycles of Permutations
5	Distributions: Occupancy
6	Partitions, Compositions, Trees and Networks

7 Permutations with Restricted Position I
8 Permutations with Restricted Position II

Biometrika, 1959, **46**, 271.

" There is no tie-up with statistical method or with probability theory. Prof. Riordan's book should, however, be made required reading for all who attempt to work in the field of so-called nonparametric methods. The standard of exposition is high and it is very easy to learn from."

J. Inst. Actuar., 1959, **85**, 112.

" Riordan's book is well written and treats with commendable thoroughness those parts of combinatorial analysis which it includes. There are, however, a few notable omissions. For instance, there is no treatment of the ' ballot problem ' and its ramifications. . . . The book might have been enlivened by the mention of more applications to other branches of mathematics. . . . However, these are minor criticisms and the important thing is that the author has filled a long-felt gap with a sound and readable text-book. . . . To sum up, Riordan's work is an essential addition to the shelves of the mathematician, whether amateur or professional, and is destined to be the standard book on combinatorial analysis for a long time to come."

Nature, 1959, **183**, 970.

" The author has given a careful exposition of various developments of recent decades which have until now remained locked away in scattered journals and proceedings. . . . The book includes a large number of problems and explicit results at the end of each chapter. . . . They are . . . ' put in a form to aid rather than baffle ', and they assume, as does the text itself, a considerable degree of mathematical maturity on the part of the reader."

Rev. Int. Statist. Inst., 1959, **27**, 71.

" Combinatorial analysis is an important part of mathematics and could be characterized from a more abstract point of view, as, for instance, the theory of finite sets. Therefore, combinatorial deliberations can be found in many mathematical branches, for instance, in the theory of graphs, theory of groups, probability theory and mathematical statistics and theory of numbers. There are indications of all these applications in this book, although the author seems to be interested especially in theory of graphs, which is of course a natural field for combinatory methods. The elementary basic tendency of this book has prevented the author's pursuing all of these very far. . . . At the end of each chapter there are many problems which serve not only as exercises for the reader but are also appropriate for widening the view of the subject under consideration."

TAKÁCS, L. *STOCHASTIC PROCESSES—PROBLEMS AND SOLUTIONS*
 1960. Reprinted with minor corrections 1962, Methuen, London; Wiley, New York, xi + 137 pp.

Chapter   Contents
1   Markov Chains
2   Markov Processes
3   Non-Markovian Processes
4   Solutions of Problems

J. Amer. Statist. Ass., 1961, **56**, 1024.

" This is another in the new series of Methuen's monographs on applied probability and statistics, edited by M. S. Bartlett. By definition, it is inexpensive, pocket-sized but substantially-bound, and intended as an introduction to a specialized topic; in this case, stochastic processes of the most important types for applications in physics.

"The three principal chapters are devoted to Markov Chains, Markov Processes, and Non-Markovian Processes. In each case, the main results are given without proof and with rather brief discussion of the implications. Strategically placed in each chapter are lists of problems, the raison d'etre of the book. Each problem can be solved by use of the basic theorems given in the text and it is in the solution of these problems that the reader is expected to develop understanding of the methods. The reader who has given a problem an honest try and has not succeeded in solving it, may turn to Chapter 4 to find complete solutions of all problems. Thus, the book has some similarities to teaching machines as well as to solitaire card games with cheating condoned.

" The reader should be familiar with the equivalent of the first ten chapters of Feller's Probability. Chapters 1 and 2 of Takács give an alternative treatment as noted (with some extensions) of the subsequent portion of Feller."

VON MISES, R. *PROBABILITY, STATISTICS AND TRUTH* 1957. 2nd Revised English Ed., prepared by Hilda Geiringer, Allen and Unwin, ix+244 pp.

Chapter	Contents
1	The Definition of Probability
2	The Elements of the Theory of Probability
3	Critical Discussion of the Foundations of Probability
4	The Laws of Large Numbers
5	Applications in Statistics and the Theory of Errors
6	Statistical Problems in Physics

J. R. Statist. Soc. A, 1958, **121**, 238.

" This book contains a semi-popular account of a philosophy of probability that has been influential since 1919. The author did as much as anyone to convert many budding probabilists and statisticians to ' frequentism ', i.e. to the interpretation of probability in terms of long range relative frequency. . . . A very good feature of the exposition is the frequent use of summaries. . . . This is a stimulating and provocative book; especially provocative."

J. Inst. Actuar., 1958, **84**, 110.

" So much informed criticism has been directed against the theory of von Mises in the last three decades that one might wonder whether, in his closing years, its creator found his views significantly altered under the bombardment to which they were so persistently subjected. Let it be said at once therefore, that the new work follows closely the lines of the old, many passages being verbatim reproductions, and gives no indication of any fundamental change. . . . The book may be summed up as a last attempt by the author to restate his essentially unchanged theory in a way that will make it more difficult to attack. He has done something towards overcoming the difficulties associated with the definition of a collective, but it is clear that other objections will remain."

WOLD, H. *A STUDY IN THE ANALYSIS OF STATIONARY TIME SERIES*
1954. 2nd Ed., Almqvist and Wicksell, vii+236 pp.

Chapter   *Contents*
1   A Survey of Hypotheses and Methods Proposed for the Analysis of Time Series
2   On the Theory of the Discrete Stationary Random Process
3   On the Theory of Some Special Stationary Processes
4   On the Application of Some Stationary Schemes

Appendix
1   Notes to the Second Edition
2   By P. Whittle. Some Recent Contributions to the Theory of Stationary Processes.

Biometrika, 1955, **42**, 538.

" The emphasis laid throughout on the mathematical and structural, rather than the statistical aspects of time series analysis, is likely to make the book of greater utility to the mathematical statistician than to one who is interested in the application to economics, physics, meteorology etc."

J. R. Statist. Soc. A, 1954, **117**, 484.

" Professor Wold's little classic, though written as a research report and an expository survey, has in fact been a standard text since its first publication in 1938 and a second edition is very welcome. Except for a few minor alterations, the original text has been reproduced. The new matter consists of a few notes on that text and a new appendix of 33 pages by Dr. Whittle on recent developments in the theory of stationary processes."

Econ. J. 1956, **66**, 327.

" There are many excellent things in the book. Even though its scope is restricted, since for the greater part it deals with what was known up to 1938, the treatment has the merit of being in the main mathematically rigorous. It therefore represents a consolidation of the theoretical position for the ' early modern ' period.

"Dr. Whittle's appendix is an admirable summary of certain aspects of modern research, including testing of the values of autoregressive approximations to time series for significance."

Econometrica, 1955, **23**, 221.

" . . . the practising econometrician will probably find this book less immediately relevant to his usual problems than other recent publications devoted more exclusively to econometrics, such as *Statistical Inference in Dynamic Economic Models* (ed. Koopmans), *Econometrics* (Tintner), and *Demand Analysis* (Wold, in association with Juréen). This is because the correlation or equivalent spectral analysis of time series requires a more extensive length of series than is often available in economics, and while Wold's examples included the Beveridge wheat-price and Myrdal cost of living indices, other series such as sunspot numbers or air pressures were more readily available for analysis of this kind. Nevertheless, Wold's book will remain a fundamental and permanent contribution to the analysis of time series which every serious econometrician should possess."

SAMPLE SURVEYS: THEORY AND PRACTICE

ACKOFF, R. L. *THE DESIGN OF SOCIAL RESEARCH*
1953. Chicago University Press, xi+420 pp.

Chapter	Contents
1	The Meaning of Methodologically Designed Research and Experiments
2	Formulating the Problem
3	The Idealized Research Problem
4	The Practical Research Design: Sampling
5	The Logic of Statistical Procedures
6	Tests of Hypotheses (1)
7	Tests of Hypotheses (2): The Analysis of Variance and Covariance
8	Tests of Hypotheses (3) and Estimation Procedures
9	The Observational Phase of the Practical Research Design
10	The Operational Phase of the Practical Research Design

Appl. Statist., 1955, **4**, 128.

" Professor Ackoff's book is in many ways unconventional in approach; it is also in parts difficult reading. His aim has been ' to provide a (not *the*) methodology of social research . . .'. Where other books are content simply to stress the importance of defining carefully any concepts used in the research, this one uses some ten pages to explain how to go about this task, what criteria to use for judging the soundness of a definition, and so on. Again, most writers in this field emphasize the need for establishing an order of priorities for the various objectives of a research; Professor Ackoff pursues this to its logical conclusion by proposing ways and means of ranking ' a set of objectives in a non-arbitrary way '. At times one may feel that he is making life unnecessarily complex, but his approach does have the great merit that it forces the researcher to think about choices he might otherwise have made almost unconsciously. . . . Altogether his book should prove widely useful."

Inc. Statist., 1955, **5**, 208.

" This book forms an excellent addition to the literature now emerging, and strikes a fair balance between the limitations of both theory and practice. It will be useful for reference to those specializing in practical statistical work and also of some value to those who want to get a practical perspective through broader reading, although these latter will have to gloss certain chapters. . . . Considerable attention is paid to statistical hypotheses and the relevant tests of significance. The systematic listing of these is quite comprehensive for practical work, and may be found useful, as also will the schedule showing the structure of different practical sampling methods. The mathematics is understandable, although here and there one could wish for its re-expression in more prosaic terms. The author attempts to introduce in figure form the principles involved in cost considerations. But your reviewer feels that these have to be simplified, and the models produced seem too simple to be achieved in practice."

Social Forces, 1955, **3**, 137.

" It must be admitted at once that a great deal of the book is excellent and contains much that will be of interest to the student. The chapters on sampling, on the logic of statistical procedures and on testing hypotheses are especially worthy of mention. The detailed directions for carrying out significance tests, however, savour a little of the cookery book and would in my view have been better omitted from a work of this kind. . . . The section on the operational phase of social research is also well written and remarkably free of the platitudes with which so many works on the subject abound. The sections concerned with the formulation of research problems and with problems of definition are rather less successful. . . . The terms used are often difficult to define and even more difficult to evaluate. . . . Nevertheless, Dr. Ackoff is always stimulating and interesting, even when one is in disagreement with him."

CANTRIL, H. *GAUGING PUBLIC OPINION*
    1944. Princeton University Press, xiv + 318 pp.

Chapter   *Contents*
   1   The Meaning of Questions

2	The Wording of Questions
3	The Measurement of Intensity
4	The Use and Value of a Battery of Questions
5	Secret vs. Non Secret Ballots
6	" Trained " vs. " Untrained " Interviewers
7	The Reliability of Interviewers' Ratings
8	Interviewer Bias and Rapport
9	Refusals as a Source of bias
10	Some General Principles of Sampling
11	How Representative are " Representative Samples "?
12	The Use of Small Samples
13	The Use of Breakdown
14	Education and Economic Status as Determinants of Opinion
15	Information as a Determinant of Opinion
16	Use of Trends
17	The Measurement of Civilian Morale

Brit. J. Psychol., 1945, **35**, 46.

" This book makes it clear that public opinion research has reached a stage where its scientific claims cannot be denied consideration. In it Hadley Cantril and his associates describe and discuss all the most important problems which face users of the polling technique. Repeated analysis of old material and new experiments provide a basis for evaluating the proper criticisms of the method and comparing the relative merits of the most important means of overcoming the difficulties discussed. The sections of the book which deal with the framing of questions and interviewing are the most thorough. . . . A very interesting part of the book deals with motivation and factors determining opinion. Unfortunately, there is no reference to the more qualitative methods of investigating these things, which are probably more successful. This limitation is a self-imposed one and has good reason, but it tends to put the methods discussed in a false perspective."

J. Amer. Statist. Ass., 1944, **39**, 541.

" Public opinion polls are likely to become more numerous rather than less . . . polls can have a great influence in the political field. . . . If polls can have even half the influence claimed for them it is essential that their weaknesses and degree of reliability be more readily understood. Those who are, and are going to be engaged in the art of interviewing will find this volume extremely useful for both specific technical information as well as general principles."

COCHRAN, W. G. *SAMPLING TECHNIQUES*
1953. Wiley, xiv + 330 pp.

Chapter	Contents
1	Introduction
2	Simple Random Sampling
3	Sampling for Proportions and Percentages
4	The Estimation of Sample Size
5	Stratified Random Sampling
6	Ratio Estimates
7	Regression Estimates
8	Systematic Sampling
9	Type of Sampling Unit
10	Subsampling with Units of Equal Size
11	Subsampling with Units of Unequal Size
13	Double Sampling
14	Sources of Error in Surveys

Biometrika, 1954, **41**, 565.

" The would-be worker in sample surveys will find his subject presented with freshness and imagination . . . everything that could and should be said has been written down. The applied statistician will find the discussion and results useful; the theoretical statistician will find out where to go in the literature in order to develop his own problems a stage further. Perhaps the one flaw is in the algebraic formulation of the sampling problem which is not elegant."

Econometrica, 1955, **23**, 350.

" This book will serve as an excellent basis for a course in sampling theory. The student is supposed to have had a first course in statistical methods, including the simpler types of analysis of variance and regression. With this background he will find the

book relatively easy reading, and it will be extremely helpful for the teacher in organising a course. The exposition of theory is very clear, principles are emphasised rather than details, and references are carefully selected with a view to supplementing the text both with regard to details omitted and to more advanced theory. . . .
" Each chapter is provided with a number of exercises, and answers are given at the end of the book."
Economica, 1954, **21**, 171.
" There is little fault to be found with the exposition, which is smooth and natural. Occasional clumsiness of notation is the fault of the subject rather than of the writer . . . the book as a whole is admirable, and is strongly recommended to the student, practitioner and teacher of sampling."

DALENIUS, T. *SAMPLING IN SWEDEN*
   1957. Almqvist and Wiksell, viii+247 pp

Chapter	Contents
1	Synopsis of Sample Survey Methods and Theories
2	Swedish Sample Survey Practice Past and Present
3	The Use of the Sample Survey Method in the Acreage and Livestock Inventory of 1950
4	The Survey Research Center of the Central Bureau of Statistics
5	Possibilities of Improving Swedish Sample Survey Practice
6	Two Contributions to the Treatment of the Frame Problem in Swedish Sample Survey Practice
7	The Problem of Optimum Stratification
8	Determining the Optimum Number of Strata
9	Multiparametric Stratified Sampling
10	The Problem of Regional Statistics
11	Contributions to the Treatment of the Non-response Problem
12	Prospects of Swedish Sample Survey Practice

J. Amer. Statist. Ass., 1958, **53**, 1036.
" After a preliminary chapter giving a synopsis of sample survey

methods and theories, the following five chapters deal with aspects of sample survey practice in Sweden. Lest it appear that these chapters detract from the value of the book for the non-Swedish reader I should like to stress that the discussion will be found to be of interest to almost all. In discussing Swedish experience the author introduces in connection with events that have actually occurred the important practical problems that occur in survey practice and organisations and shows the relation of theoretical work to the solution of these problems. . . .

" The book does not emphasize proofs but the technical language used in chapters 7 through 10 will probably be too difficult for the reader who has not previously studied some sampling theory or mathematical statistics. . . .

" Readers who have not previously seen Dalenius' own research in optimum stratification, the estimation of several parameters from a single sample survey, and the use of linear programming techniques in sample survey design will find this book of great assistance.

" Almost any statistician concerned with surveys will welcome this book for at least one of the following reasons:

a) The study of sample surveys in another country than his own.

b) The summarization of research previously available only in journal articles.

c) The worked out examples and illustrations.

"The only objection this reviewer has is a minor point in Chapter 1. Surveys have many uses other than description and estimation."

J. R. Statist. Soc. A, 1959, **122**, 246.

" The author is well known as a sampling statistician and this book, his Ph.D. thesis, presents an account of his contributions to the field. It is no disparagement of the book to describe it as a hotch-potch of dissimilar constituents. The author's work has been mainly in an official sampling organization and this has given rise to a diversity of experience whose range is well illustrated by the topics treated in the thesis."

DEMING, W. E. *SOME THEORY OF SAMPLING*
1950. Wiley, xvii + 602 pp.

Chapter	Contents
1	The Planning of Surveys
2	The Various Errors of a Survey
3	Moments and Expected Values
4	Some Variances in Random Sampling
5	Multistage Sampling, Ratio Estimates, and Choice of Sampling Unit
6	Allocation in Stratified Sampling
7	Distinction Between Enumerative and Analytic Studies
8	Control of the Risks in Acceptance Sampling
9	The Sample as a Basis for Action
10	Estimation of the Precision of a Sample
11	Inventories by Sampling
12	A Population Sample for Greece
13	Detailed Study of Some Binomial and Related Distributions
14	The Gamma and Beta Functions
15	Distribution of the Variance in Samples from a Normal Universe
16	Tests for Hypotheses in Normal Theory
17	The Distribution of the External and Internal Variances

J. Inst. Actuar., 1951, **77**, 153.

" The Author is the fortunate possessor of an attractive style of writing which makes the book a pleasure to read even when the reader disagrees with the opinions expressed. Let it be said at once that such disagreement is rarely on technical matters. Dr. Deming's treatment of the theory and methods of application is, in itself, clear and unexceptionable. It is only the occasional odd opinion which arouses doubt."

J. R. Statist. Soc. A, 1951, **114**, 100.

" The author sets himself the two-fold task of instructing both the non-mathematical reader and the student of statistics who knows some mathematics. Where the book fails is in its two-fold aim. . . . The non-mathematician will very quickly find himself troubled, while the mathematics student will find that he can read a statistical text-book with greater profit. It is to be regretted that Dr. Deming did not do what this present volume suggests he is eminently qualified to do, and that is write two books."

DEMING, W. E. *SAMPLE DESIGN IN BUSINESS RESEARCH* 1960. Wiley, xx+517 pp.

Chapter	Contents
1	Responsibilities in Planning a Survey
2	Some Remarks on the Theory of Sampling
3.	The Frame and Elements of a Sampling Plan
4	Operational Definitions of Expected Value and of Standard Error
5	Uncertainties not Attributable to Sampling
6	Some Simple Replicated Designs
7	A Survey of Business Establishments with Correction for Nonresponse
8	Examples in Sampling Accounts
9	Evaluation of Inventory of Materials
10	Exercise in a Replicated Survey of a Small Urban Area
11	General Theory and Procedure for Replicated Sampling of a Large Area
12	Field Procedure for the Creation of Segments and for the Selection of People Within Families
13	A Statistical Aid to Supervision
14	Sampling New Material
15	Stratified Sampling
16	Evaluation of Expected Value and of Bias in Sampling Procedures
17	Theory of Variances
18	The Poisson Series and the Square-Root Transformation
19	Optimum Number of Segments per Block
20	Theory for the Formation of Strata
21	Choice of Zoning Interval and Number of Subsamples

Inc. Statist., 1961, **11**, 173.
" The title of this book might suggest to the ordinary reader in

this country that it deals mainly with the quick and somewhat less rigorous survey techniques of the kind sometimes used in commercial research on the grounds that when time and money are short then less rigorous research methods are better than a guess. No impression could be further from the truth. In an early chapter Dr. Deming dismisses techniques such as quota sampling in a few sentences with a contempt which will startle even the most vigorous opponents of such methods in this country. He writes as a statistician in the most exclusive and exalted sense of the term and clearly regards any non-statistical evidence about the reliability and usefulness of a research technique as quite beyond the pale of his interest. So this is a book about probability sampling methods applicable to a wide range of social, economic and commercial research.

". . . The arrangement of the book is unsystematic to a degree and anyone wishing to use it as a reference book is likely to be faced with a kind of 'treasure hunt' for the information which he is seeking.

" Thus although this book can be warmly recommended as a tonic to experienced practitioners, who will certainly find their patience in the 'treasure hunt' rewarded by a number of valuable ideas, it is difficult to recommend the book to a learner, who would surely profit from a very much more systematic treatment of the subject. The book in fact contains in one place or another all the material required for a really first class textbook on the subject—if only it could be systematically re-arranged! "

J. Amer. Statist. Ass., 1961, **56**, 740.

" This important and well-written book should have great success with a broad audience. It will influence and improve the practice of sampling and will be used widely, especially in business research, but also in other areas of survey sampling. The book's aims are clear and are achieved boldly and well: to carry to a broader audience the goal and the methods the author has been teaching, preaching as well as practising in research and as consultant to governments, to business and to industry."

Operat. Res. Quart., 1961, **12**, 191.

" Deming maintains that the statistician does not need to be an expert in the subject matter he is handling and it is abundantly clear that he is far more interested in the techniques of sampling than in the problems sampling is designed to answer. This attitude of his has dangers. Firstly, it makes it difficult for a statistician to contribute to the important problem of whether the right questions are being posed for examination. Secondly, it can lead to a lack of perspective verging on the ludicrous. . . .

"A final danger in Deming's attitude is one very germane to the whole problem of sampling. It is that he may be led to overlook the interviewing-situation involved in a particular survey. The sampling expert needs to know that certain subject matters cause an impossible situation if enquiries are made about them in the home. . . .

"But let us list Deming's virtues, on which the book can be highly commended:

(*a*) Deming is crystal clear, with a style that is not tedious. American writers please copy.

(*b*) He has had wide practical experience and draws on this not only for the purpose of theory but to show how problems in the fieldwork can and should be tackled.

(*c*) He has a sane insistence on his belief that the place for arithmetic is before and not after the sample is drawn and the fieldwork done. Simplicity in the computation of results is the theme that he constantly reiterates."

EDWARDS, F. (Editor). *READINGS IN MARKET RESEARCH* 1956. British Market Research Bureau, xxxvi+235 pp.

Author	Title of Paper
M. G. Kendall	The Statistical Approach
T. Corlett and F. Edwards	Sampling Methods
P. G. Gray, T. Corlett and P. Frankland	The Register of Electors as a Sampling Frame
P. G. Gray, T. Corlett and P. Jones	The Proportion of Jurors as an Index of the Economic Status for District
J. E. Fothergill and H. D. Willcock	Interviewers and Interviewing
J. Downham	The Function of Coding

A. I. Harris	The Work of a Coding Section
R. N. Wadsworth	The User's Point of View
J. A. P. Treasure	Retail Audit Research
The Market Research Society	Readership Surveys—A Comparative Study
The Institute of Practitioners in Advertising	1954 National Readership Survey Techniques
H. Durant	The Gallup Poll and Some of its Problems
R. Silvey	B.B.C. Audience Research
L. Moss	Sample Surveys and the Administrative Process
H. F. Lydall	The Methods of the Savings Survey

Econ. J., 1957, **67**, 317.

" Altogether this is a most interesting and useful book in a field where potentialities are only just beginning to be explored. Anyone who is at all interested could hardly fail to learn a great deal from it."

Inc. Statist., 1956, **7**, 120.

" [The papers] . . . have been well selected and certainly include much of the best *British* literature on the subject which has appeared in recent years. They are also prefaced by a long ' editorial ' on the scope, nature and development of market research in this country, which is well up to the standard of the remaining contributions . . . The non-technical reader will at least obtain from the whole book an appreciation that a good deal more is involved in market research than just thinking up a few questions and putting them to a few people, haphazardly chosen. . . . But for all this, and for all the care and attention which has gone into this volume . . . it is difficult to read it without a feeling of its inevitable inadequacy."

J. R. Statist. Soc. A, 1957, **120**, 231.

" No substantial text-book on market research has yet been written in this country and Mr. Edwards and his colleagues have set out to fill the gap by republishing in a single volume fifteen articles by British authors which bear on market research techniques and practices. . . . All the fifteen articles are good but their sum is perhaps ill-balanced. Over half the material is provided by academicians and civil servants concerned primarily with social surveys and not with market research. . . . One consequence of this is that, relatively, far too much space is given to technique of sampling . . . too little to the construction of questionnaires and the problems of interviewing. . . . However, even as it stands, the book is sufficiently valuable to make us look forward to new editions with additional material."

FESTINGER, L. AND KATZ, D. (Editors). *RESEARCH METHODS IN THE BEHAVIORAL SCIENCES*
    1953. Dryden Press,
    1954. Staples Press, xi+660 pp.

Chapter	Contents
1	The Sample Survey: A Technique for Social Science Research
2	Field Studies
3	Experiments in Field Settings
4	Laboratory Experiments
5	Selection of the Sample
6	Problems of Objective Observation
7	The Use of Documents, Records, Census Materials and Indices
8	The Collection of Data by Interviewing
9	Observation of Group Behaviour
10	Analysis of Qualitative Material
11	Theory and Methods of Social Measurement
12	Distribution-Free Statistical Methods and the Concept of Power Efficiency
13	The Utilization of Social Science

Brit. J. Psychol., 1955, **46**, 67.
" Books on research methods tend to be rather tedious, particularly in fields where there is little agreement on methodology. Books written by a large number of different authors tend to be repetitive,

lacking in uniformity of style, and evincing no clear-cut plan or design. ' Research Methods in the Behavioral Sciences ' is singularly free from both these faults. It is well planned and put together, the individual papers complement each other without overlapping, the style of writing is uniformly good throughout, and the contributors almost without exception have written at a very high level of professional competence indeed. The book is likely to become the standard text in this field for many years to come. . . . For the serious student, this book will certainly become required reading, and even the expert will learn a good deal from it."

J. Amer. Statist. Ass., 1954, **49**, 919.

" This very excellent volume might more appropriately have been titled ' Research Methods in Social Psychology ', for the actual title seems merely to capitalize on a new and popular term. As soon as the reader realizes that the authors are not trying to make social psychology synonymous with the behavioral sciences, resentment dies out and the real merits of the book are more clearly seen. . . . All chapters include good bibliographies and lots of live, illustrative material. The book will, quite properly, find a wide market as a text and reference book in research methods."

J. R. Statist. Soc. A, 1955, **118**, 246.

" This is a substantial book involving the work of nineteen contributing authors who are psychologists or sociologists connected with the University of Michigan and its Institute for Social Research. . . . To one who is not a psychologist the book is in places difficult to read as an unfamiliar jargon is sometimes used. As a text book it is full of suggestions and well documented, and will fulfil its purpose well. As an attempt at coding research techniques it shows that the behavioral sciences need much more experience before this can be done satisfactorily, and hence is not very convincing, and one even wonders whether the approach is along the right lines. . . . The work is a valuable summary of investigations and experiments which will help in the ultimate coding of research methods in the behavioral sciences."

HANSEN, M. H., HURWITZ, W. N. AND MADOW, W. G. *SAMPLE SURVEY METHODS AND THEORY*
1953. Wiley. Vol. I Methods and Applications, xxii+638 pp.
Vol. II Theory, xiii+332 pp.

Chapter	Contents
	Vol. I
1	An Elementary Survey of Sampling Principles
2	Biases and Non-sampling Errors in Survey Results
3	Sample Designs for Some Common Sampling Problems
4	Simple Random Sampling
5	Stratified Simple Random Sampling
6	Simple One- or Two-Stage Cluster Sampling
7	Stratified Single- or Multi-Stage Cluster Sampling
8	Control of Variation in Size of Cluster in Estimating Totals, Averages, or Ratios
9	Multi-Stage Sampling with Large Primary Sampling Units
10	Estimating Variances
11	Regression Estimates, Double Sampling, Sampling for Time Series, Systematic Sampling and other Sampling Methods
12	Case Studies—Designs and Results of Some Actual Sample Surveys
	Vol. II
1	Introduction and Definitions
2	Operations, Events and Probability
3	Random Variables, Expected Values, Variances, Covariances and Convergence in Probability
4	Simple Random Sampling
5	Stratified Simple Random Sampling
6	Simple One- or More Stage Cluster Sampling
7	Stratified Single- or Multi-Stage Cluster Sampling
8	Control of Variation in Size of Cluster in Estimating Totals, Averages or Ratios
9	Multi-Stage Sampling with Large Primary Sampling Units
10	Estimating Variances
11	Regression Estimates, Double Sampling, Sampling for Time Series and Other Sampling Methods

12   Response Errors in Surveys

Biometrika, 1955, **42**, 272.

" Vol. I sets out the methods in common use in sampling surveys and the way in which the methods are applied.

Vol. II can either be read in conjunction with Vol. I or separately when it can be looked on as an elementary text-book exercise in statistical algebra.

The two books taken together cover fully the whole field of sample surveys, and are unlikely to be superseded for some years to come."

Operat. Res., 1954, **2**, 221.

" These two volumes are almost a ' must ' as reference volumes in sampling for the operations researcher who should ever be on the alert for possible applications of sampling techniques for his clients, even though he may at times feel that such application is not strictly an operations research problem.

On the other hand, through my experience in teaching from these volumes, I feel quite strongly that the books do not represent adequate texts at the graduate level."

HENDRICKS, W. A. *THE MATHEMATICAL THEORY OF SAMPLING*
    1956. Scarecrow Press.
    1957. Bailey Bros. & Swinfen, vii+364 pp.

Chapter	Contents
1	Introduction
2	Random Sampling With Equal Probabilities of Selection
3	Probability Theory and its Relation to Sampling
4	Random Sampling in a Universe Defined by a Continuous Frequency Distribution
5	Stratified Sampling
6	Measurement of Heterogeneity Within a Universe
7	Multistage Sampling
8	Sampling Units and Their Selection
9	Sampling with Unequal Probabilities of Selection

10   Ratio and Regression Estimates
11   Control of Errors in Sample Surveys

J. Amer. Statist. Soc., 1958, **53**, 598.

" The author has combined a theoretical approach involving some mathematical literacy with numerous simple numerical examples to illustrate the ideas and to indicate the nature of the applications. Also considerable space is devoted to topics in general statistical methods and theory which other texts in survey sampling assume as prerequisites. As a consequence the book is hardly suitable as a beginning methods course in survey sampling of the type of Volume I of *Sample Survey Methods & Theory* by M. H. Hansen, W. N. Hurwitz, and W. G. Madow. On the other hand, no attempt is made to present a complete formal mathematical treatment and hence, in this sense, it cannot be classed as an advanced text. Nevertheless, this reviewer recommends this book to students of survey sampling who have some knowledge of mathematics through calculus and who wish a self-contained treatment of the subject including related topics in general statistics at the intermediate level."

J. R. Statist. Soc. A, 1957, **120**, 353.

" This is a sound statistical textbook of roughly intermediate level, with special emphasis on sampling techniques."

HYMAN, H. H. et al. *INTERVIEWING IN SOCIAL RESEARCH*
   1954. Chicago University Press, xvi+415 pp.

Chapter   *Contents*
1   A Frame of Reference for the Study of Interviewer Effect
2   The Definition of the Interview Situation
3   Sources of Effect Deriving from the Interviewer
4   Respondent Reaction in the Interview Situation
5   Situational Determinants of Interviewer Effect
6   Interviewer Effects under Normal Operating Conditions
7   Reduction and Control of Error

Social Forces, 1955, **34**, 84.

" [This book] . . . represents a milestone in research on the degree and kind of interviewer effect, for it combines a number of ingenious experiments and investigations at the National Opinion Research Center with a thorough and theoretical re-examination of the psychological and polling literature. The authors cite two general objectives: ' (1) to determine and evaluate empirically the factors that may operate within the interview to produce error in the data derived from it and (2) to test the amenability of these factors to methods of control designed to minimize their effects ' . . . Readers looking for concrete and simple rules of procedure for the reduction of interviewer effect will find the book somewhat disappointing, a fact which reflects not on the authors' comprehensive study but on the complexity of the problem and the state of research in this area."

Sociological Review, 1955, 3, 308.

" Anybody with a serious interest, whether academic or practical, in the interview ought to read it with care, heavy going though much of it is. Dr. Hyman and his associates concern themselves chiefly with one rather special kind of interview. In this the interviewer collects, in a planned or partly planned encounter, data regarding the degrees of belief, attitude or opinion current in a social group. A public opinion poll is a simple instance. . . . This is a contribution which cannot be disregarded by any who are concerned with the development of techniques in social science."

HYMAN, H. H. *SURVEY DESIGN AND ANALYSIS*
1955. The Free Press, xxviii+425 pp.

Chapter	Contents
1	The General Context of Survey Research and the Proper Orientation of the Analyst
2	Variations in Technical Context and the Proper Orientation of the Analyst
3	Theoretical Problems in the Descriptive Survey
4	Technical Aspects of the Analysis of the Descriptive Survey
5	Problems in Treating Simple Relations Between Two Variables

6	The Introduction of Additional Variables and the Problem of Spuriousness
7	The Introduction of Additional Variables and the Elaboration of the Analysis
8	Utilization of Descriptive Survey Findings and the Functions of the Analyst
9	Utilization of Explanatory Survey Findings and the Functions of the Analyst

Social Forces, 1956, **35**, 91.

" The main purpose of the volume seems to be to help the reader learn how to ask theoretically meaningful questions of survey data. It deals only incidentally with how to ask people questions. Since answering theoretical questions from the data has important implications for the sorts of questions that are asked people, design is treated from this point of view. It should be fairly obvious that the sorts of questions one wants to answer with the data collected determine the substantive areas to be covered in the survey, but experience indicates that many people do not give this point sufficient thought. . . . This volume should result in improved surveys from this point of view. The illustrations throughout the entire text are drawn from seven well-known surveys. The use of these same basic materials throughout the book adds considerably to understanding."

MOSER, C. A. *SURVEY METHODS IN SOCIAL INVESTIGATION*
1958. Heinemann, xiii+352 pp.

Chapter	Contents
1	The Nature of Social Surveys
2	The Evolution of Social Surveys in Great Britain
3	The Planning of Social Surveys
4	The Coverage of Social Surveys
5	Basic Ideas of Sampling
6	Types of Sample Design
7	Further Aspects of Sampling

8	An Example of a National Random Sample Design
9	Methods of Collecting the Information I—Documents and Observation
10	Methods of Collecting the Information II—Mail Questionnaires
11	Methods of Collecting the Information III—Interviewing
12	Questionnaires
13	Response Errors
14	Processing of the Data
15	Analysis, Interpretation and Presentation
16	Concluding Remarks

Econ. J., 1959, **69**, 153.

" Here one finds discussion of most of the problems encountered in the design, execution and analysis of large-scale social surveys. Alongside an extremely clear description of the technical aspects of the work (sampling theory, mechanical methods of analysis and the like) the author does not eschew common-sense advice on such important matters are ensuring that the survey is not overlapping with others, or on the writing up and presentation of conclusions. . . . Indeed it is to be hoped that it will be read by many of those now working in the survey field, who may then take note of the plea that it contains for more experimentation both at the pilot and main survey stages."

J. Inst. Actuar., 1958, **84**, 309.

" One of the author's aims is to ' give due prominence both to the strengths and the limitations of the social survey approach ' and in the reviewer's opinion this aim has been achieved. . . . It is the theoretical parts of the book which are least satisfactory. In these there is evidence of loose thinking and imprecise writing . . . [these] are comparatively unimportant when considering the book as a whole, but it is a pity that an otherwise good book should be marred in this way."

J. R. Statist. Soc. A, 1958, **121**, 360.

" This book is based on lectures given by the author on survey methodology to students in the social sciences at the London School of Economics. It is aimed primarily at this class of reader and gives an admirable introduction to the subject. The student will appreciate the absence of that rash of E's which must so often frighten the non-mathematical reader of text-books on this subject. ... Practitioners, too, might spare a little time for this readable book."

Nature, 1958, **182**, 1256.

" It is made plain in the introductory chapter of this book that the techniques with which it deals are more relevant to ' extensive ' rather than ' intensive ' inquiries; that is to say, it is primarily concerned with official surveys of the kind conducted by the Central Office of Information, market and opinion research, and the large-scale operations of social sciences. ... The main section of the book on sampling methods provides a useful text on which those actively engaged on large-scale inquiries can rely."

Occupational Psychology, 1960, **34**, 217.

" This book is a practical guide to the non-statistical problems in sample surveys and at the same time the more general aspects of sampling are discussed. It is not only of value to those who may wish to use the sample survey techniques but also to those who, in the course of business activities, may find themselves commissioning others to do such work for them. There are still some business firms it seems, who are willing to place a contract for a sample survey with that agency which offers the largest number of interviews at the lowest price. This book, to them, will act as a ' Consumers' Guide ' and enable the quality of the different types of products to be identified."

PARTEN, M. *SURVEYS, POLLS, AND SAMPLES*
1950. Harper, xii+624 pp.

Chapter	Contents
1	Social Surveys and Polls in the United States
2	Planning the Procedure
3	Methods of Securing Information
4	The Role of Sampling
5	Organization and Personnel of the Survey

6	Construction of the Schedule or Questionnaire
7	Types of Sampling
8	Procedures for Drawing Samples
9	Size of Sample
10	Interview Procedures
11	Mail Questionnaire Procedures
12	Sources of Bias
13	Editing the Schedule Data
14	Coding the Data
15	Tabulation of the Data
16	Evaluation of the Data and Sample
17	Preparation and Publication of the Report

Compilers Note: It appears that this valuable, practical book has not been reviewed in the regular journals.

PAYNE, S. I. *THE ART OF ASKING QUESTIONS*
1951. Princeton University Press, xiv+249 pp.

Chapter	Contents
1	Why Concern Yourself?
2	May We Presume?
3	Who Left It Open?
4	Boy or Girl?
5	Win, Place, or Show?
6	How Else?
7	Still Beat Your Wife?
8	Can You Make It Brief?
9	What's the Good Word?
10	What's Wrong With " You "?
11	Isn't That Loaded?
12	How Does it Read?
13	Is it Possible?
14	How's That Again?

J. Amer. Statist. Ass., 1952, **47**, 97.

" This is a book on question wording as an art. . . . The task that Payne sets himself is to codify some of the ' know-how ' accumulated in the polling profession in regard to the problem of framing single questions on matters of information or opinion. Within these self-imposed limits he has done a thoroughly creditable job that should be widely useful, especially to the neophyte but also to the seasoned practitioner."

J. R. Statist. Soc. A, 1952, **115**, 442.

" The discussion centres round the form of a question when considered apart from others in a questionnaire or interview, and it is mainly concerned with the choice of the right words in constructing a single question. One field excluded, therefore, is the relationship between questions and the problems that are met with in designing a battery of questions or in deciding the order in which questions should be asked. Further, since many of the readers of this review will no doubt regard the asking of questions primarily as a means of obtaining statistical data, it should be noted that all matters concerned with statistical aspects have been excluded. Thus, the book deals neither with the scaling and rating of the answers nor with the statistical analysis and reduction of data. . . . The book brings together in one place many important points and hints on question design which otherwise could only be found by an extensive search through the literature. . . . The book is well written; in fact it reads so smoothly that on first reading one is likely to under-estimate the care with which it has been compiled. Mr. Payne has succeeded in conveying in a very simple manner the basic ideas, without becoming involved in a discussion of semantics. Finally, the reviewer would like to single out two features for special praise: firstly the list of 1,000 frequent and familiar words, and secondly, the discussion of problem words."

SLONIM, M. J. *SAMPLING IN A NUTSHELL*
 1960. Simon and Schuster, xiii+145 pp.

Chapter	Contents
1	Introduction
2	Steps in a sample survey
3	Sampling and nonsampling errors
4	Some applications of sampling

5	Sampling of accounting data
6	Polls, prognosticators and program ratings
7	Simple random sampling
8	Stratified sampling
9	Cluster sampling
10	Systematic sampling
11	Interpenetrating replicate subsamples
12	Other sampling methods
13	Estimating procedures
14	Size of samples
15	Quality control
16	Acceptance sampling
17	Some case histories

J. Amer. Statist. Ass., 1961, **56**, 192.

" This small volume is an expansion of a layman's pamphlet prepared by the author for the U.S. Air Force, and later reprinted in this Journal [**52** (1957), 143-61]. To the original material there has been added some further discussion, including the subject of sample size, and some material on quality control charts and acceptance sampling and almost half the book is now devoted to applications and case histories. The style is similar to that of the original paper, and makes entertaining as well as informative reading—a difficult task for an author.

" . . . It should be very useful, as was the original pamphlet, for conveying the elements of sampling to persons who are not technicians (or not even statisticians) but have occasion to use sampling or participate in sampling projects. The case histories may also be helpful in persuading administrators of the practicability and value of sampling by the example of large and respected business as well as government. The author has succeeded very well in his objectives."

SUKHATME, P. V. *SAMPLING THEORY OF SURVEYS*
                   WITH APPLICATIONS
   1954. Indian Society of Agricultural Statistics, Iowa State College Press, xxviii + 491 pp.

Chapter	Contents
1	Basic Ideas in Sampling

2   Basic Theory
3   Stratified Sampling
4   Ratio Method of Estimation
5   Regression Method of Estimation
6   Choice of Sampling Unit
7   Sub-Sampling: Equal Selection Probabilities
8   Sub-Sampling (continued): Varying Selection Probabilities
9   Systematic Sampling
10 Non-Sampling Errors

Appl. Statist., 1954, **3**, 208.

" No book on this subject can avoid a good deal of algebra, but the amount in this one is likely to seem formidable to the new student, and in fact the book is intended as an advanced course and as a work of reference. . . .

" This point made, it must be said that the book has the virtue of thoroughness. There is a final chapter on non-sampling errors (including some new results) which is worthy of every sampler's attention."

Biometrika, 1955, **42**, 273.

" . . . Dr. Sukhatme has written a textbook on the algebraical development of the standard branches of sample-survey theory. On this basis the treatment is painstaking and clear and the book will be most valuable to the student or research worker who requires an *ad hoc* treatment of the theory appropriate to any particular sampling method."

J. Amer. Statist. Ass., 1957, **52**, 587.

" Since this book follows on the heels of several recent books on the subject, some comparisons seem inevitable. The organization of the contents follows most closely that of W. G. Cochran's ' Sampling Techniques '. This reviewer found Sukhatme to be preferable if used for an advanced course in which there is emphasis on a complete algebraic treatment and for which the students are moderately well prepared. However it is not as lucid in many of the descriptive sections. . . . the inclusion of many advanced topics and the very extensive treatment given in certain sections make this book a welcome addition. This reviewer feels that it

may also be used to great advantage as reference material and as supplementary reading in courses which are at a modest level."
J. R. Statist. Soc. A, 1954, **117**, 484.
"... The mathematics is nowhere very difficult, but some of the formulae, e.g. for unbiased estimates and for the variances of such estimates, are more complicated than usual owing to the conditions of the sampling, and in particular because account is taken of the finite size of the population.

"The book is informative and easy to read, the necessary formulae being worked out and displayed in full detail. A beginner to the subject with some mathematical competence should therefore have no difficulty in following the theoretical treatment."
Rev. Int. Statist. Inst., 1954, **22**, 172.
"The new book is a splendid presentation, which in spite of the wide range of topics, and in spite of remarkable thoroughness of coverage, turns out to be delightfully clear, and a tribute to Dr. Sukhatme's obvious efforts.

"... the book will be indispensable to the teacher and to the serious student."

YATES, F. *SAMPLING METHODS FOR CENSUSES AND SURVEYS*
1960. 3rd Ed., Griffin, xvi+440 pp.

Chapter	Contents
1	The Place of Sampling in Census Work
2	Requirements of a Good Sample
3	The Structure of Various Types of Sample
4	Practical Problems Arising in the Planning of a Survey
5	Problems Arising in the Execution and Analysis of a Survey
6	Estimation of the Population Values
7	Estimation of the Sampling Error
8	Efficiency
9	Further Notes on the Critical Analysis of Survey Data
10	Miscellaneous Developments
11	Electronic Computers

Reviews of 2nd Ed., 1953:
Biometrika, 1954, **41**, 284.

" The first edition of this book immediately became the standard manual for survey practitioners. . . . This new edition leaves unchanged the earlier text, but adds two new chapters. Chapter 9 is devoted to methods of critical analysis of surveys of an investigational character . . . Chapter 10 is a collection of miscellaneous developments, largely devoted to bringing up to date the exposition in the first edition. . . . The select bibliography which was a feature of the first edition has been supplemented, and, for the benefit of those new to the subject, a short course of reading in the book has been indicated.

" It is a tribute to the quality of the first edition that no competitor has appeared; despite the jump in price . . . none is likely to rival this second edition."

Econometrica, 1956, **23**, 85.

" . . . it is fair to say that in these few years it has established itself as a classic of statistical literature. The outstanding merit of the book for the student lies in the logical manner in which different aspects of sample design are presented. Thus, as much in the general chapter on the structure of samples as in the technical chapters dealing with the estimation of population values, the estimation of sampling error and with efficiency, the unity underlying sample design is brought out. A number of the results presented in the first edition were new at the time and have had important applications in sample design. In the second edition here under review, two new chapters and a supplementary bibliography have been added, while the remainder of the text has been left unchanged (apart from minor corrections). The first new chapter deals with the critical analysis of survey data, that is with the situations in which one is interested less in estimating the overall characteristics of a population than in studying the relationship between different variables and in making comparisons between different parts of the population covered. The other new chapter brings together a number of miscellaneous developments since the last edition. . . . "

Review of 3rd Ed., 1960:
J. R. Statist. Soc. A, 1961, **124**, 576.

" In the twelve years since its publication, *Sampling Methods for Censuses and Surveys* has established itself as perhaps the outstanding book on the subject of sampling methods. The scheme of the original edition has been kept for succeeding editions, and remains very satisfactory. In the second edition Dr. Yates added a chapter on complex survey analysis and another bringing together miscellaneous developments. Now, in the third edition, the only major addition is a chapter on electronic computers, which gives a concise and characteristically clear account of the operations of computers, and their use in survey analysis. The bibliography has also been brought up to date, and now extends to some 30 pages of references on sampling theory and applications.

". . . The book is, and will remain, essential study material for anyone teaching or learning about sample surveys and, no doubt, for anyone concerned with their design."

DESIGN OF EXPERIMENTS

CHEW, V. (Editor). *EXPERIMENTAL DESIGNS IN INDUSTRY* 1954. Wiley, xi+268 pp.

Part I. Review of Experimental Designs Useful in Industrial Research

V. Chew	Basic Experimental Designs
R. L. Anderson	Complete Factorials, Fractional Factorials and Compounding
R. J. Hader and A. H. E. Grandage	Simple and Multiple Regression Analysis
G. E. P. Box and J. S. Hunter	Experimental Designs for Exploring Response Surfaces

Part II. Industrial Experiences with Experimental Designs

W. S. Connor	Experiences with Incomplete Block Designs
W. H. Horton	Experiences with Fractional Factorials
M. B. Carroll and O. Dykstra Jr.	Application of Fractional Factorials in a Food Research Laboratory
R. M. DeBaun and A. M. Schneider	Experiences with Response Surface Designs
C. A. Bicking	Experiences and Needs for Designs in Ordnance Experimentation

Biometrika, 1959, **46**, 266.

" The outstanding feature of the first part of the book is the coherence and continuity of the four papers contained in it. This is an unusual quality in a symposium, possibly due to luck, but more probability reflecting some care in planning. . . .

"It would be quite possible for the unaided, mathematically inclined, student to obtain a good idea of modern experimental design from these four papers. They do not, of course, form an ' ideal ' text-book —in particular, the theoretical bases underlying the numerical procedures are not always sufficiently clearly described for pedagogical purposes—but they do describe, in a clear unambiguous fashion, the procedures which are actually used.

"The papers on specific industrial applications naturally form a rather less closely knit group. They are, however, of considerable intrinsic interest, enhanced by the fact that they give actual designs, data and analyses. The topics covered include examples of incomplete block design, fractional replication, and response surface design; and a short paper on ' Design in ordnance experimentation '.

"This is a book which should prove of real value to serious students of statistics and others wishing to learn something of the techniques and outlook of modern experimental design. It is an unpretentious book (typescript with a number of surprising slips in spelling) and does not claim more for its subject than is justified. It is also quite inexpensive, by present-day standards."

J. Amer. Statist. Ass., 1959, **54**, 320.

"Whenever I hear that the proceedings of a symposium have been published in book form, I immediately become prejudiced against it, since such books are, in my experience, generally of uneven quality, and lacking in any real integration. I therefore picked up this book with some misgivings; these, however, were quickly dispelled. I read it through, from cover to cover, and found it almost uniformly clear, instructive and interesting. Perhaps when one studies the list of 37 participants and contributors at the Symposium this becomes less surprising; it reads like the Statisticians' *Who's Who*, ranging all the way from Anderson to Youden.

"The value of the book is greatly enhanced by Chew's Introductory Chapter, which offers a bird's eye view of the whole subject. It is very succinct and very much to the point; it is also diplomatic."

J. R. Statist. Soc. A, 1959, **122**, 104.

"On the whole the papers tend to be concerned with details of advanced methodology rather than with fundamental principles. The level of knowledge assumed of the reader varies substantially, both between and within authors. A rough indication of the standard is that an applied statistician familiar, say, with some of the later chapters of the book edited by O. L. Davies, *Design and Analysis of Industrial Experiments*, should find most of the papers reasonably understandable.

" In commenting on the book as a whole, one cannot but say that a series of rather uncoordinated papers by different authors, writing on overlapping topics, is not a very satisfactory form for an expository book; something done collectively by at most a small group seems much more likely to produce a coherent review of a field. On the other hand, the applied statistician, in any field, not necessarily industrial, who has much to do with analysis of variance and experimental design, is likely to find useful things in the book, and hence its publication is to be welcomed."

COCHRAN, W. G. AND COX, G. M. *EXPERIMENTAL DESIGNS* 1957. 2nd Ed., Wiley, xiv+617 pp.

Chapter	Contents
1	Introduction
2	Methods for Increasing the Accuracy of Experiments
3	Notes on the Statistical Analysis of the Results
4	Completely Randomized, Randomized Block and Latin Square Designs
5	Factorial Experiments
6	Confounding
6A	Factorial Experiments in Fractional Replication
7	Factorial Experiments With Main Effects Confounded: Split-Plot Designs
8	Factorial Experiments Confounded in Quasi-Latin Squares
8A	Some Methods for the Study of Response Surfaces
9	Incomplete Block Designs
10	Lattice Designs
11	Balanced and Partially Balanced Incomplete Block Designs
12	Lattice Squares
13	Incomplete Latin Squares
14	Analysis of the Results of a Series of Experiments
15	Random Permutations of 9 and 16 Numbers

Biometrika, 1958, **45**, 287.

" It is evidence of the soundness of the first edition that very little of the original text has been altered or removed in the present edition. A number of additional paragraphs have been inserted, usually on points of detail omitted in the first edition. . . . The overall effect of the changes has been to consolidate the position of an already well-established text-book. . . . The second edition is about one-third larger than the first. . . . The book is still excellent value for the practising statistician."

J. R. Statist. Soc. A, 1958, **121**, 237.

" The first edition of this book . . . has deservedly established itself as a standard text-book. . . . For the second edition the authors have added two new chapters and a number of additional sections and plans. . . . The new material maintains the high standard of lucidity of the first edition."

J. Amer. Statist. Ass., 1958, **53**, 214.

" The framework of the book is unchanged, but a good deal of new material has been added, and some topics have been treated more briefly. . . . The added material includes two new chapters, one dealing with fractional replication of factorial experiments, the other with factorial experiments in which the factors represent quantitative variables measured on a continuous scale. At the end of Chapter 9 there has been added an index to incomplete block designs now available. A number of sections have been added to various chapters. . . . The numbers of new chapters, sections, and tables carry the letter A to identify clearly the material that is new in this edition."

Operat. Res. Quart., 1958, **9**, 260.

" By the end of the war the main principles and techniques of the design of experiments in agriculture and biological research had been well established and the resulting body of knowledge was authoritatively set out in 1950 in the first edition of this excellent book. Since then however, there have been extensive developments in other fields of application such as industrial, social and medical research. The attempt to cover these developments as well as elaborations of previous material has led to a size increase of about a third compared with the first edition. . . . A minor criticism from the technologist's point of view is that most of the designs described were constructed so as to allow all treatments to be compared. In practice however, what we often want to do is pick out the best treatment. Once we have done this we are not very interested in comparisons between the remainder. It is a pity that recent work on this problem by Somerville, Bechhofer and others was not mentioned."

Operat. Res. Quart., 1957, **5**, 872.

" This is a revised and enlarged second editon of a book which first presented a comprehensive coverage of the type of experimental design most frequently encountered in practice. It deals with a number of real problems in research, points out practical approaches, and identifies the methodology developed for these problems.

" The industrial experimenter will find areas of particular interest which were not included in the first edition. In its new form this book includes the use of (i) response surface explorations, (ii) attribute data and (iii) multiple-decision procedures, all of which are extremely valuable in the industrial applications of experimental designs. . . . The wide selection of suitable designs, particularly in the more complicated cases, which are given at the end of each chapter, makes this a welcome library addition as a reference book."

Inc. Statist., 1958, **8**, 141.

" The great advantage of this book is its extensive use of practical examples to illustrate the working of particular experimental schemes. Theoretical experimental arrangements never carry the conviction of one that has been tried and proved. At the end of each chapter there are useful bibliographies providing both experimental results and experimental designs so that the text can be amplified from the original sources."

Cox, D. R. *PLANNING OF EXPERIMENTS*
1958. Wiley, vii + 308 pp.

Chapter	Contents
1	Preliminaries
2	Some Key Assumptions
3	Designs For The Reduction of Error

4   Use of Supplementary Observations to Reduce Error
5   Randomisation
6   Basic Ideas About Factorial Experiments
7   Design of Simple Factorial Experiments
8   Choice of Number of Observations
9   Choice of Units Treatments and Observations
10 More About Latin Squares
11 Incomplete Nonfactorial Designs
12 Fractional Replication and Confounding
13 Cross-over Designs
14 Some Special Problems

Biometrika, 1959, **46**, 492.

" Dr. Cox's book is extremely welcome in that it concentrates on just those matters where little guidance is available elsewhere. The practical aspects of experimental design are here dealt with in a highly individual way—the discussion avoids mathematical technicalities yet is careful and detailed; it is mostly in terms of concrete examples, taken from many different fields. It ... requires no specialised knowledge for its understanding. . . . it should be made required reading for all students of statistics."

J. R. Statist. Soc. A, 1959, **122**, 241.

" Dr. Cox has written a skilful and, to my mind, admirable book on comparative experimentation. The book contains virtually no mathematics, and very little arithmetic. . . . One attractive feature of the book is the wealth of examples . . . . carefully chosen from a very wide variety of fields of research. The book is intended primarily for the experimental worker . . . the professional statistician will find much food for thought in the thorough discussion of basic ideas which is characteristic of this book."

Operat. Res. Quart., 1959, **10**, 172.

" The whole emphasis of the book is on the experimental situation being studied. This is discussed, illustrated with examples drawn from a wide variety of sources, and it is shown how the statistical treatment follows logically from practical considerations. The style in which the book is written is clear and direct. . . . The book should be welcomed by all who are concerned in any degree with experimentation. Those who are new to the subject, whether mathematicians or otherwise, would be well advised to read this book first."

Operat. Res., 1959, **7**, 266.

" This is a good introductory book on experimental design. . . . Cox is superlative in the quality, quantity and diversity of examples that he uses in this book."

Nature, 1959, **183**, 1766.

" The book could be an admirable introduction to statistical ideas for a biological or industrial scientist; from it he would learn little about the standard procedures of statistical analysis, such as are to be found in most elementary text-books, but he would acquire something of greater practical value, an appreciation of the manner in which the design of an experiment affects the precision of the results and the efficiency with which the experimenter's time and resources are used."

J. Inst. Actuar., 1959, **85**, 317.

" The ideas put forward in this book should not be accepted uncritically, not because they are ' incorrect ', but because uncritical acceptance, though easy, can be no substitute for individual judgment. With this reservation, the book ought to prove of unique value as an introduction to experimental designs requiring no mathematics beyond arithmetic and an understanding of the use of symbols. . . . For those who are neither ' experimentalists ' nor professional ' experimental design ' statisticians, the book is one of the best ways of gaining some insight into present day statistical work in the experimental field."

DAVIES, O. L. (Editor). *THE DESIGN AND ANALYSIS OF INDUSTRIAL EXPERIMENTS*
1956. 2nd Ed., Oliver and Boyd, xiii + 637 pp.

Chapter	Contents
1	Introduction
2	The Planning of Simple Comparative Experiments

3   Sequential Tests of Significance
4   Investigation of Sampling and Testing Methods
5   Randomised Blocks and Latin Squares
6   Incomplete Randomised Block Designs
7   Factorial Experiments: Elementary Principles
8   Factorial Experiments with Factors at more than Two Levels
9   Confounding in Factorial Designs. Factorial Experimentation when Uniform Conditions Cannot be Maintained Throughout the Experiment
10 Fractional Factorial Experiments
11 The Determination of Optimum Conditions
    Glossary of Technical Terms

Inc. Statist., 1959, **9**, 107.

"This second handbook sponsored by Imperial Chemical Industries and companion to *Statistical Methods in Research and Production* is comprehensive with regard to the elementary and standard designs as well as the modern developments. These experiment designs, together with a vast amount of practical illustration and a thorough discussion of assumptions and general reasoning, are given in a fashion which is essentially literary. . . . In short the approach is ideal for the practising statistician who needs to know what is ready for use in this particular part of the 'tool-box' before delving, if needs be, into the more esoteric parts of the literature."

FEDERER, W. T. *EXPERIMENTAL DESIGN*
   1955. Macmillan, xix + 544 pp.

Chapter   Contents
   1   Introduction
   2   Some Useful Statistical Tools and Concepts
   3   Plot or Pen Technique
   4   The Completely Randomized Design
   5   Randomized Complete Block Design
   6   The Latin Square Design

7	The Choice of Treatments and the Factorial Experiment—p^n Series
8	Other Factorial Experiments
9	Confounding in Factorial Experiments
10	Factorial Experiments with Main Effects Confounded—Split Plot and Split Block Designs with Variations
11	Incomplete Block Designs—General Considerations and the One-Restrictional Lattices with Treatments in Complete Replicates
12	Lattice Designs with More than One Restriction on the Allocation of Treatments in the Complete Block
13	Other Incomplete Block Designs
14	Balanced Designs
15	Some Additional Designs
16	Covariance

Biometrika, 1956, **43**, 491.

" Prof. Federer's book . . . deals with experimental design only in the narrowest methodological sense, and within these limits is concerned to be comprehensive and detailed, which it certainly is. Also, it has a bibliography that is well chosen and extensive."

J. Amer. Statist. Ass., 1956, **51**, 669.

" This reviewer's over-all evaluation of the book is that Federer has tried to cover too many topics. The table of contents would lead one to believe that this is a much more comprehensive book than any of its competitors, yet it lacks many of the details needed by the user of statistical methods. For example, the author tries to cover the complicated subject of long term experiments in eight pages. In addition, how can an experimenter set up a confounded factorial experiment or use an incomplete blocks design without a set of plans? Yet the only design plans included in this book are those illustrated in examples. . . . However, if an experimenter desires another reference on experimental designs in addition to that containing his design plans, Federer's book is strongly recommended. It certainly deserves to be on every statistician's desk; even in those cases where the discussion is too brief, the bibliography is excellent."

J. R. Statist. Soc. A, 1956, **119**, 341.

" This book is primarily a student's text-book and is based on lecture notes for University courses. . . . The examples in the text are heavily biased towards the biological sciences, and agriculture in particular. Probably it is this bias which leads the author to neglect sequential experimentation, which has found applications chiefly outside biology. . . . The standard of printing is very high throughout the book. . . . All tables are reproduced in a ' typewriter ' script, but are clearly legible none the less. Its price seems likely to put it outside the range of the student, to whom it would probably be of most use."

Nature, 1956, **178**, 1139.

" Comparison with Cochran and Cox, whose similarly titled book has established a high standard is inevitable. Federer includes a greater range of designs, especially in respect of factorial sets of treatments and types of lattice, and his instructions for analysis of these will be widely used. He is less successful in showing relations between designs, his system of classification tending to emphasize distinctions rather than connexions. . . . The impressive list of 340 references is of interest for many unfamiliar items, and remarkable for some of the omissions. . . . Teachers of statistics, including even those who do not find it suitable as a manual of instruction, will welcome this book. Not only does the text contain detailed working of many numerical examples, but also at the end is a very fine collection of problems for further study."

FINNEY, D. J.   *EXPERIMENTAL DESIGN AND ITS STATISTICAL BASIS*
    1955. Cambridge University Press, xi+169 pp.

Chapter	Contents
1	Statistical Science
2	Counts
3	Measurements
4	Randomized Blocks and Latin Squares
5	Incomplete Block Designs

6 Factorial Experiments
7 Sequential Experiments
8 Biological Assay
9 The Selection of a Design

Ann. Hum. Genet., 1956, **21**, 97.

" This book is a general survey of experimental design, principally for biologists who have had no mathematical or statistical training. The details of statistical analysis have been largely kept in the background, leaving the author free to emphasize the logical principles behind the designing of experiments. Among many examples in pure and applied science, clinical medicine (which seems to have been neglected in many such books) is given some consideration."

Appl. Statist., 1957, **6**, 73.

" This book is good propaganda for statisticians and can warmly be recommended to Unconverted Biologists. It should, however, be added that although the author has taken great pains in writing the book, it is not an easy one to read. Dr. Finney has tried to give the reader the benefit of his many years of practical experience. He has distilled his wisdom down to its essentials; but it is not too easy to grasp when expressed in a rather general form and compressed into a moderately sized book."

Biometrika, 1956, **43**, 491.

" Dr. Finney's book is at once remarkable and remarkably good. It aims not at teaching statistics but at explaining what statisticians do. It discusses experimental design from the point of view of logic and common sense and shows how many scientific arguments can be expressed in numerical form."

J. R. Statist. Soc. A, 1956, **119**, 210.

" On the one hand this is a book which will certainly be read with profit by those for whom it is primarily intended: namely research workers in all branches of biological science. Many of these have not had specialised mathematical or statistical training. Nevertheless, they cannot escape quantitative studies and are in fact obliged to use some kind of experimental design, which will probably be unsatisfactory if special steps are not taken to ensure a statistically appropriate choice. On the other hand, even professional

statisticians should derive some pleasure from the book, not so much for the information it contains, as for the masterly way in which it presents a wide range of modern techniques in experimental design in concise and simple language."
Nature, 1956, **178**, 1015.

". . . [biological research workers and students] should find it a valuable and well written account of the principles of a difficult subject. The basic ideas are clearly stated, and examples drawn from many fields of biological work are given at each stage of development. The most important experimental arrangements or plans are surveyed, including randomized blocks, Latin squares and incomplete blocks. An excellent short account of factorial experiments is also included. . . . Technical detail has been kept to a minimum throughout the book; but some discussion of methods of analysis has been considered necessary."

FISHER, R. A. *THE DESIGN OF EXPERIMENTS*
1960. 7th Ed., Oliver and Boyd, xiv+248 pp.

Chapter	Contents
1	Introduction
2	The Principles of Experimentation, Illustrated by a Psycho-physical Experiment
3	A Historical Experiment on Growth Rate
4	An Agricultural Experiment in Randomised Blocks
5	The Latin Square
6	The Factorial Design in Experimentation
7	Confounding
8	Special cases of Partial Confounding
9	The Increase of Precision by Concomitant Measurements. Statistical Control
10	The Generalisation of Null Hypotheses. Fiducial Probability
11	The Measurement of Amount of Information in General

Compiler's Note: There are no reviews of recent editions of this well-known classic book. Reviews of earlier editions may be found in, for example, the first version of this Bibliography (1951) or Buros, O. K., *Statistical Methodology Reviews* (1951). New York: Wiley.

KEMPTHORNE, O. *THE DESIGN AND ANALYSIS OF EXPERIMENTS* 1952. Wiley, xix+631 pp.

Chapter	Contents
1	Introduction
2	The Principles of Experimental Design
3	Elementary Statistical Notions
4	An Introduction to the Theory of Least Squares
5	The General Linear Hypothesis or Multiple Regression and the Analysis of Variance
6	The Analysis of Multiple Classifications
7	Randomization
8	The Validity of Analyses of Randomized Experiments
9	Randomized Blocks
10	Latin Squares
11	Plot Technique
12	The Sensitivity of Randomized Block and Latin Square Experiments
13	Experiments Involving Several Factors
14	Confounding in 2^n Factorial Experiments
15	Partial Confounding in 2^n Factorial Experiments
16	Experiments Involving Factors with 3 Levels
17	The General p^n Factorial System
18	Other Factorial Experiments
19	Split-Plot Experiments
20	Fractional Replication
21	The General Case of Fractional Replication
22	Quasifactorial or Lattice and Incomplete Block Designs
23	Lattice Designs
24	Lattice Designs with Two Restrictions
25	Rectangular Lattices
26	Balanced Incomplete Block Designs

27   Partially Balanced Incomplete Block Designs
28   Experiments on Infinite Populations and Groups of Experiments
29   Treatments Applied in Sequence

Ann. Eugen., 1953, **18**, 96.

" . . . its prime concern is with the details of *why*, and is to be regarded as supplementing Cochran and Cox's details of *how* an experiment is designed. With this objective, however, it is impossible not to employ a fair amount of complicated mathematical statistics, and Mr. Kempthorne tackles this task with insight and vigour. . . . Numerical examples are given of the analysis of many of the designs, though sometimes not as many as the reader would wish. This, in itself, is not a serious drawback if the book is regarded as a supplementary volume to a practical manual, but the casual reader is likely to be led to an unbalanced view of this subject if he confines his reading to this volume alone. However, as a reference book to the theory of experimental design, this volume is indispensable in any statistical library."

Appl. Statist., 1953, **2**, 70.

" This is a good book; it deals comprehensively with experimental designs used in agricultural research and introduced and developed by the Rothamsted school. . . . The book also deals with confounding and fractional replication and lattice designs.

" . . . it is definitely not a book for the beginner, as a fair knowledge of mathematics and statistical analysis is required to obtain a reasonable understanding of the book."

Biometrika, 1953, **40**, 470.

" . . . this new book is not for the beginner, nor is it suitable for superficial and easy reference. It should be looked upon as a comprehensive and advanced textbook and studied with the concentration and patience such a book deserves.

" . . . Professor Kempthorne must be congratulated for carrying through so successfully the enormous task of providing a systematic treatment of experimental designs. . . . The mathematical theory is given for all the designs, together with explanations and numerical examples."

J. R. Statist. Soc. A, 1952, **115**, 586.

" The book . . . sets out to give . . . a comprehensive account both of the general principles and of the detailed mathematical theory of the special designs.

" Several different types of reader will be interested in the book. The statistician familiar with the basic ideas and requiring the theory of the complex designs should find it an admirable reference book. For the student or the reader interested mainly in general principles the book is perhaps rather less satisfactory. The chapters on the basic ideas are not the best in the book and tend to be obscured by detail. . . . The professional mathematician may find the mathematical parts of the book a trifle laboured. . . . the author has obviously tried very hard to produce a generally understandable book and on the whole he has succeeded remarkably well, although one would have welcomed a more incisive style."

Nature, 1952, **170**, 991.

" This book will unquestionably be valuable to statisticians, yet perhaps its value lies in the details of methods that it contains rather than in the whole view of experimental design that it presents. . . . Possibly Prof. Kempthorne has attempted too much, even for a large volume. The great need today is for a book that displays the fundamental ideas of experimental design and analysis fully and systematically for the serious student while retaining the comprehensive outlook of Fisher's ' The Design of Experiments '; ' The Design and Analysis of Experiments ' tries to combine with this a manual of detailed instructions for analysis and, in so doing, fails to attain the highest level for either. Prof. Kempthorne is to be congratulated on so nearly succeeding in a difficult task. . . ."

MANN, H. B. *ANALYSIS AND DESIGN OF EXPERIMENTS* 1949. Dover, x + 198 pp.

Chapter	Contents
1	Chi-square distribution and analysis of variance distribution
2	Matrices, quadratic forms and the multivariate normal distribution

3   Analysis of variance in a one way classification
4   Likelihood ratio tests and tests of linear hypotheses
5   Analysis of variance in an r-way classification design
6   The power of analysis of variance tests
7   Latin squares and incomplete balanced block designs
8   Galois fields and Orthogonal Latin squares
9   The construction of incomplete balanced block designs
10 Non-orthogonal data
11 Factorial experiments
12 Randomized designs, randomized blocks and quasi-factorial designs
13 Analysis of covariance
14 Interblock estimates and interblock variance

Biometrika, 1951, **38**, 260.

" . . . it is to be wished that Prof. Mann had given a more accurate indication of the contents of his book in the title he assigned to it. An essential phrase in this title should be ' mathematical theory of ', or words to the same effect. . . . It should be clearly understood that this is a mathematical text book written in an advanced and concise style. . . .

" Despite its austere style and the inequalities of treatment of the various parts of the subject, this book is a useful summary of the modern mathematical theory which has grown up around the analysis of variance."

Nature, 1951, **167**, 580.

" Those engaged in the teaching of experimental design have for some time felt the need of a book on the theoretical aspects of the subject. This work satisfies that need, and read in conjunction with a treatise of a more practical nature, it should provide an excellent survey of contemporary experimental design. . . . In addition to the discussion of methods of analysis, there are excellent sections on the construction of Galois fields, hyper-Graeco-Latin squares, balanced incomplete block configurations and confounded factorial designs. . . . It is possible to regret certain omissions, notably those of fractional replication and of partially balanced incomplete block designs."

QUENOUILLE, M. H. *THE DESIGN AND ANALYSIS OF EXPERIMENT*
1953. Griffin, xiii + 356 pp.

Chapter	Contents
1	The Design and Analysis of Experiments
2	Randomised Blocks and Latin Squares
3	Simple Factorial and Split Plot Designs
4	General Factorial and Split Plot Designs
5	Factorial Designs Involving Factors at Two Levels
6	Factorial Designs Involving Factors at Three Levels
7	Complex Factorial Designs
8	Incomplete Block Designs for a Single Set of Treatments
9	Long-term Experiments
10	Planning of Groups of Experiments
11	Combination of Experimental Results
12	Special Designs and Analyses
13	Missing Observations
14	Scaling of Observations

Biometrika, 1953, **40**, 471.

" . . . (The book is an) advanced non-mathematical text-book on statistical methods excellently illustrated with examples, mostly biological, which are handled with great skill and with a clear sense of the practical purpose of the statistical analysis. The main fault is an occasional carelessness of writing. . . .

"*The Design and Analysis of Experiment* begins with a twenty-page account of the general principles of design. This is so terse that it is unlikely to make much appeal to an experimenter not already fairly familiar with the methods described. . . .

" The following chapters deal with randomised blocks, Latin squares and with simple and general factorial and split-plot designs. The emphasis tends to be on the appropriate forms of analysis of variance and covariance.

" Section B consists of four chapters on incomplete block designs. The main types of confounding and fractional replication are well described. . . .

" Sections C and D entitled 'Long-term Policy' and 'Experimental Complications' contain a good deal of interesting material, the discussion of the combination of results from a series of experiments being particularly good. . . ."

J. R. Statist. Soc. A, 1953, **116**, 453.

". . . let it be said that Quenouille's book is a first-rate one, that it contains a good deal of most useful material not easily available elsewhere, and that it should become a standard work. . . . The only general criticism of substance is that the chapters have been fitted into a rather Procrustean scheme of four sections, dealing successively with elementary principles and designs; incomplete block designs, long term policy, and experimental complications, with the result that a good deal of simple material (such as missing plot techniques and variate transformations) is encountered later than the deeper complications of partial confounding and long-term experiments. Most experimental workers should find the book extremely useful; but they would do well to skip with determination passages they find obscure at a first reading and to keep a professional statistician handy to elucidate the more difficult sections. . . .

"One merit of this book is clearly the amount of ground covered. Another is the very practical flavour which is evident throughout . . . the examples have an air of realism conspicuously absent from many statistical texts."

Appl. Statist., 1954, **3**, 60.

"The book covers a lot of ground and contains much material which appears for the first time in a text-book. However, the claim in the blurb that 'This book provides a comprehensive and detailed account of available methods' is much exaggerated, although the book comes nearer to fulfilling this condition than any other book known to the reviewer.

"The scope of the first part of the book is fairly conventional, dealing with randomised blocks, Latin squares, factorial designs, split-plot designs, incomplete block designs, confounding, fractional replication etc. . . .

"The second half of the book strikes much new ground as far as text-books are concerned.

"The book should prove a most useful and valuable addition to the libraries of all statistical research units."

Nature, 1953, **172**, 785.
" The author has, perhaps, tried to include too many topics in one volume. This results in the first half containing insufficient detail for those entirely new to experimental design, while in the latter half are included some sections (such as that on sequential analysis) in which the treatment is too brief to be of much value. It is difficult to recommend this book wholeheartedly to experimenters or to statisticians; however, it contains material which should be interesting and useful to both groups."

WISHART, J. AND SANDERS, H. G. *PRINCIPLES AND PRACTICE OF FIELD EXPERIMENTATION*
1955. 2nd Ed., Commonwealth Bureau of Plant Breeding and Genetics, vii+133 pp.

Chapter	Contents
1	What is the Difficulty
2	The Statistical Processes
3	The Object of an Experiment. A Suggested Method
4	The Analysis of Variance
5	Reduction of Error by Local Control. Method of Randomized Blocks
6	Method of the Latin Square
7	Extensions of Procedure. Multiple Factor Experiments
8	Split-Plot Experiments. Confounding
9	Experiments with Large Numbers of Varieties
10	Sampling Experimental Plots
11	Analysis of Covariance
12	Considerations of Policy and General Procedure
13	The Agricultural Significance of Experimental Results
14	Observation Plots
15	Size, Shape and Arrangement of Plots
16	Observations on Plots. Sampling
17	Matters of Detail

J. Amer. Statist. Ass., 1956, **51**, 387.
" The authors have collaborated to write an excellent manual on

field experimentation. Wishart wrote the first part which presents practically, and with no mathematical proofs, the statistical methods commonly needed in the reduction of agricultural field trial data for the common experimental designs with worked numerical examples. In the second part by Sanders advice is given on experimental policy, on the agricultural significance of experimental results, and on many practical points in experimental lay-outs and the taking of observations from plots."

J. R. Statist. Soc. A, 1956, **119**, 89.

" This book provides one of the best introductions to experimentation for the practical worker in the field of agriculture. . . . In 80 pages, Dr. Wishart covers the basic statistical techniques. . . . There is no mention of experiments extending over more than one season, but within its chosen limits the only serious criticism that can be raised is the somewhat undue emphasis placed upon significance testing, a lack of balance that is shared by almost all the current elementary text-books. Dr. Sanders' contribution, though it contains little of direct statistical interest, is probably the more valuable part of the book since it presents information that is extremely hard to come by elsewhere. The practical flavour of this section is very marked and the author is clearly writing from a considerable (and sometimes bitter) experience."

Nature, 1956, **177**, 680.

" The first edition of this book, published twenty years ago and for a long time out of print, was a landmark in so presenting the statistical outlook on field experimentation that it could be understood and used without advanced training in statistics. A new edition is therefore of considerable interest. . . . The contribution by Dr. H. G. Sanders . . . remains perhaps one of the best published guides to experimental policy and details of field technique. . . . This book should be in the hands of all who conduct field experiments."

o

QUALITY CONTROL AND INSPECTION

COLUMBIA STATISTICAL RESEARCH GROUP. *SAMPLING INSPECTION* (Edited by H. A. Freeman, M. Friedman, F. Mosteller and W. A. Wallis) 1948. McGraw-Hill, xx+395 pp.

Chapter	Contents
1	Nature, Purpose and Scope of this Book

Part II

2	Sampling Inspection as an Acceptance Program
3	Properties of Sampling Inspection Plans
4	Single-, Double-, and Sequential-sampling Plans
5	Installation and Operation of Sampling Plans
6	Use of Sampling Inspection for Quality Control
	Appendix to Part 2. Relation of Sampling Inspection to Design Specifications

Part III

7	General Description of the Standard Procedure
8	Establishment of Standards
9	Installation of the Procedure
10	Operation of the Procedure
11	Review of Past Results
12	Suggested Forms
13	Application of the Standard Procedure to Control Sampling

Part IV

14	Introduction
15	The Collection of Sampling Plans
16	The Standard Procedure for Selecting a Sampling Plan
17	Methods of Computation

J. Amer. Statist. Ass., 1948, **43**, 606.

" It will meet the needs of three kinds of readers: those who want a ready-made sampling-inspection programme, those interested in building their own programmes, and students of acceptance sampling . . . the book treats the subject of sampling inspection by attributes in great detail. The bases for the decisions necessary in installing and operating acceptance sampling are discussed from almost every angle. The methods of constructing the sampling plans are carefully illustrated . . . unable to think of any question regarding the tables which has not been answered somewhere in the book. . . . This insistence on complete coverage makes the book a valuable reference, especially in view of the scarcity of general publications in the field. . . . Using well-chosen examples the authors describe single, double and group sequential sampling. . . . It is an expert job and major excerpts will, no doubt, be quoted in many an inspection manual.

" The somewhat limited class of readers who are concerned with methods of constructing sampling tables will welcome Part IV with enthusiasm . . . this is an outstanding book. Anyone who is at all concerned with the problem of acceptance sampling by attributes needs to be thoroughly conversant with its content."

COWDEN, D. J. *STATISTICAL METHODS IN QUALITY CONTROL*
1957. Prentice Hall, xxiv + 727 pp.

Chapter	Contents
1	Probability, Statistics, and Quality Control
2	Summarization of Statistical Data
3	Elementary Principles of Probability
4	The Binomial and Multinomial Distributions
5	The Normal Distribution
6	Criteria for Choice of Estimators of Parameters
7	Principles of Estimation
8	Tests of Hypotheses and Confidence Limits: Mean and Fraction Defective
9	Tests of Hypotheses and Confidence Limits: Standard Deviation and Chi-Square
10	Analysis of Variance

11	Tests of Control of a Variable Based on Amounts of Variability
12	Tests of Control Based on the Pattern of Variability
13	Analysis of Historical Data
14	Analysis of a Process Subject to Sporadic Changes in Cause System and Systematic Differences Among Categories
15	Specifications, Parameters and Statistics
16	Use of Control Charts for Variables During Production
17	Selection of Statistic and Computational Procedures
18	Operating Characteristic of Control Charts for Variables
19	Comparison of Process Control Plans
20	Systems of Frequency Curves for a Continuous Variable
21	Control Charts for Non-Normal Distributions
22	Miscellaneous Control Charts for Variables
23	Analysis of Number or Fraction Defective: Large Samples
24	Analysis of Defectives: Selected Techniques
25	The Poisson Distribution
26	Control Charts for Number of Defects
27	Estimating with an Equation of Relationship
28	Sloping Control Lines
29	The Economics of Control Charts
30	Single Sampling Plans for Mean, Standard Deviation Known
31	Principles of Lot Acceptance Sampling for Attributes
32	The Hypergeometric Distribution
33	Single Sampling Plans for Attributes: Small Lots
34	Single Sampling Plans for Attributes: Large Lots
35	Double Sampling
36	Item-by-Item Sequential Sampling
37	Multiple Sequential Sampling
38	Military Standard 105A
39	Single Sampling Plans for Variables, Unknown
40	Analysis of Pattern of Variability

Appl. Statist., 1958, **7**, 202.

". . . though the book may contain all that a 'quality control practitioner', or so-called 'analyst', may require, it is doubtful whether there are many such equipped to master this book. . . . It is, in fact, the text of a formal course in statistical methods directed at all stages towards methods for control of quality."

Biometrika, 1957, **44**, 537.

" The book would probably make a difficult course in statistics for a student to work through on his own because it is very hard to see the wood from the trees. . . . The volume would, however, be very useful as a textbook for a course on quality control when the teacher could signpost the way and use much of the material in the book for illustration and consolidation. As a refresher and reference work, too, the book should have an assured place."

J. Amer. Statist. Ass., 1957, **52**, 583.

" This book brings together under a single cover descriptions of a great number and variety of statistical techniques useful in the control of quality of manufactured products. . . . It is not a book that the casual student would read for general knowledge of quality control because of the great attention given to detail. A reader would do well to have some prior knowledge of elementary statistics and introductory quality control and an acquaintance with the calculus. . . . Throughout the book emphasis is on the ' best ' statistical procedure. . . . The discussion of process control is very comprehensive. . . . The discussion of techniques of process control is generally excellent . . . Although the discussion of acceptance sampling is of a high order, it is a little disappointing in at least two instances. . . . On the whole this is a very fine book. The author has taken great pains in presenting concise explanations of a large variety of statistical techniques. The quality control engineer should find it exceptionally useful in presenting him with new and statistically sound procedures for attaining process control. The teacher may find it a suitable text for advanced courses, and certainly an excellent source of reference for statistical theory as applied to quality control."

J. R. Statist. Soc. A, 1957, **120**, 355.

" The mathematical ability demanded of the reader is not heavy; the understanding of the meaning of an integral sign is the most that is necessary for the main text. A few more mathematical sections form short appendices at the ends of the appropriate chapters, but the book can be read with profit even if these appendices are omitted.

" Frequent practical and numerical examples, and a good selection of diagrams, are given. . . . The approach to the logic of acceptance sampling seems unnecessarily complicated. . . . Apart from rather a large number of misprints, some of which could be misleading, the standard of accuracy is quite high. . . . Criticisms are few compared with the merits of the book, and with the skill and good sense which are apparent throughout."

DODGE, H. F. AND ROMIG, H. G. *SAMPLING INSPECTION TABLES*
1959. 2nd Ed., revised and expanded, Wiley, xi+224 pp.

Chapter   Contents
1   A Method of Sampling Inspection
2   Single Sampling and Double Sampling Inspection Tables
3   Using Double Sampling Inspection in a Manufacturing Plant
4   Operating Characteristics of Sampling Plans

Appl. Statist., 1960, **9**, 67.

" In later years other inspection tables, employing other systems based on different assumptions, have been published and there is no reason to believe that the process will cease. Hence the present edition faces more ' competition '. Each system has its advocates and it is not my intention to compare the systems here. Suffice it to say that Dodge and Romig provide a consistent system whose primary object is to satisfy the quality requirements with the minimum inspection."

Biometrika, 1960, **47**, 490.

" This is the second edition revised and expanded of sampling inspection tables first produced in 1944. The additions are:
    (i) Use of the tables when rejected lots are not screened;
    (ii) Choosing a sampling plan for a specific application;

(iii) A new chapter on the ' operating characteristic curve ' (OC);
(iv) OC curves for all the single and double sampling tables.
The additions have been made at the request of users who have found this book of practical importance."

J. R. Statist. Soc. A, 1960, **123**, 72.

" The schemes offered in the new edition are the same as in the first, but the outstanding advantage is the addition of diagrams of the operating characterics for all the single- and double-sample A.O.Q.L. schemes, together with a new chapter to support them. Another helpful addition, in the Introduction, is advice on choosing schemes and on using the tabled schemes for straightforward acceptance without rectification. . . . The textual arrangement, the printing and the binding, make the book a pleasure to use."

Nature, 1961, **189**, 259.

" This new edition on a much larger page has grown almost out of recognition, mainly because of the addition of a set of diagrams of operating characteristic curves. The four chapters which precede the tables are themselves a valuable introduction to the theory and method of sampling inspection. . . . This is an essential book for the serious student and the factory operator, written with the authority of long experience in teaching and practical application."

DUNCAN, A. J. *QUALITY CONTROL AND INDUSTRIAL STATISTICS*
1959. Revised edition, Irwin, xxxiii + 946 pp.

Chapter	Contents
1	Introduction
2	Probability
3	Frequency Distributions
4	Frequency Distributions (continued)
5	The Sampling Distribution of a Proportion or Fraction
6	Other Important Sampling Distributions
7	Acceptance Sampling by Attributes: Single-Sampling Plans
8	Acceptance Sampling by Attributes: Double and Sequential Fraction-Defective Sampling Plans

9	Acceptance Sampling by Attributes: Multiple Fraction-Defective Sampling Plans
10	Acceptance Sampling by Attributes: Sampling Plans of the Department of Defense
11	Acceptance Sampling by Variables to Control the Fraction Defective: Normal Lots with Known Standard Deviation
12	Acceptance Sampling by Variables to Control the Fraction Defective: Normal Lots with Unknown Standard Deviation
13	Acceptance Sampling by Variables to Control the Fraction Defective: Sampling Plans of the Department of Defense
14	Comparison of Various Types of Sampling Plans to Give Assurance Regarding the Lot Fraction Defective
15	Acceptance Sampling by Variables to Give Assurance Regarding the Mean or Standard Deviation of a Lot
16	Rectifying Inspection for Lot-by-Lot Sampling
17	Sampling Plans for Continuous Production
18	The General Theory of Control Charts
19	Control Charts for Fraction Defective (p-Charts)
20	Control Charts for Number of Defects per Unit (c-Charts and u-Charts)
21	Variables Control Charts
22	Operating Characteristics of $\bar{X}$- and $\bar{R}$-Charts used to Control Current Output
23	Special Devices and Procedures
24	Estimation of Lot and Process Characteristics
25	Tests of Hypotheses Pertaining to Proportions, Means, and Variances
26	Tests Pertaining to the Difference Between Two Proportions, Means, or Variances
27	Tests of Normality
28	Contingency Tables and χ^2 Tests
29	Analysis of Variance
30	Analysis of Variance (continued)
31	Analyses Supplementary to and Associated with Analysis of Variance
32	Regression and Correlation: Two Variables

33	Regression and Correlation: Three and More Variables
34	Analysis of Covariance
35	The Design of Experiments
36	The Design of Experiments (continued)
37	Mapping Response Surfaces and Determination of Optimum Conditions

Biometrika, 1960, **47**, 212.

" The second enlarged and revised edition is to be very warmly welcomed. . . . The reviewer feels that for a reference book of this type, some small space at least could be given to sampling techniques, and two or three of the most useful non-parametric techniques . . . would have added little extra to the length."

J. R. Statist. Soc. A, 1959, **122**, 548.

" The book is, in fact, a book on statistical methods with the greater number of its examples from the manufacturing field. . . . The revision has greatly lengthened it, chiefly by the addition of the 384-page section entitled ' Some statistics useful in industrial research '. . . . Though all the mathematical proofs are relegated to appendices (43 of them), the remaining text is freely interspersed with formulae and statements of theorems. Because of this and its great length the book is not likely to appeal to the British reader. Those who are able to cope with the mathematics will use the more thoroughgoing and general texts which are available; the others will be put off by the semi-formal treatment. The treatment is, in outline, that of a conventional text in statistical methods. When the book is used, as no doubt the author intends, as a text to supplement a fairly long lecture course these drawbacks might disappear."

Operat. Res. Quart., 1959, **10**, 255.

" It is too long and all-inclusive to be read as an exposition. . . . But it would form a good accompaniment to a course of lectures or study, and provides an excellent reference book. Very little that has been done on the subject covered seems to have been missed, and the list of references is formidable. There are also copious appendices giving mathematical proofs. It is doubtful, however, if this is the book on statistics that operational researchers are looking for. . . . operational researchers are sophisticated people who are more likely to be interested in such subjects as the design of experiments and the mapping of response surfaces, which is dealt with only in an introductory way in about seventy pages, or in the ramifications of queuing theory or stochastic processes, which are not dealt with at all."

GRANT, E. L. *STATISTICAL QUALITY CONTROL*
1952. 2nd Ed., McGraw-Hill, xvi+557 pp.

Chapter	Contents
1	Objectives of Statistical Quality Control
2	Some Representative Applications
3	Some Fundamental Statistical Concepts
4	Why the Control Chart Works. Example of a Process in Control
5	Why the Control Chart Works. Examples of Processes Out of Control
6	Directions for Simple $\bar{X}$ and $\bar{R}$ Charts
7	The Selection of Rational Subgroups
8	Different Adaptations of the Control Chart for Variables
9	Some Fundamentals of the Theory of Probability
10	The Control Chart for Fraction Defective
11	The Control Chart for Defects
12	Some Statistical Aspects of Tolerances
13	Some Fundamental Concepts in Acceptance Sampling
14	Acceptance Sampling by Attributes—Dodge-Romig Tables and Procedures
15	Acceptance Sampling by Attributes—Tables and Procedures Based on Acceptable Quality Level
16	Acceptance Sampling by Variables
17	Some Cost Aspects of Quality Decisions
18	Organization for Statistical Quality Control
19	The Place of Statistical Quality Control in Representative Manufacturing and Inspection Operations

J. Amer. Statist. Ass., 1953, **48**, 363.

"The most extensive additions are in the area of acceptance sampling. . . . Another new feature of importance is the introduction of acceptance sampling by variables. . . . There is a good deal of revision in other sections of the book, too. The section on the cost aspect of quality decisions has been somewhat expanded . . . of greater importance is that the new edition contains 302 problems as compared with 145 in the first edition.

"It should be remembered that this is a pre-calculus text and written for the student either in school or in a shop who has the very practical aim of making statistical quality control methods work. The reviewer . . . is convinced that the second edition only keeps this book considerably the best in its field . . . the engineering point of view in this book is authentic and Grant keeps his feet firmly on the ground. This, in combination with its clear and systematic exposition, its wealth of examples, and its numerous problems makes its merits far outweigh the few imperfections noted."

SCHROCK, E. M. *QUALITY CONTROL AND STATISTICAL METHODS*
1957. 2nd Ed., Reinhold, xiii+246 pp.

Chapter	Contents
1	The Development of Modern Quality Control
2	Organizing for Quality Control
3	What Statistical Methods Have to Offer
4	Case Histories
5	The Meaning of Numbers
6	Summarization of Data
7	Pictorial Presentation of Data
8	The Quality Control Chart for Variables
9	Using the Quality Control Chart to Identify Assignable Causes
10	Application and Interpretation of the Quality Control Chart
11	The Quality Control Chart for Attributes
12	The Quality Control Chart for Defects per Unit
13	Modified Control Chart Limits
14	Use of Control Chart when Known Trend Exists
15	Quality Control by Limit Gaging

16	Relationship between Control Limits and Specification Limits
17	Use of the Variables Control Chart as a Basis for Reducing Volume of Inspection
18	The Binomial and Poisson Distributions
19	Significance of Obtained Differences of Sample Means and Standard Deviations
20	Some Rapid Approximate Tests of Significance
21	Acceptance Sampling
22	Sequential Analysis
23	Least Squares and Correlation
24	Analysis of Variance

Compiler's Note: It appears that this practical book has not been reviewed in the regular journals.

SHEWART, W. A. *ECONOMIC CONTROL OF QUALITY OF MANUFACTURED PRODUCT*
1931. van Nostrand, xiv+501 pp.

Chapter   Contents

Part I
Introduction

1	Characteristics of a Controlled Quality
2	Scientific Basis for Control
3	Advantages Secured Through Control

Part II
Ways of Expressing Quality of Product

4	Definition of Quality
5	The Problem of Presentation of Data
6	Presentation of Data by Tables and Graphs
7	Presentation of Data by Means of Simple Functions or Statistics
8	Basis for Determining how to Present Data
9	Presentation of Data to Indicate Relationship

Part III
Basis for Specification of Quality Control
10 Laws Basic to Control
11 Statistical Control
12 Maximum Control

Part IV
Sampling Fluctuations in Quality
13 Sampling Fluctuations
14 Sampling Fluctuations in Simple Statistics under Statistical Control
15 Sampling Fluctuations in Simple Statistics, Correlation Coefficient
16 Sampling Fluctuations in Simple Statistics, General Remarks

Part V
Statistical Basis for Specification of Standard Quality
17 Design Limits on Variability
18 Specification of Standard Quality

Part VI
Allowable Variability in Quality
19 Detection of Lack of Control in Respect to Standard Quality
20 Detection of Lack of Control
21 Detection of Lack of Control, continued

Part VII
Quality Control in Practice
22 Summary of Fundamental Principles
23 Sampling Measurement
24 Sampling
25 The Control Program

J. R. Statist. Soc., 1932, **95**, 546.

" . . . in the course of his work at the Bell Telephone Laboratories, Dr. Shewart gradually came to see the need for the application of statistical theory and this book is the result of his experience. . . .

" The term quality is used in the objective sense as a measurable attribute of some product of the production process . . . the theory of control is based on the postulates that while chance systems of causes are not all alike, constant systems of chance causes do exist and that assignable causes of variation may be found and eliminated.

. . .

" This book opens up what is largely a new field for the application of statistical methods and in time should have an important influence on manufacturing practice."

ECONOMETRICS, TIME SERIES AND INDEX NUMBERS

DAVIS, H. T. *THE ANALYSIS OF ECONOMIC TIME SERIES*
1941. Principia Press, xiv+620 pp.

Chapter	Contents
1	History of the Problem
2	The Technique of Harmonic Analysis
3	Serial Correlation Analysis
4	Theory of Random Series
5	The Degrees of Freedom in Economic Time Series
6	The Analysis of Trends
7	Periodogram Analysis
8	The Evidence and Explanation of Cycles
9	The Nature of Wealth and Income
10	The Dynamics of Trends from the Point of View of Equation of Exchange
11	Forecasting Economic Time Series
12	Interpretation and Critique

J. Amer. Statist. Ass., 1942, **37**, 294.

" The book is concerned chiefly with developing and analyzing the components of economic time series such as trends and cycles. In this connection considerable attention is given to the technique of harmonic analysis and its application to economic time series. . . . The first chapter of the book presents a concise history of the problem and serves as a splendid introduction to the treatment given in detail in the chapters that follow. . . . Professor Davis has made a distinct contribution in making available to the student a brilliant presentation of powerful techniques of analysis which promise much for the future development of economics as a science."

J. R. Statist. Soc. A, 1942, **105**, 127.

" Broadly speaking, the book falls into two main sections. In the first the author gives an account of the statistical techniques of time-series analysis, particularly of the analysis of oscillatory movements. In the second he proceeds from statistics to economics and considers the economic features which can account for the phenomena he has described. . . . Chapter 7, on periodograms, is exceptionally good, and would alone make this book worth reading. . . . No mention is made of the theory of relaxed oscillation which can alone explain the shifting phase and varying amplitude characteristic of stationary time series. . . . One would like to see illustrations of the interesting concept of statistical hysteresis which is discussed only in general terms. . . .

"But taking it by and large, this book is a notable achievement. It is probably the most comprehensive book in economic time series that has yet been written and one which every serious student of the subject should read without delay. It provides something which teachers have long been wanting, a conspectus of a difficult and tortuous subject and an unbiased account by a man who thoroughly appreciates that example is better than precept. . . ."

Sankhyā, 1946, **8**, 83.

". . . the discussion on serial correlation is more interesting . . . similar ideas have been used . . . without any reference to the time series. Auto-correlation of adjacent quods of a random field can be exactly likened to that of a random series. . . .

"There is no doubt that the book is a masterly presentation of the more advanced mathematical and statistical tools as employed in the analysis of time series. . . ."

JOHNSTON, J. *STATISTICAL COST ANALYSIS*
    1960. McGraw-Hill, ix+197 pp.

Chapter	Contents
1	Introduction
2	Theoretical Hypotheses about the Relationships Between Costs and Output
3	Problems of Statistical Estimation and Procedure
4	Empirical Results
	Section 1 Electricity Generation

Section 2 Road Passenger Transport
Section 3 Multiple-product Food-processing Firm
Section 4 Costs in Coal Mining
Section 5 Building Sodieties
Section 6 Life Assurance Companies
Section 7 Labor Productivity and Size of Establishment
Appendix
5   A Summary of the Empirical Evidence
6   A Critique of the Critics

J. R. Statist. Soc. A, 1961, **124**, 255.

" This book sets out to find empirical data concerning the relation of output to cost in contemporary industry. The argument is well set out and the difficulties of finding and interpreting evidence are not shirked.

" It includes painstaking and original studies of electricity generation, road passenger transport, a firm in the food processing industry and some financial institutions. There is also a very useful summary of the main studies that have been made in this field.

" The interest of this study . . . lies in its methods rather than its conclusions."

KLEIN, L. R. *ECONOMETRICS*
1953. Row Peterson, ix+355 pp.

Chapter   Contents
1   The Econometric Approach
2   Statistical Groundwork
3   Estimation of Aggregative Models
4   Computational Design
5   Methods of Sector Analysis
6   Econometric Applications
7   Special Problems of Econometrics

Econometrica, 1954, **22**, 124.

" This book offers a very happy combination of the various elements of econometric work. . . . The statistical methods used are described very clearly—*inter alia*, least squares, maximum likelihood, and limited information methods—but no proofs of the

P

fundamental theorems are given. .... The readability of the book might be further increased if its subdivisions were somewhat more accentuated, say by subtitles or subsections, whenever a new theme or even a new example is begun. ... Important concepts might also be announced in sub-heading. ... All these deficiencies, if the author would recognise them as such, could be very easily eliminated. They do not affect the main quality of the book, however, namely to offer an optimal combination of the econometrician's tools."

PRAIS, S. J. AND HOUTHAKKER, H. S. *THE ANALYSIS OF FAMILY BUDGETS*
1955. Cambridge University Press, xx+372 pp.

Chapter	Contents
1	The Analysis of Family Budgets
2	The Theory of Consumers' Demand
3	The Collection of Information on Consumers' Expenditure by Household Surveys
4	The Limitations of the Data
5	The Estimation of Statistical Relationships
6	Computational Methods
7	The Engel Curve
8	Quality Variations in the Consumption Pattern
9	Household Composition and Unit-Consumer Scales
10	Economies of Scale in Consumption
11	Social, Occupational and Regional Factors in Consumption
12	Some Conclusions from the Inquiry

Econ. J., 1956, **66**, 322.

" Even allowing for the substantial technical assistance which they could command, the sheer amount of detailed work that the authors have put into this book must evoke admiration. But it is much more than a monument of ant-like industry. They have plunged into their work with obvious gusto, and have produced a piece of research which is not only ingenious in its conception but which, in exposition and treatment alike, will be found interesting and even exciting by many workers in this field. . . . In spite of the considerable amount of precise and detailed work that has gone into this book, it is in many parts sketchy. The authors' enthusiasm and ingenuity carry the reader along; yet intermittently he may wonder how much solidity the samples employed can infuse into this lofty mathematical structure. But after such moments he will usually either be brought down safely on to solid ground by a common-sense discussion of the technical difficulties inherent in the collection and analysis of household accounts or else he will be stimuated afresh to follow the authors' exploits, by the exhilarating character of the mathematical enterprise."

J. R. Statist. Soc. A, 1958, **121**, 119.

" While the lack of integration may seem to be the main weakness of the book, the authors nevertheless appear to have been too ambitious. The results of each stage, with the exception of the analysis of quality variations, leave important questions unanswered. But progress is bound to be slow in what is still a fairly new field of research. The outstanding merit of the book, for which all who work in this field will be grateful, is that it sets out the analytical problems and the formal relationships between them clearly and systematically."

THEIL, H. *ECONOMIC FORECASTS AND POLICY*
1958. North-Holland Publishing, xxxi+562 pp.

Chapter   *Contents*
1   Introduction
2   Elementary Aspects of the Methodology of Forecasting
3   Postwar Macroeconomic Forecasts in the Netherlands and Scandinavia
4   Accuracy Analysis of Entrepreneurial Predictions by Means of Business Test Data
5   Underestimation of Changes
6   Analysis of Interrelationships among Expected, Planned, and Actual Prices

7   Forecasts and Policy: Problems and Tools
8   Forecasts and Policy: Analysis and Applications
9   Conclusion

J. Amer. Statist. Ass., 1960, **55**, 378.

" The primary focus of the book is the application of the techniques of mathematical economics and statistics to the problem of forecasting. The analysis—devoted primarily to evaluating forecasts and forecasting procedures in mathematical terms—reaches its culmination in chapters VII and VIII, which deal with the role of forecasting in the dynamic context of decision-making under uncertainty. . . .

" Of most direct interest to the statistician is the appraisal of methods for making and testing forecasts. . . .

" The reader is warned that the book does not provide much easy reading. Basically, it is written for professionals in econometrics, and large parts of it will be incomprehensible to anyone not versed in the mathematics of matrix relations. Nevertheless, there are certain values the practical forecaster can realize (not without study but without understanding the mathematics fully). Among them are a knowledge of rigorous methods for testing forecasts, a summary of forecasting experience, especially in Europe, and numerous insights into forecasting processes and relationships in a setting of the kind of problems forecasts are intended to solve."

TINBERGEN, J. *ECONOMETRICS*
1951. Allen and Unwin, xii+258 pp.

Chapter   Contents
1   The Relationship of Econometrics to Economics and Statistics
2   Mathematical Formulation
3   Statistical Testing
4   The Psychic Reactions
5   The Technical Relations
6   Reactions of Business Life
7   The Functioning of Economic Systems
8   The Use of Econometric Research for the Purpose of Economic Policy (An Example)

Appendices
   A   The Use of Correlation Analysis in Economic Research
   B   Statistical Evidence on the Acceleration Principle
   C   Long Term Foreign Trade Elasticities

Econometrica, 1953, **21**, 202.
"Tinbergen's volume is . . . selective, literary rather than mathematical, and primarily concerned with results. . . . The book is written with the urbanity and persuasiveness that one expects from its author, and he has been well served by his translator. Yet one wonders how much insight the non-specialist to whom it is addressed, really will obtain. Certainly the untutored reader will not receive from Tinbergen any clear impression of the doubts and difficulties that surround the econometrician, or of the highly provisional character of his results in the present state of our knowledge."

Econ. J., 1953, **63**, 118.
". . . It is a first introduction to the subject, inadequate as a guide in actual research, but valuable as a means of getting the main ideas and the logical structure of the subject into the mind of a beginner."

Economica, 1954, **21**, 163.
"This is not a manual of detailed procedure for the expert practitioner of econometrics, but on the contrary, a book that every student of economics could profitably read."

TINTNER, G. *ECONOMETRICS*
   1952. Wiley, xiii + 370 pp.

Chapter	Contents
1	Scope and Method of Econometrics
2	A Short Sketch of Regression Methods
3	Some Illustrations of Econometric Research
4	The Practical Importance of Econometrics
5	Multiple Regression and Correlation
6	Some Applications of Multivariate Analysis to Economic Data

7   Stochastic Models with Errors in the Equations
8   The Trend
9   Oscillatory and Periodic Movements
10 The Interdependence of Successive Observations
11 The Transformation of Observations

Biometrika, 1953, **40**, 234.

" Earlier books on econometrics have dealt mainly with the economic background or with special parts of the field, and this is the first attempt that has been made at a systematic exposition of the statistical methodology of the subject. The book is a compendium of known procedures rather than a research monograph, and thus will be of great value to the practical worker although containing little that will be new to the mathematical statistician."

Econometrica, 1959, **21**, 202.

" . . . the range of topics treated is quite astonishing. Tintner is to be especially commended for the clarity with which he distinguishes between errors in the observed variables and in the structural equations themselves. . . . The book, which could equally well have been called *Statistical Methods for Economists*, has among other virtues: ample numerical illustrations, copious references to the literature, and frank—some (not this reviewer) will think too frank—reminders of the limitations of individual methods."

Econ. J., 1953, **63**, 118.

" Professor Tintner leaves too much unproved; his book is the ideal source for the man who wants a full bag of tools, but does not care to know how they do their work. . . . Professor Tintner's mastery of the subject appears in every page—not least in the way in which he can illustrate much of it by reference to his own work . . . in the later parts of the book [this addiction to footnotes] . . . proves its merit; for here we have presented, one after another, the econometric methods and problems—each with enough explanation to give a clear mathematical formulation and with those invaluable footnotes to take one to the original sources."

J. R. Statist. Soc. A, 1953, **116**, 206.

" The main point to be made about this book is that it does not cover the field of Econometrics as a whole but is at best an account,

and in the reviewer's judgement, a one sided account, of some aspects of it. . . .
"It seems one cannot but admire Professor Tintner for his ingenuity; one cannot but despair at his ingenuousness."
Nature, 1953, **171**, 275.
". . . it is not a text-book of econometrics, simply because in the present state of knowledge there cannot be such a thing. . . . What Prof. Tintner has done is bring together a great many of the attempts made by econometricians to quantify parts of their subject and to expound the statistical techniques which are required. . . . One of the most useful features of the book is that Prof. Tintner, who has a very extensive acquaintance with the literature of statistics and econometrics, has given full references to original sources, so that his book is a useful introduction for anyone who wants to take his studies deeper. . . . Prof. Tintner would, I am sure, be the first to acknowledge the shortcomings of this book. . . . But all students of econometrics will want to read it, and it should do much to widen interest in a frustrating but extremely important field awaiting scientific exploration."

VALAVANIS, S. *ECONOMETRICS*
    1959. McGraw-Hill, xvii+223 pp.

Chapter	Contents
1	The Fundamental Proposition of Econometrics
2	Estimating Criteria and the Method of Least Squares
3	Bias in Models of Decay
4	Pitfalls of Simultaneous Interdependence
5	Many-equation Linear Models
6	Identification
7	Instrumental Variables
8	Limited Information
9	The Family of Simultaneous Estimating Techniques
10	Searching for Hypotheses and Testing them
11	Unspecified Factors
12	Time Series

J. R. Statist. Soc. A, 1960, **123**, 494.

" This is a fine book, but its value is greatly reduced by unnecessary blemishes. . . . If the blemishes were removed and the treatment extended to cover the whole field of econometrics, or cut back to its central core, it would be a first-rate text-book. Meanwhile I hope that the list of what seemed to me the more important of Professor Valavanis's slips might help economists to read it with profit as well as enjoyment."

[The reviewer gives, in the course of a long review, a list of errors in the book.]

VON HOFSTEN, E. *PRICE INDEXES AND QUALITY CHANGES* 1952. Bokforlaget Forum, 136 pp.

Chapter	Contents
1	Price Index Problems in Theory
2	Price Index Problems in Practice
3	The Quality Problem in Outline
4	Some Numerical Results from the Swedish Computations Index
5	The Quality Problem and the Indifference Defined Index
6	The Quality Problem and the Divisia Integral Index
7	The Problem of Aggregation

Econometrica, 1953, **21**, 359.

" In summary, the author has carried forward a technical analysis with meticulous care and has produced a scholarly study that deserves the most careful attention by every index number maker."

Econ. J., 1953, **63**, 145.

" It is very difficult to sum up in a few words the general impression that this book makes on the reader. . . . It seems that the author has failed to indicate at any point the rough outline of his method of approach and has also omitted to take stock of the position, to which his argument has so far led him, at suitable breathing stops in the text. . . . This failure to lead the reader gently and firmly by the hand while whispering words of encouragement in his ear prevents this book from fulfilling its earlier and remarkable promise."

Rev. Int. Statist. Inst., 1954, **22**, 179.

" The book deserves to be studied carefully by anyone who, in national statistical offices and in international agencies, is responsible for the compilation of index numbers. The theoretical sections are illustrated by numerous references to empirical results, which readers should compare with their own experience."

WOLD, H. in association with JURÉEN, L. *DEMAND ANALYSIS* 1953. Wiley, xvi+358 pp.

Chapter	Contents
1	The Ends and Means of Demand Analysis
2	Least-Squares Regression Under Debate
3	The Theoretical Requisites of Demand Analysis
4	Individual Preference Fields
5	The Specification of Demand Patterns
6	Relations Between Individual Demand Elasticities
7	Market Demand
8	Some Further Applications of Preference Fields
9	The Notion of a Stationary Process
10	Fundamental Types of Stationary Processes
11	Structural Problems in Time-series Analysis
12	Least-squares. Regression as a Linear Approximation
13	Sampling Aspects of Regression Analysis
14	The Analysis of Family Budget Data
15	The Analysis of Market Statistics
16	Income Elasticities Obtained from Family Budget Data
17	Elasticity Calculations Based on Market Statistics
18	Consumption Prediction

Biometrika, 1955, **42**, 538.

" Originating in a study of consumer demand for food in Sweden undertaken in 1938 by Prof. Wold and Mr. Juréen, this book sets out to present a self contained account of both methods and results. . . . The theoretical sections are of considerable incidental interest for econometrics generally, although the developments, on an abstract level, are occasionally only remotely relevant to the reported empirical study. . . . The book is very fully annotated; there is an extensive bibliography (although several of the dated references in the text are omitted), and important sets of exercises accompany the theoretical parts. Based on years of research into the foundations of the subject, this is a very thorough work of scholarship."

Econ. J., 1954, **64**, 376.
" This book is a happy example of econometrics as it should be: the union of common sense and powerful mathematical techniques in the analysis of important aspects of the real economic world."

J. R. Statist. Soc. A, 1954, **117**, 235.
" The first impression made by this book is one of excitement. Here, at last, it seems is a book which deals with an econometric question in all its aspects and uses recent developments in methods of analysis. On closer study, however, one is left with a growing feeling of disappointment. Professor Wold discusses a large number of topics connected with demand theory and the statistical analysis of demand. His treatment of the topics is always interesting and frequently revealing, but in many cases one feels that they have little direct connection with his main theme. This would not matter if it did not lead to compression, and sometimes obscurity, in the treatment of more important and relevant questions. One is also liable to get rather irritated at the frequency with which one is told that ' we shall now state without proof . . .'. . . . The critical nature of this review must largely be blamed on the high hopes raised by the book. In spite of all its faults it remains a very notable addition to econometric literature which must be read by all who wish to keep abreast of the subject."

Rev. Int. Statist. Inst., 1953, **21**, 81.
" . . . Prof. Wold undertook an exhaustive study of the theoretical foundations of the subject. . . . The result of these labours, theoretical and practical, are presented together in this monograph. Since the treatment ranges over many fields, the book is of considerable interest to a wide variety of readers. . . . The applied economist will find much to interest him, not only in the skilful and thorough handling of the data, but also in the use that is made of them for short and long term forecasting of Swedish post-war food

consumption. . . . The economic theorist will find in Part II of the book a rigorous development of the theory of consumer and market demand based mainly on work published earlier by Professor Wold. The third part, dealing with the theory of stationary processes, displays at its best the author's power of synthesis and concise exposition of a theoretical subject. The brief account of ergodic theory and of the various types of stationary process, together with the associated references and notes, will be invaluable to all statisticians. The most controversial feature of the book is the author's treatment of regression analysis. He has plumped fairly and squarely for the ordinary method of least squares and has few reservations about its superiority over other possible methods of analysis. He has thus taken a stand counter to that of the econometricians of the Cowles Commission. . . ."

STATISTICAL DECISION AND INFORMATION THEORY

BLACKWELL, D. AND GIRSHICK, M. A. *THEORY OF GAMES AND STATISTICAL DECISIONS*
1954. Wiley, xi+355 pp.

Chapter	Contents
1	Games in Normal Form
2	Values and Optimal Strategies in Games
3	General Structure of Statistical Games
4	Utility and Principles of Choice
5	Classes of Optimal Strategies
6	Fixed Sample-Size Games with Finite Ω
7	Fixed Sample-Size Games with Finite A
8	Sufficient Statistics and the Invariance Principle in Statistical Games
9	Sequential Games
10	Bayes and Minimax Sequential Procedures when both Ω and A are Finite
11	Estimation
12	Comparison of Experiments

Biometrika, 1956, **43**, 490.

" The present book shows how statistical problems of various types can be handled via games theory and decision functions. . . . The first few chapters are devoted to a thorough exposition of games theory . . . even so a preliminary reading of McKinsey's *Introduction to the Theory of Games* will be useful. . . . The book contains many stimulating exercises and is well produced."

Economica, 1955, **22**, 279.

" This excellent book is unfortunately too mathematical to be available to the average economist without the considerable amount of specialised training that would be necessary to read it. It addresses itself primarily to mathematical statisticians ; however there are some features which merit the attention of the economist . . . the discussion of action under uncertainty merits his attention."

Inc. Statist., 1955, **5**, 208.

" The title of this book by two American professors would be clearer if prefaced by ' The relationship between . . .'. It deserves attention by specialists or the mathematical philosopher since it contains much basic analysis of what goes into and underlies decision-making. But those not versed in the algebra and geometry of point sets will find it tough going. . . . It is a pity no index of definitions is attached, since every word is used rigorously in a precise technical sense, and this enforces an academic discipline on the reader."

J. Amer. Statist. Ass., 1956, **51**, 388.

" The book is dedicated to A. Wald. . . . The style also is like Wald's in avoiding verbal philosophy, history, polemics and judicious repitition. The result is cold and austere, but it is nearly always unambiguous. It can hardly be misunderstood, but it will also not be understood except by the careful and patient reader. For those who are already fairly familiar with the subject matter it will make a very useful reference book. For this purpose its value would be increased if it had an index of symbols, since the symbol to-word ratio is high."

J. R. Statist. Soc. A, 1955, **108**, 102.

" The authors have given us a very thorough text-book, within self-imposed limitations, of a mathematical discipline about which many feel enthusiastic. . . . [The presentation] is formal and makes reading rather difficult. The assertion in the Preface that elementary analysis and algebra suffice to understand the text is surely disingenuous. What is most required is a taste for abstract formulation and a tremendous memory. . . . However, judged by the standards which the authors have set themselves, this is a very good book."

BROSS, I. D. J. *DESIGN FOR DECISION*
1953. Macmillan, viii+276 pp.

Chapter	Contents
1	History of Decision
2	Nature of Decision
3	Prediction
4	Probability
5	Values
6	Rules for Action
7	Operating a Decision-Maker
8	Sequential Decision
9	Data
10	Models
11	Sampling
12	Measurement
13	Statistical Inference
14	Statistical Techniques
15	Design for Decision

Biometrika, 1954, **41**, 283.

" The author has taken considerable trouble to produce an interesting, popular text without hiding real difficulties inherent in his subject. It is to be hoped that administrators, and scientists in general, will read this book with serious attention . . . professional statisticians should find it of very real value. It should stimulate renewed, and serious, thought about the foundations of their subject."

J. Inst. Actuar., 1955, **81**, 102.

" This book is about ' statistical decision ', and much of it is so good that it is a pity to have to cavil at certain parts of it. From Chapter 6 onwards there is little to complain about. In fact, any statistical student should find these later chapters a great help as background reading. . . . The main trouble, however, about his book lies in the confused treatment of the subject of probability. No harm will come to the reader who has a clear grip of his own attitude to probability, and the novice will be unable to make head or tail of it anyway. To the impressionable student, however, there is considerable danger if he is unable himself to sense the confusion.

... There are a number of other fundamental points in this book that could be questioned, but there are also many things worthy of approval."

CHERNOFF, H. AND MOSES, L. E. *ELEMENTARY DECISION THEORY*
1959. Wiley, xv+364 pp.

Chapter	Contents
1	Introduction
2	Data Processing
3	Introduction to Probability and Random Variables
4	Utility and Descriptive Statistics
5	Uncertainty Due to Ignorance of the State of Nature
6	The Computation of Bayes Strategies
7	Introduction to Classical Statistics
8	Models
9	Testing Hypotheses
10	Estimation of Confidence Intervals

Econometrica, 1961, **29**, 87.

" The book under review now presents an introduction to the foundations of statistics in terms of decision theory which is very elementary and quite complete. It is only natural that the authors stress the careful discussion of methodological principles and foundations. This is done very simply with the help of artificial examples. . . . Naturally, as the authors emphasize, this book should be supplemented by a consecutive second course in the field."

Inc. Statist., 1960, **10**, 146.

" In 1950 Wald published his book on ' Statistical Decision Functions '; but this was at a high level of mathematical sophistication, and the book presented here aims at presenting the essential features of the theory in an elementary manner. It does, in fact, succeed admirably, Chernoff and Moses's account of the theory is both lucid and amusing. It requires careful reading in places, but the authors have supplied an abundance of exercises to help the reader. . . . In short, this book can be highly recommended to all who wish to learn something about methods of decision making on the basis of statistical data. The reviewer's only serious doubt is whether the authors have not made their presentation so light-hearted that the reader may wonder whether the subject has any serious applications at all. They can be reassured on this point; a very large part of the statistician's work is advising on decisions. These may not always be arrived at quite so formally and rigidly as described in this book; but the apparatus of statistical decision theory does suggest how to proceed."

J. Amer. Statist. Ass., 1960, **55**, 584.

" In their preface, the authors recommend the first seven chapters for a first course in the fundamental ideas of statistics, requiring only high school mathematics. They feel that some background in statistics or mathematics would be desirable before attempting to cover chapters 9 and 10. The text is very clearly written, and there are many illustrative examples and exercises. . . . Although there is little doubt that as time goes on more and more first courses in statistics will be given from the decision theory point of view, at present this is rarely done. One reason for this inertia has been the lack of suitable text-books. The text by Chernoff and Moses requires more mathematical maturity (which is not identical with formal course work) than most of the current pre-calculus texts for first courses in statistics, but it should be considered by those instructors who would like to introduce a more modern (and a more logical) approach in a basic course in statistics."

DAVIDSON, D. AND SUPPES, P. in collaboration with SIEGEL, S. *DECISION MAKING—AN EXPERIMENTAL APPROACH* 1957. Stanford University Press, ix+121 pp.

Chapter	Contents
1	Introduction: Problems of Empirical Interpretation
2	Experimental Test of the Basic Model
3	Experimental Test of a Linear Programming Model
4	Utilities and Incomparable Outcomes

Econometrica, 1959, **27**, 522.

" This little book represents one of the first excursions into the difficult area of experimental research on individual's utility functions and subjective probabilities. As such, it must leave many important questions unanswered or inconclusively answered; but it investigates several points which were previously untouched, and in the reviewer's opinion this careful and self-critical study is a genuine contribution and one which is always interesting and sometimes fascinating to read."

KULLBACK, S. *INFORMATION THEORY AND STATISTICS*
1959. Wiley, xvii+395 pp.

Chapter	Contents
1	Definition of Information
2	Properties of Information
3	Inequalities of Information Theory
4	Limiting Properties
5	Information Statistics
6	Multinomial Populations
7	Poisson Populations
8	Contingency Tables
9	Multivariate Normal Populations
10	The Linear Hypothesis
11	Multivariate Analysis; the Multivariate Linear Hypothesis
12	Multivariate Analysis; Other Hypotheses
13	Linear Discriminant Functions

J. Amer. Statist. Ass., 1959, **54**, 825.

"The merit of this book lies in the unity of the treatment based on the fundamental ideas. . . . To summarize: this is an advanced book on the large-sample theory of tests involving Poisson, Multinomial and Normal distributions treated mathematically by a new unifying approach which is open to objections but which yields results, seen to be satisfactory by other methods. Incidentally, it is a book only for the expert statistician; others interested in information theory will find almost nothing of value to them."

Q

J. R. Statist. Soc. A, 1959, **122**, 380.

" The author presents this book as a study of logarithmic measures of information and their application to the testing of statistical hypotheses, in an attempt to give a unified derivation of known results, with some extensions. Matters relating to communication channels receive only passing mention; the applications are limited to samples of fixed size. . . . Considerable familiarity with statistical theory is assumed. The author writes at a pleasing mathematical level which combines generality with precision; measure theoretic concepts are used with restraint, and are carefully explained when introduced. A glossary is included, and there are three numerical tables. There are copious references, many worked examples, and numerous problems at the ends of chapters. Obviously a great deal of work has gone into the book. . . . It is here . . . [chapter V] . . . the heart of the book . . . that judgment must be passed on the degree to which the author has attained his object of unification. In the reviewer's opinion he has not attained it; the development is highly arbitrary and unappealing. . . . The reviewer has considerable sympathy with the author's intention; it is the more disappointing to find that such an inadequate attempt has been made towards achieving it."

Nature, 1960, **186**, 507.

" This book provides a treatise upon the general statistical theory of information, as complete, thorough and up to date as any single book today. . . . It covers and relates the work of Fisher, Shannon, Chernoff, Kolmogorov, of Good, Woodward, Barnard and many others well known within the field. . . . In this book [the author] aims at unification—conceptual, notational and methodological—of scattered works by West Europeans, Americans and Russians too. . . . The book is essentially mathematical in treatment and in its purpose. . . . The many worked and unworked examples form a particularly valuable feature of the book; it is well provided, too, with a glossary of mathematical terms and with a comprehensive bibliography of several hundred references."

SCHLAIFER, R. *PROBABILITY AND STATISTICS FOR BUSINESS DECISIONS*
1959. McGraw-Hill, xii+732 pp.

Chapter	Contents
1	The Meaning of Probability
2	Expected Value and Utility
3	Random Variables and Probability Distributions
4	The Simplest Problems of Inventory Control; Incremental Analysis
5	Measures of Location; Fractiles and Expectations; Linear Profits and Costs
6	Assessment of Probabilities by Smoothing Historical Frequencies
7	Opportunity Loss and the Cost of Uncertainty
8	Lump-sum Losses; Scrap Allowances
9	Conditional and Joint Probability
10	The Bernoulli Process: The Binomial Distribution
11	The Bernoulli Process: The Pascal Distribution
12	Conditional Models and Marginal Probability
13	The Poisson Process: The Poisson Distribution
14	The Poisson Process: The Gamma Distribution
15	Min-Max Inventory Control
16	Measures of Dispersion: The Variance and the Standard Deviation
17	The Normal Approximation to Distributions of Sums of Random Variables
18	The Normal Approximation to Empirical Distributions
19	Waiting Lines
20	The Monte Carlo Method
21	Revision of Probabilities in the Light of New Information
22	Two-action Problems with Linear Costs
23	Samples from Finite Populations: The Hypergeometric Distribution
24	Interdependent Decision Problems; Finite vs. Infinite Populations
25	Samples from Many-valued Populations; Sufficient Statistics

26	Samples from 'Normal' Populations with Known Variance
27	Samples from 'Normal' Populations with Known Mean
28	Nuisance Parameters: 'Normal' Populations with Both Parameters Unknown
29	Populations of Incompletely Specified Form; "Large-sample Theory"
30	Normal Prior Distributions
31	Biased Measurement and Biased Selection
32	Comparison of Two Unknown Quantities; the Importance of Sample Design
33	Evaluation of a Decision to Sample and Then Act; Pre-posterior Analysis
34	Two-action Problems with Linear Costs: Expected Loss and the Prior Distribution of the Posterior Mean
35	Two-action Problems with Linear Costs: Optimal Sample Size
36	Interdependent Two-action Problems under a Stationary Distribution
37	Many-action Problems with Proportional Losses; General-purpose Estimation
38	Sequential Decision Procedures
39	The Classical Theory of Testing Hypotheses
40	Evaluation of Statistical Decision Rules in Terms of Expected Loss
41	Tests of Significance as Sequential Decision Procedures
42	Confidence Intervals

Inc. Statist., 1960, **10**, 95.

" In the opinion of this reviewer . . . one of the most important books of interest to the practising statistician which has crossed the Atlantic during the last five years. . . . This is essentially a book on the application of the statistical approach to the real world where decisions have to be taken upon the basis of information and not where such information is regarded merely as an addition to man's stock of knowledge. Hence, as soon as each new technique of analysis is introduced, the author is at pains to apply it to a realistic business problem. . . . One feature which this reviewer would wish otherwise is the complete absence of references to background literature. . . . It is quite possible that this book, like those of its kind in other fields, will draw the fire of some statistical purists. Nevertheless, the practising statistician stands in need of just this kind of book and will do well to examine this one closely in order to sharpen the impact of his usefulness to management."

J. Amer. Statist. Ass., 1959, **54**, 813.

" This is an elementary exposition of the science of decision making under uncertainty, by one who has accepted L. J. Savage's *Foundations of Statistics* and related literature and is not hindered by a compulsion to reiterate what has been said in previous elementary texts. . . . Although the mathematical level is very low, it is a book for adults, and is not too likely to prove useful for undergraduates. The integrity of the style is quite astonishing. The great length is due to careful and detailed explanations of calculations and to subtle discussions of the proper framing of problems. The line of argument can be followed easily, there are no pointless digressions or clutter, everything serves the main purpose. . . . A curious feature of the book is that it is entirely without references. . . . To sum up: Professor Schlaifer is to be congratulated on an extraordinary achievement."

J. R. Statist. Soc. A, 1959, **122**, 549.

" This very wordy book is a text for a one-year course for students of business administration and contains in its first three chapters an introduction to probability, expectation and utility. It is then divided into five parts, proceeding from a naive use of expectation to distributions, Bayes' theorem, sampling and risk. It contains much arithmetic, though very little mathematics. . . . The author was developing his manuscript for about four and a half years and this accounts for some unevenness of presentation. . . . There are many exercises for the reader; for solutions we are referred to a ' Student's Manual '. The book contains a great amount of information and might be useful to teachers of statistics in search of examples."

WALD, A. *STATISTICAL DECISION FUNCTIONS*
1950. Wiley, ix+179 pp.

Chapter	Contents
1	The General Statistical Decision Problem: Definitions and Preliminary Discussion
2	Zero Sum Two-Person Games with Infinitely Many Strategies
3	Development of a General Theory of Statistical Decision Function
4	Properties of Bayes Solutions when the Chance Variables are Independently and Identically Distributed and the Cost of Experimentation is Proportional to the Number of Observations
5	Application of the General Theory to Various Special Cases

J. Amer. Statist. Ass., 1951, **46**, 130.

" Abraham Wald's recent book . . . presents a new theory of the foundations of statistics. . . . The treatment and many of the topics are quite advanced mathematically. . . . The technical nomenclature and notations seem unnecessarily complicated and unsuggestive. . . .

" Wald's report on the current state of the theory of statistical decision is of great scholarly value and its possible influence for the good on statistics, through the enthusiastic few who are able to study it, is inestimable. . . . For a long time to come, scholars in the field will turn to this book for what is stored up in it of the guidance and stimulation which used to flow so copiously from its author."

J. R. Statist. Soc. A, 1951, **114**, 251.

" . . . Prof. Wald had for his object a formulation and solution of what Prof. Neyman has called the problem of inductive behaviour. . . . . In order to examine the theory of statistical decision functions it is convenient to recognize three aspects of Prof. Wald's treatment. First there is the problem of decisions . . . and the introduction of weight and cost functions. Second, there are notions of average loss and average cost, which are combined to give the concept of average risk. . . . Finally there is the problem of the minimax solution . . . these three divisions are worth making because their respective values from the point of view of their importance in statistical theory are widely different . . . this book ought to be read by all statisticians . . . suggest reading the excellent chapter one first, possibly more than once . . . then dip into chapter five and to a lesser degree chapter four. . . . The remaining two chapters are perhaps best only skimmed, except for the rare avis who is prepared to meet four different topologies on the same page. . . ."

Nature, 1951, **167**, 1044.

" Wald, by training and inclination, was a synthesizer and a generalizer. He was at his best and his happiest when extending the scope of previous results and bringing apparently distinct lines of thought into one canon. Although his exposition is usually clear and never loose, this tendency towards generality makes his work rather abstract and difficult for a beginner to follow. . . . In short this is a very difficult book, and the ordinary reader will require a certain amount of preparation for it. Nevertheless it represents some extremely stimulating lines of development in the theory of inference and experimentation which look as if they may have a permanent value."

DEMOGRAPHY, BIOMETRY AND MEDICAL STATISTICS

BANCROFT, H. *INTRODUCTION TO BIOSTATISTICS*
1957. Cassell, x+210 pp.

Chapter   *Contents*
1   Introduction
2   Classification and Tabulation
3   Tabular Presentation
4   Graphs
5   Frequency Distributions and Centering Constants
6   Measures of Variation
7   Sampling Variation
8   Significance of Differences in Means
9   Rates and Ratios
10   Sampling Variation of Proportions
11   Significance of Difference in Proportions
12   Sampling—Adequacy and Size
13   Chi Square Test
14   Correlation and Regression
15   t-Test for Small Samples
16   Life Tables
17   Modified Life Tables in Follow-up Study
18   Bio-assay

Compiler's Note: It appears that this book has not been reviewed in the regular journals.

BARCLAY, G. W. *TECHNIQUES OF POPULATION ANALYSIS*
1958. Wiley, xiii+311 pp.

Chapter   *Contents*
1   The Nature of Demography

2 Rates and Ratios
3 Accuracy and Error
4 The Life Table
5 The Study of Mortality
6 Measurement of Fertility
7 Growth of Population
8 Migration and the Distribution of Population
9 Manpower and Working Activities
10 Conclusion

Eugen. Rev., 1959, **51**, 123.

" Dr. Barclay's book is designed more as an introduction to the subject of demography for those who are going to perform as well as use the results of population analysis, and he seems to have in mind the needs of beginners the world over. His illustrations are drawn from the data of many countries, and so give a welcome breadth of view, although they do not make the techniques of analysis that he describes any more general in their application. . . . He also has a useful section on errors and their detection. . . . He deals at some length with population growth and distribution and with manpower and working activities."

J. Amer. Statist. Ass., 1959, **54**, 817.

" This work represents a non-mathematical introductory text on methods of population analysis addressed to the general student of social statistics. It explains many of the more important methods of analyzing population data, including the newer developments, with instructions in steps in computation, and with explanations of the logic of the methods and of ways of interpreting the results. Examples are drawn from the data of many countries, especially the underdeveloped countries. . . . The system of cross-referencing is excellent, worthy of imitation by other text writers. On the other hand, the division of material between the main text and footnotes leaves much to be desired, as if there was a lack of principle in the division made. The instructions on methods of computation have a commendable clarity. . . . In spite of the weaknesses noted, the volume represents a scholarly job and is well recommended for the statistician or social scientist who wishes to train himself in the specific techniques of demographic analysis."

BENJAMIN, B. *ELEMENTS OF VITAL STATISTICS*
1959. Allen and Unwin, 352 pp.

Chapter	Contents
1	Introductory
2	Population Census
3	Registration of Births, Deaths and Marriages
4	Fertility—Measures and Trends
5	Mortality—Death Rates and Causes
6	Mortality Indices: Life Tables
7	Environmental Factors Affecting Mortality
8	The Measurement of Morbidity
9	Statistics of Infectious Diseases
10	Tuberculosis
11	Maternity and Child Welfare
12	Statistics of the Health of School Children
13	Other Public Health Statistics
14	Industrial and General Incapacity
15	Hospital Statistics
16	Cancer Statistics
17	Mental Health Statistics
18	General Practitioner Statistics
19	Field Studies

Eugen. Rev., 1959, **51**, 123.

" Dr. Benjamin's book has been written for the benefit of medical officers of health, administrators of welfare services of all kinds, and other social and public health workers whose decisions depend on statistical indices, in order to help them fully to understand the implications of those indices. About two-thirds of his text is devoted to the analysis of morbidity and disability statistics and comprises a very thorough and enlightening account that should be of great service to his readers. . . . The remainder of *Elements of Vital Statistics* is given over to demography. . . . As befits the needs of the intended audience, these subjects are treated less fully than disability. . . . Even so the approach to these subjects is by no means over-simplified and the retention of the word ' elements ' in the title can be described only as a piece of modesty on the author's part."

J. Inst. Actuar., 1959, **85**, 460.

" This book began as a revision of an earlier work by the late Sir Arthur Newsholme and ended as a complete new text . . . the main emphasis . . . [lies on] . . . medical statistics, i.e. on mortality and morbidity. . . . Only one chapter is devoted to the measurement of fertility, including the analysis of nuptiality; while the subject of migration occupies three pages in the course of a chapter on ' Population Census ' . . . this reveals a marked lack of balance and it may be wondered whether the title is altogether apt. . . . This reservation having been made, let it be said at once that the book under review admirably serves its expressed purpose. It is lucid and succinct, the logical arrangement of the material is masterly and the extensive references reveal the author's wide range of scholarship. It deliberately avoids the intricacies of theoretical statistics and the result is a book which the layman can read with ease and even, thanks to the author's limpid style, with enjoyment. Yet so great is the fund of knowledge contained in its pages—and more particularly in the chapters on morbidity—that the expert, too, will find it an invaluable work of reference."

J. R. Statist. Soc. A, 1959, **122**, 251.

" Dr. Benjamin . . . has written a very comprehensive guide for all those who are concerned with public health and welfare. His knowledge of statistical inquiries into disability is impressively wide and he is able to quote a long list of references at the end of each chapter. Moreover he begins his account of each different aspect with a detailed history of the origin and advancement of the study of the subject and the collection of data bearing upon it."

BLISS, C. I. *THE STATISTICS OF BIO-ASSAY*
1952. Academic Press, i+184 pp.

Chapter	Contents
1	General Principles of Biological Assays
2	The Dosage Response Curve and its Error
3	Designs for Segregating Non-random Variation
4	Measurement of Relative Potency

5 The Correction of Quantitative Variables: Covariance
6 Assays where the Variation in Response is a Function of the Dose
7 Slope-Ratio Assays
8 Multiple or Repeated Assays

Biometrika, 1953, **40**, 473.
" Inevitably in so brief a compass, Bliss's book is little more than a collection of recipes—indeed he refers his readers to Finney . . . *Statistical Method in Biological Assay* . . . for all mathematical details. Within this limitation it should prove very valuable. The needs of the practising biologist are always kept in mind, and the author is bold enough to suggest approximate rule-of-thumb techniques for important problems, rather than to decline to commit himself on the grounds that no exact solution is yet available. . . . Biologists may like to keep Bliss's book on the bench (not least because of its handy size), but a study of Finney's book will be necessary for non-routine problems, and may well enable them to improve on their accepted techniques."

BLISS, C. I. AND CALHOUN, D. W. *OUTLINE OF BIOMETRY*
1954. Yale Co-operative Corporation, x+272 pp.

Chapter	Contents
1	General Computing Instructions
2	A Taste Experiment
3	The Binomial Distribution
4	The χ^2 Test
5	Analysis of Proportionate Frequencies
6	The Normal Distribution
7	Numerical Analysis of Normal Samples
8	Interval Estimation
9	The Comparison of Two Groups
10	The Comparison of Several Groups
11	Simple Experimental Designs
12	Regression
13	Factorial Experiments

14   Bioassays From Parallel Regressions
15   Associated Measurements
16   Two Discontinuous Distributions
17   Meeting the Assumptions of the Analysis of Variance

Biometrika, 1955, **42**, 541.

" This book will be extremely useful to those who teach biometry, and to statisticians who work in a biological field or who wish to have biological examples to illustrate their teaching of statistics. Each chapter consists of a number of very concise explanatory notes, together with several illustrative worked examples and exercises chosen from a wide range of experimental matter. . . . The professional statistician will find this book packed with information such as short-cut formulas, precise statements of the limits within which approximate tests can be relied on and alternative parametric and non-parametric tests. A number of useful tables and charts are included. A long list of references enables the reader to consult the original papers whenever necessary, except for work yet unpublished. The exposition is always lucid and the reviewer has noticed few errors (apart from those already covered by a list of errata). . . . The book is too condensed for the unassisted student, but one working through the course under a teacher's guidance will find it very useful."

J. Amer. Statist. Ass., 1955, **50**, 975.

" Although described by the authors as a lecture manual its close gearing to practice makes it rather a laboratory recipe manual. Yet it does not read as stiltedly as that description might suggest owing to the logical development from one topic to another and the skill with which the recipes are collated. . . . No attempt is made to teach theory, although the source whence methods derive is lightly indicated. At the same time, so differently from many elementary texts, it is clear that the underlying theory is thoroughly understood by the authors themselves. Difficulties are not slurred over. . . . An interesting collection of 18 tables and 5 figures contains some which are not usually given in textbooks. . . ."

J. R. Statist. Soc. A, 1955, **118**, 107.

" ' Biometry ' here means ' statistical methods '; non-statistical biomathematics is excluded. The contents and the order in which they occur are interesting and unusual. . . . The general approach is nonmathematical. The text is written rather concisely in short numbered sections. This means that, although a surprising amount of material can be included, the exposition is on the whole not suitable for a first introduction to the subject. . . . On the whole the book would be found useful by the biologist who has previously acquired a background in statistics. I think the authors are right in hoping that ' he will welcome its compact presentation and the inclusion of much specialized material '. At times the search for brevity seems to lead to obscurity or (very occasionally) inaccuracy. . . . Two features of this book make it particularly attractive. The first is the superb collection of over 200 numerical examples, drawn from published work in many branches of biology. Some of these are fully worked out; others are left for the student to complete, the authors having done most of the routine computing of sums of squares etc. These examples should be of great interest to all teachers of statistics. . . . The other especially interesting feature of the book is the publicity given to various post-war methodological developments which are often ignored even in post-war textbooks."

Cox, P. R. *DEMOGRAPHY*
1959. 3rd Ed., Cambridge University Press, xiv+346 pp.

Chapter	Contents
1	Introductory
2	The Census
3	Vital Registration
4	Other Sources of Information about the Population
5	The Analysis of Mortality Data
6	Methods of Comparing Mortality Experiences
7	The Incidence and Influence of Marriage
8	The Statistical Investigation of Fertility
9	Population Estimates and Projections
10	Some Notes on World Population and on the Demography of Particular Countries
11	A Short Account of the Population of Great Britain
12	The Measurement of Disability

13   Some Suggestions for Further Study and Research
Appendix
     An Introduction to Population Mathematics

J. Inst. Actuar., 1960, **86**, 228.

"Though writing primarily for the actuarial student, the author goes in places beyond the confines of the examination syllabus and gives a complete account of the subject of demography, particularly of the practical side, namely the collection, analysis and use of populations data. . . . For the third edition the text has been largely rewritten and now forms a harmonious whole, free from the drawback of a disjoined appendix. . . . All students, and all others who are interested in demography, owe a very great debt to the author of this practical and clearly written work."

J. R. Statist. Soc. A, 1960, **123**, 211.

"This third edition has a new look but many less obvious improvements have been carried out. . . . The author's lucid style and his obvious command of his subject have established him as a demographic authority with an influence far beyond the confines of the actuarial profession. It must be a matter of considerable pride to the Institute that they have supplied not only their own text book but one which is evidently acceptable to many other teaching authorities."

EMMENS, C. W. *PRINCIPLES OF BIOLOGICAL ASSAY*
   1948. Chapman and Hall, xv+206 pp.

Chapter   *Contents*
1   The Application of Mathematics to Biological Measurements
2   Means, Variances and Degrees of Freedom
3   Comparisons Between Groups
4   Dose-Response Lines
5   Further Discussion of Dose-Response Lines
6   Restrictions in Design
7   Polynomial Coefficients
8   Covariance

9	Predicting from Dose-Response Lines and Planning Assays
10	The Estimation of Relative Potency
11	The Estimation of Relative Potency with Unbalanced Dosage Groups
12	A 2×4-Point Assay with Restrictions in Design
13	Further Designs for Assays
14	Discontinuous Variation
15	Calculations Involving Probits
16	Probit Assays
17	Assays Based on Reaction Times
18	Groups of Tests
19	Choosing and Measuring the Response
20	The Response Linearly Related to the Dose

J. Amer. Statist. Ass., 1949, **44**, 448.

". . . attempts to cover a wider approach and includes quantitative as well as quantal responses on biological assays with one chapter devoted to the work of Finney and Wood on microbiological assays . . . the entire book deals with the statistical design and analysis and not with the pharmacological aspects of assays. . . . On the whole the book will be a welcome addition to the library of a pharmacological laboratory, particularly as a source book for formulas, and very helpful in promoting the use of statistics in biological assay."

FINNEY, D. J. *STATISTICAL METHOD IN BIOLOGICAL ASSAY*
1952. Griffin, xix+661 pp.

Chapter	Contents
1	Introduction
2	Direct Assays
3	Quantitative Dose-Response Relationships
4	Parallel Line Assays
5	Symmetrical Designs for Parallel Line Assays
6	Efficiency, Reliability, and Sensitivity
7	Slope Ratio Assays

8	Efficiency in Slope Ratio Assays
9	Incomplete Block Designs
10	Cross-Over Designs
11	Multiple Assays
12	The Use of Concomitant Information
13	Composite Responses
14	The Combination of Estimates
15	Validity and the Choice of Metameters
16	The 'General' Method
17	Quantal Responses and the Tolerance Distribution
18	Assays Based on Quantal Responses
19	The Design of Assays Based on Quantal Responses
20	Alternative Methods of Analysis for Quantal Responses
21	Special Problems with Quantal Responses
22	Time as a Response

Biometrika, 1953, **40**, 473.

" Finney's book is substantial to the point of being encyclopaedic, and some of the theory set out is well ahead of practice, at any rate in the assay field. The reader is supposed to be reasonably familiar with the basic statistical techniques, but apart from this, the suggested analytical methods are explained in full detail with an excellent set of worked examples. The underlying logic of bio-assay is discussed at length, and a number of incomplete-block designs are given which should prove of great practical use. Four chapters are devoted to quantal assays, and these are noteworthy for a very full discussion of the various alternatives to probit analysis that have been suggested from time to time. The book includes a 40 page Appendix of Tables, many of them new."

J. Inst. Actuar., 1954, **80**, 428.

" [It should] . . . be welcomed as an excellent example of the best features of modern British statistical thought—a complete acceptance of all that mathematical theory can offer combined with a clear understanding of the final purposes of the analyses described. . . . This book can be read with profit by anyone with a solid grounding in elementary statistics, provided he realises that it is a reference work of techniques applicable in a certain restricted field rather than a general text-book."

R

J. R. Statist. Soc. A, 1953, **116**, 85.

" It is intended for four classes of reader—the professional statistician desiring a short course in biological assay, the non-mathematical user of biological assays, the reader who requires a general survey of the function of statistical science in biological assay, and the reader mainly interested in quantal responses. Appropriate courses of reading for these four groups are suggested at the beginning of the book. . . . The main purpose of the book appears to be didactic; it is a guide for the future rather than a survey of the past, but controversial points are fully discussed and the bibliography includes 266 items."

GUILFORD, J. P. *PSYCHOMETRIC METHODS*
1954. 2nd Ed., McGraw-Hill, x + 597 pp.

Chapter	Contents
1	Psychological Measurement
2	Psychophysical Theory
3	A Mathematical Introduction
4	The Method of Average Error
5	Method of Minimal Changes
6	The Constant Methods
7	The Method of Pair Comparisons
8	The Method of Rank Order
9	Scaling from Interval and Ratio Judgments
10	The Method of Successive Categories and Other Scaling Methods and Problems
11	Rating Scales
12	Principles of Judgment
13	Theory of Psychological Tests
14	Reliability and Validity of Measures
15	Test Development
16	Factor Analysis

Brit. J. Psychol., 1955, **46**, 145.

" The student who wishes to obtain guidance on how to carry out one of the many specific techniques dealt with in this volume may consult it to his advantage. However, the more sophisticated reader will often retain mental reservations concerning the assumptions which have to be made in order to proceed with the more elaborate techniques. In a volume this size more space might profitably have been devoted to the qualitative implications of the assumptions which particular techniques force upon the investigator, and of the precise meaning of their end-products. It is quite clear from short interpolated paragraphs that Prof. Guilford is well aware of the necessity of stating clearly what assumptions can legitimately be made. However, he repeatedly throws upon the reader the responsibility for a decision on this point in applying the techniques outlined to practical problems. The beginner for whom the mathematical introduction is intended will not be in a position to decide such questions for himself. Furthermore, the sections on psychological scaling, on the psychometrics of mental testing, and on Factor Analysis seem to be more advanced than the non-mathematical reader can approach in an intelligent and critical manner. Readers in the United Kingdom may regret the scanty reference to relevant work originating in this country. . . . *Psychometric Methods* is probably best regarded as a reference book which should be included on the shelves of the psychological section of all libraries."

J. Amer. Statist. Ass., 1956, **51**, 413.

" The book is written for the non-mathematical student who possesses a good introduction to fundamental arithmetic and algebraic processes. Some familiarity with statistical symbols and elementary computations is also desirable. Many of the necessary arithmetical and statistical ideas are presented in a special chapter designed for this purpose. . . . In summary, the reviewer believes that this revision provides researchers and advanced students with a well-documented summary of developments in the various areas of psychological measurement. The effort to organize and provide logical continuity to these areas is commendable."

HILL, A. B. *PRINCIPLES OF MEDICAL STATISTICS*
    1955. 6th Ed., The Lancet, ix+314 pp.

Chapter	Contents
1	The Aim of the Statistical Method

2	Selection
3	Presentation of Statistics
4	The Average
5	The Variability of Observations
6	Calculation of the Standard Deviation
7	Problems of Sampling: Averages
8	Further Problems of Sampling: Proportions
9	Further Problems of Sampling: Differences
10	Further Problems of Sampling: χ^2
11	Further Examples and Discussion of χ^2
12	The Coefficient of Correlation
13	Calculation of the Correlation Coefficient
14	Life Tables and Survival after Treatment
15	Common Fallacies and Difficulties
16	Further Fallacies and Difficulties
17	Further Fallacies and Difficulties
18	Calculation of Standardised Death-Rates
19	Calculation of Standardised Indices
20	Clinical Trials
21	General Summary and Conclusions

J. Amer. Statist. Ass., 1956, **51**, 170.

" The book was originally published in 1937 to meet the needs of research workers on medical problems. For this objective, the tone and level of the language were well chosen and the exposition was both lucid and logical. On the other hand, the development of new statistical tools plus the spreading familiarity of old tools suggest that such standard techniques as Student's t-test and the analysis of variance and covariance are not above the comprehension of research workers in the medical sciences. . . . [these] . . . have been conspicuously absent in the later and present revisions. . . . this book is still unchallenged as the best text in its field."

J. R. Statist. Soc. A, 1955, **118**, 487.

" It is . . . most useful that in the 6th edition of his book he has added a new chapter on clinical trials, which, as well as describing with great clarity the principles of their design and analysis, contains a masterly discussion of the apparently new ethical problems which they sometimes raise. . . . In other respects the new edition is little changed. . . . In his preface the author regrets that he was unable to achieve his ambition of issuing this new edition ' revised and greatly reduced '. His readers will be content to differ and will welcome it once more ' revised and enlarged '."

KEMPTHORNE, O. *AN INTRODUCTION TO GENETIC STATISTICS*
1957. Wiley, xvii+545 pp.

Chapter	Contents
1	Elementary Probability
2	Random Mating Populations
3	Elementary Selection Problems
4	The Elementary Stochastic Theory of Genetic Populations
5	Inbreeding
6	The Generation Matrix Theory of Inbreeding
7	Tests of Genetic Hypotheses
8	The Estimation of Genetic Parameters
9	The Planning of Experiments
10	Statistical Problems in Human Genetics
11	Introduction to Chapters 12 to 23
12	The Analysis of Variation
13	The Partition of Variance
14	Multiple Regression, Correlation, and Adjustment of Data, and Path Analysis
15	Inheritance of Quantitative Characters in a Random Mating Population
16	Non-Random Mating Diploid Populations with the Locus Segregating
17	Correlations Between Relatives Under Inbreeding with One Locus Segregating
18	One-Locus Polyploid Populations
19	Diploid Populations with Arbitrary Number of Segregating Loci and Arbitrary Epistacy
20	Inbreeding with an Arbitrary Diploid Population
21	Populations Derived from Inbred Lines
22	Infinitesimal Equilibrium Theory of Assortative Mating
23	Selection for Quantitative Characters

Ann. Hum. Genet., 1960, **24**, 188.

" . . . in the reviewer's opinion this book will be suitable only for a statistics student of some maturity with more than a smattering of the mathematical techniques which are nowadays considered necessary for the delineation of statistical methods. Given that there is such a student interested in genetics, and there are many, will this book prove of both interest and profit for him to read? and the answer is undoubtedly yes. Prof. Kempthorne has presented the theory of genetics, with special emphasis on population growth, as he sees it. While this may or may not be acceptable to everyone, there is no doubt but that any student reading and assimilating the theory and methods presented here will be very well qualified indeed to proceed to further reading and self questioning."

J. R. Statist. Soc. A, 1958, **121**, 358.

" This is the first book covering in one volume all important topics in genetical statistics. . . . It is clear that Prof. Kempthorne has taken an immense amount of trouble to put the material in a connected and logical form, and has himself filled in some gaps in the known results to achieve this. The book is very clearly written, and very readable. The mathematics required to read it extends only up to simple differential calculus and an understanding of the summation notation; matrices, etc., are defined in the text when required, and where a rigorous proof would require more advanced mathematics, this fact is clearly stated and an intuitive justification given instead where possible. In short, this book is indispensable for all, both geneticists and statisticians who wish to know something of the application of statistics to genetics."

Nature, 1958, **182**, 899.

" . . . the bulk of the book is devoted to the mathematical development of genetical concepts, theories and problems. . . . To many however the great appeal of the book will be its very full treatment of the theory of biometrical genetics both in populations and in the descendants of deliberately crossed inbred lines. . . . Few . . . will fail to find Dr. Kempthorne's text to be hard going, and many geneticists will undoubtedly give it up in despair. They will however be the losers if they do."

MATHER, K. *STATISTICAL ANALYSIS IN BIOLOGY*
1949. 3rd Ed., Methuen, 267 pp.

Chapter	Contents
1	Introductory
2	Probability and Significance
3	Distributions
4	Tests of Significance
5	The Significance of Single Observations, Sums, Differences and Means
6	Degrees of Freedom and the Analysis of Variance
7	Planning Experiments
8	The Interrelations of Two Variables
9	Polynomial and Multiple Regressions
10	Correlation
11	The Analysis of Frequency Data
12	Estimation and Information
13	Some Transformations

Reviews of 2nd Ed., 1946:
J. Amer. Statist. Ass., 1947, **42**, 477.
" This edition is practically identical with the first, except that in Chapter XIII . . . a transformation . . . has been added. . . . Most of the examples . . . are drawn from the fields of genetics or agronomy.
" The brief section on sampling distributions brings out admirably the relation between the normal t, χ^2 and Z distributions. . . . Of particular interest . . . is the detailed presentation on the partitioning of the variation among individual degrees of freedom."

Sankhyā, 1948, **8**, 389.
" . . . deals in a simple manner with the various statistical methods used in biological investigation and shows keen practical grasp of the essentials of good experimentation . . . explains not so much the statistical principles as the practical procedure for solving the problem and thus the whole treatment has become perhaps a little more mechanical than it need have been even under the restriction of simplicity."

SPIEGELMAN, M. *INTRODUCTION TO DEMOGRAPHY*
1955. Society of Actuaries, xxi+390 pp.

Chapter	Contents
1	Introduction
2	The Collection of Census Statistics and Vital Statistics
3	Errors in Census Statistics and Vital Statistics and their Adjustments
4	Measures of Mortality
5	The Construction of Life Tables
6	Projections of Mortality
7	Morbidity Statistics
8	Family Formation, Composition and Dissolution
9	Fertility and Reproduction
10	The Distribution of Population
11	The Working Population
12	Population Estimates and Projections

Biometrika, 1956, **43**, 237.

" This book was commissioned by the Society of Actuaries for the use of students preparing themselves for the Society's examinations. . . . The book should be admirably suited to the needs of actuarial students in that the items of necessary information are set out clearly in (usually) short sections. On the other hand, there tends to be the typical text-book drawback of a lack of deep critical discussion. . . . To sum up, this is a good text-book of real value to students, though it breaks little significantly fresh ground in the demographic field."

J. Amer. Statist. Ass., 1956, **51**, 409.

" Although the author speaks of designing it for the actuarial student, its context is general enough to interest a far wider group. This is fortunate because the text is a superb one, being tightly organized and meeting high standards throughout its length. . . . The style of writing is succinct and lucid. Only rarely does it become so terse or detailed as to give difficulty. A detailed table of contents is provided as well as name and subject indexes. Almost no footnotes appear. Instead a careful list of references, grouped by chapter sub-sections, is given in the back of the book. . . . The focus of methodology makes it a specialized book. Nor is all of it assignable unless a background of elementary calculus is assumed.

... The book provides no practice problems. ... In summary, this is a splendid, specialized text-book on population methods which will interest the practitioner and the advanced student, but not the beginner."

J. Inst. Actuar., 1956, **82**, 162.

" The proper treatment of statistical methods applicable to demography involves considerable descriptive material, and any manual which attempts compression runs the risk of giving inadequate rationalisation of currently accepted methods. It is a tribute to Spiegelman's lucidity that he avoids this risk throughout most of the book, though one would have wished to see more critical treatment of such topics as occupational mortality, population concepts . . . and mortality and fertility indices. . . . This is a text-book of very high quality which will be of great value to students; but it is also so readable that it will itself do much to stimulate an interest in the study of population changes in a wider circle of readers."

J. R. Statist. Soc. A, 1957, **120**, 95.

" Ideally, a book of this nature should be written in such a way that it assists in the student's gradual acquisition of knowledge of a new subject. It must therefore develop systematically, express itself with complete clarity and try to convey its meaning equally to the student who likes to learn from a mathematical formula and to one who prefers verbal applications. It must also be indexed and cross-referenced in such a manner that the student can locate quickly any section on which he wishes to refresh his memory. By these criteria Mr. Spiegelman's text-book must be judged a good one."

WOLFENDEN, H. H. *POPULATION STATISTICS AND THEIR COMPILATION*
1954. Revised Ed., Chicago University Press, xxiii+258 pp.

Chapter   *Contents*
  1   Introductory
  2   The Census
  3   The Registration of Births, Deaths, and Marriages

4	The Reliability of Census and Registration Statistics, and the Nature of the Errors Therein
5	Preliminary Adjustments for Errors of Age in Census and Registration Statistics; and Estimates of Population
6	The Mathematical Relationships Between Births, Deaths, and Populations, and the Formulae for the Rates of Mortality
7	The Construction of Mortality Tables from Population Statistics
8	The Construction of Abridged Life Tables from Population Statistics
9	Methods of Comparing the Mortalities of Different Communities
10	The Forecasting of Mortality Rates
11	Mortality by Cause of Death
12	Occupational Mortality
13	The Use of Census and Registration Data in the Compilation of Statistics Relating to Marriages, Births, Orphanhood, Unemployment, Etc.
14	The Theory of Reproductivity
15	Sickness Data
16	Conclusion

Appendix

Some Theory in the Sampling of Human Populations By W. Edwards Deming

Appl. Statist., 1956, **5**, 71.

" The author is at pains in his conclusions to point out that his book is intended to describe methods of compilation and not to discuss their interpretation or ' other allied problems which are more particularly interesting to the general statistician '. In brief, therefore, it may be a useful *vade mecum* for the actuarial student, but it is doubtful whether—apart from the first few chapters—it is likely to be of great interest to others."

Biometrika, 1955, **42**, 275.

" Comprehensiveness has evidently been the author's ideal. While he has succeeded in making his book a mine of information on particular topics, it is to be expected that students may experience difficulty in sorting out really important material from items now mainly of historical interest. The dust-cover claims that ' this book is the only presentation, by an actuary, of the particular actuarial view points and methods necessary to the production of modern population statistics '. Apart from the fact that this statement ignores books published by the Institute of Actuaries in recent years, the catalogue-like assembly of methods presented makes difficult the disentanglement of the more modern methods. Despite these criticisms the book should prove useful as a comprehensive, yet handy, work of reference. There is no index, though there is a detailed ' Table of Contents ' by paragraphs (not by pages). There are nearly one hundred footnotes which bear witness to the author's devotion to the ideal of comprehensiveness. Most of them contain useful information, though they tend to interrupt the textual line of argument."

J. R. Statist. Soc. A, 1954, **117**, 363.

" ' Statistics ', in the title, implies indexes and standard tables. This is not primarily a manual for registrars and others whose main concern is the collection of population data, although a good introduction to census and registration methods is given. It deals only incidentally with the interpretation of assembled statistics. Its purpose is to guide students and others to the great storehouse of mathematical and statistical techniques available for the convenient summarization and standardization of the demographic material. Within this field it is very comprehensive, embracing many important studies made not only in the United States but also in Great Britain, Canada and elsewhere. It is well written and effectively presented and contains an extensive bibliography."

MISCELLANEOUS APPLICATION OF STATISTICAL METHODS

ADCOCK, C. J. *FACTORIAL ANALYSIS FOR NON-MATHEMATICIANS*
1954. Melbourne University Press, 88 pp.

Chapter	Contents
1	The Logic of Factor Analysis
2	Correlation
3	Factors
4	The Principle of Rotation
5	Finding Simple Structure
6	Cluster-Directed Analysis
7	Combining Centroid and Group Analysis
8	Interpreting the Results
9	The Role of Factor Analysis

Brit. J. Psychol., 1955, **46**, 158.

The aim of this book is ' to cover the essential processes of factor analysis in such a way as to make clear the underlying logic in simple language.' The approach is through well-chosen numerical examples. Attention is focussed on three methods: analysis for simple structure (Thurstone), cluster-directed analysis, and group factors derived from perliminary simple numeration (Burt). Criticisms from the point of view of factor analysis are that the basis of factorial methods is not said to be measurements but correlations, that no account is given of how product-moment correlation comes logically to be involved, that use of the tetrachoric coefficient is even made to appear better, and that the mistaken procedure of inserting new communalities for the calculation of each successive centroid factor is advocated. The statistician can also point to the isolation of the discussion from any general consideration of statistical methods and their requirements. The main commentary is contained in chapters on the logic of factor analysis, rotation, interpretation of factors and the role of factor analysis. Here the arguments advanced can be held to suffer from their brevity and may be found persuasive rather than logically compelling. With qualifications, therefore, the book has much to recommend it as a teaching device, and it is of interest for its straightforward presentation and comparisons of the principal methods of group factor analysis."

BARNES, R. M. *WORK SAMPLING*
1957. 2nd Ed., Wiley, x+283 pp.

Chapter	Contents
1	Introduction
2	History of Work Sampling
3	Fundamental Statistical Concepts Pertaining to Work Sampling
4	Control Charts
5	Practical Suggestions for Determining Sample Size
6	Demonstrations that Aid in Explaining How Sampling Works
7	Use of Random Number Tables
8	Procedure for Making a Work Sampling Study
9	Determining Time Standards by Work Sampling
10	Two Work Sampling Studies: A Study of Inspectors; Tool Room Machine Utilization
11	Methods Study by Random Sampling
12	Work Sampling of the Supervisor's Job
13	Sampling Technique for Determining the Percentage of a Sugar Cane Field to be Replanted
14	Work Sampling Study of How School Teachers Utilize their Time
15	Work Sampling Study of Personnel in a Hospital
16	Four Work Sampling Studies
17	A Study of Direct Factory Labor before Installation of a Work Measurement Program
18	Incentives for Indirect Labor—Warehouse Handling Group
19	Determination of Indirect Labor Allowances for Trucking and Set-up by Performance Sampling

20   Work Sampling and Waiting-Line Theory for Demand-Type Labor Allowances
21   Industrial Application of the Ratio-Delay Method
22   Performance Sampling in Work Measurement
23   Test to Determine Validity of Performance Rating in Conjunction with Work Sampling
24   A Snap-Reading Method of Making Time Studies of Machines and Operatives in Factory Surveys

J. Amer. Statist. Ass., 1958, **53**, 625.

" Ralph M. Barnes has assembled in this small book a working manual for those who have need of sampling techniques to obtain reliable information about working time, performance rating, indirect incentive measurement, demand, and allowances. . . . Barnes shows that work sampling is a rapid and economical means of obtaining the information necessary for such diverse purposes as setting work standards for indirect labour, improvement of work methods in nonrepetitive tasks, determination of amount of work to be performed, and the setting of allowances for different kinds of work. . . . The book has been written primarily for the engineer who has little or no statistical background. . . . The author emphasizes the importance of randomness in the work sampling procedures and provides several pages of random digits. . . . One of the interesting parts of the book is Chapter 22, in which Barnes reports the results of 14 different studies in 8 different companies. . . . While the book may be of little interest to statisticians, it should be valuable for industrial engineers in two ways. It presents a clear and interesting description of work sampling as a tool. Secondly, it illustrates how statistical techniques can be used by industrial engineers to reduce their work and improve the reliability of their recommendations and conclusions."

BROOKS, C. E. P. AND CARRUTHERS, N. *HANDBOOK OF STATISTICAL METHODS IN METEOROLOGY* 1953. H.M.S.O., viii+412 pp.

Chapter   *Contents*
1   Nature of observations

2	Probability
3	One-Dimensional Frequency Distributions
4	Mean Values
5	Parameters of Frequency Distributions. Standard Errors and Tests of Significance
6	Binomial Distribution
7	Normal Frequency Distribution
8	Other One-Dimensional (Empirical) Distributions
9	Analysis of Variance
10	Frequencies of Related Variables. Space Distributions
11	Distributions of Vector Quantities
12	Simple Correlation
13	Partial Correlation
14	Smoothing and Interpolation
15	Curve-fitting
16	Persistence
17	Periodicity. Introduction
18	Harmonic Analysis
19	Periodograms Based on Harmonic Analysis
20	Correlogram and Similar Methods
21	Selective Methods
22	Survey of Methods of Analysis

J. R. Statist. Soc. A, 1953, **116**, 460.

"This cheap and well printed work has a more than usual authority, being issued by the Meteorological Office of the Air Ministry. Not all methods advocated in it have the same respectability as its sponsor but this is no matter for regret. On the contrary, it is a very encouraging thing that a Government Department should promote a publication by two of its most devoted employees. . . . Methodologically speaking, the most interesting part of the work is the third, on time series. . . . Owing to the official cachet on this work a reviewer would feel justified in being particularly critical of it. But I confess to a strong desire to refrain from harrying pioneers. The important thing is that the authors have produced for the first time a book which surveys the field and gives abundant references. All meteorologists and many statisticians can read it with profit. It should do much to promote improvements in the analysis of meteorological data and to stimulate further work on the theoretical tools required for that analysis."

CATTELL, R. B. *FACTOR ANALYSIS*
1952. Harper, xiii+462 pp.

Chapter	Contents
1	The Place of Factor Analysis in Scientific Method
2	Interpretation of Correlations as Clusters and Factors
3	On Obtaining Factors from a Correlation Matrix
4	Extraction of Successive Factors
5	Rotation of Factors for Scientific Meaning
6	Factor Estimation and the Specification Equation
7	Unitariness in Relation to O-, P-, Q-, and R-Techniques
8	The Covariation Chart and the Possibilities of Obliqueness, Order, and Efficacy
9	The Chief Alternative Designs in Factorizing a Matrix
10	Working Methods for Centroid Extraction Including Communality Estimation
11	The Clustering Methods of Factor Extraction
12	The Elementary Spatial Computations in Rotations
13	The Special Problems of Oblique Factors
14	General Techniques and Criteria of Factor Resolution
15	The Basic Art of Rotation by Graphs
16	Other Specialized Techniques for Rotation
17	The Effects of Errors
18	True Factor Resolution and the Design of Experiment
19	The Chief Manipulatable Features in Classical Factor Analytic Experiment
20	Structuring Variables by Combinations of Factor Analysis with Controlled Experiment
21	Strategy and Tactics of Economy in Computing

Brit. J. Psychol., 1953, **44**, 78.
" It is indeed a fine piece of work—clearly and very objectively written, and packed with interesting ideas and helpful illustrations. Parts of it, however, are very heavy-going and the book hardly succeeds in providing the working manual which any Ph.D. student

could follow, for which there is a great need. . . . Factor analysis, for Prof. Cattell, is by no means confined to exploratory studies of mental organization and classification. He makes ambitious claims and presents strong arguments, for its wider use in general psychological research, and its combination with classical experimental, or with modern Fisherian techniques. The psychologist or statistician who is suspicious of the whole topic should certainly study Parts I and III with care. A number of doubts, nevertheless, still remain in the reviewer's mind."

J. R. Statist. Soc. A, 1953, **116**, 462.

" If this book had given a reasonably simple exposition of factor analysis methods and had not launched forth into extravagant claims it might have been a good book. . . . Although, because of its lack of balance in discussing statistical techniques the book seems hardly suitable as an introduction for undergraduates, it is a very useful comprehensive text for those whose knowledge of statistics is sufficiently advanced to enable them to take or leave the arguments in accordance with their own experience and ideas. The examples should facilitate computations and the mathematically unskilled should be able to follow the routines laid down and to grind out an answer."

FINNEY, D. J. *AN INTRODUCTION TO STATISTICAL SCIENCE IN AGRICULTURE*
    1953. Oliver & Boyd, 179 pp.

Chapter	Contents
1	The Need for Statistics
2	Some Problems of Rates and Frequencies
3	Probability
4	Properties and Uses of Distributions
5	An Experiment to Compare Two Varieties
6	The Reduction of Error
7	Factorial Design
8	Sampling
9	Correlation and Regression

J. Amer. Statist. Ass., 1954, **49**, 389.

" I have long held the view that the research scientist's most urgent statistical need is for an appreciation of the essential ideas of the design and analysis of experiments, and that those ideas can be appreciated without recourse to mathematics. Therefore I expect Finney's book will probably have wide appeal, and it seems well suited to its purpose of conveying appreciation of principles. An important feature of the book is its stress on the relation between the research worker and the statistician, and the continual emphasis on the desirability of expert statistical advice at all stages of the work but especially before experimentation is begun. This culminates in the ' Valediction ', with its twelve rules of respectable statistical conduct for research workers."

J. R. Statist. Soc. A, 1953, **116**, 325.

" In presenting this book, which developed from his lectures, Dr. Finney has adopted a scheme of presentation which students approaching statistics for the first time should find very useful. He emphasizes the principles of statistics so that the student shall understand the purposes that it can serve and know when statistical method is appropriate to any problem. Algebraic and arithmetic detail are consequently minimized and in Dr. Finney's words, ' Nevertheless I am here much less concerned that my readers shall learn to make a t-test, or to calculate a standard error of sampling, than that they should appreciate the advantages of careful choice of experimental designs, the chief features of a good sampling investigation, the need for objective statistical analysis of data, the logical basis of significance tests, and related topics.' This objective is achieved in a clear and detailed account that is full of useful practical examples and advice to the agriculturist. . . . The book concludes with a valediction consisting of twelve rules, which, if followed, would save much needless work and simplify the presentation of any that is performed."

LYLE, P. *REGRESSION ANALYSIS OF PRODUCTION COSTS AND FACTORY OPERATIONS*
    1957. 3rd Ed., revised by L. H. C. Tippett, Oliver and Boyd, xvi + 204 pp.

Chapter   Contents
   1   Introduction

2	Preparation of Data
3	Analysis of Short-Term Changes
4	Additional Variates
5	Accuracy of Estimates
6	Summary of Analysis
7	Analysis of Long-Term Changes
8	Price and Wages Levels
9	Unit Costs
10	Outliers
11	Fully Worked-Out Examples
12	Conclusion

Appl. Statist., 1958, **7**, 132.

" The book, written ' with the main object of trying to interest industrial workers in a very useful subject ' (original preface), had in mind the accountant and technologist as readers. It has probably been useful as a primer in regression analysis, but it is doubtful if the cost application has made much impression on the accountant. This is regrettable and is probably indicative of poor communication between statisticians and accountants. . . . but the time may have come, with the publication of the third edition, to think again about the possible application of statistical methods to factory costs. If the accountant might benefit from a knowledge of statistics it is equally true that the industrial statistician might benefit from a critical appreciation of the meaning of costs—particularly if he is engaged in linear programming or other operational research exercises."

Biometrika, 1958, **45**, 286.

" This well-produced book contains a wealth of material much of which will appeal to a professional statistician as well as to the industrialist with a moderate mathematical equipment who would like to learn something of statistics."

J. Amer. Statist. Ass., 1958, **53**, 220.

" This third edition prepared by L. H. C. Tippett after the death of the author, corrects the known errors in the second edition. Tippett has also ' taken the liberty of inserting a very few interpolations which are enclosed in square brackets '. He has also added

about two pages of very sound and useful comments in his Preface to the third edition."
J. R. Statist. Soc. A, 1958, **121**, 113.
" Any major revision of the text of the book would be a most difficult task, since the style of construction and the methods of working are so individual. . . . The main subject matter of the book is the fitting of regression lines to observations of weekly output and total costs for the week, and the difficulties are present which always arise when the statistician has to take data that are available rather than to collect his information by experiment. . . . In his preface to the new edition Mr. Tippett mentions some of the difficulties to be faced, and it is to be hoped that he will feel justified in incorporating some new paragraphs in the text itself when a fourth edition is called for."

THOMSON, G. H. *FACTORIAL ANALYSIS OF HUMAN ABILITY* 1950. 4th Ed., London University Press, xv+394 pp.

Chapter	Contents
1	The Theory of Two Factors
2	Multiple Factor Analysis
3	The Sampling Theory
4	The Geometrical Picture
5	Hotelling's " Principal Components "
6	Estimation and the Pooling Square
7	The Estimation of Factors by Regression
8	Maximising and Minimising the Specifics
9	Sampling Error and the Theory of Two Factors
10	Multiple-Factor Analysis with Fallible Data
11	The Influence of Univariate Selection on Factorial Analysis
12	The Influence of Multivariate Selection
13	Reversing the Roles
14	The Relation between Test Factors and Person Factors
15	The Definition of " g "
16	" Orthogonal Simple Structure "

17	Limits to the Extent of Factors
18	Oblique Factors, and Criticisms
19	Second-Order Factors
20	Sampling of Bonds
21	The Maximum Likelihood Method of Estimating Factor Loadings
22	Some Fundamental Questions

Reviews of 2nd Ed.:

J. Amer. Statist. Ass., 1947, **42**, 199.

" This book should be read by everyone interested in factor analysis. . . . As an example of the difficulties of interpretation which can and do arise in applying the quantitative method, it is of interest to all statisticians . . . considers only the application of factor analysis to mental testing . . . his comments are so well-chosen and searching that they are required reading for anyone interested in any application of factor analysis. . . .

" . . . All important principles of factor analysis are discussed but not all computational procedures. The numerical processes outlined are based on Aitken's compact and rigid schemes."

J. Amer. Statist. Ass., 1947, **42**, 342.

" . . . the reader should be warned that the book must be read in its entirety and in particular the Addenda must not be overlooked. . . . The book is more a treatise than a text. It contains no practice material, no exercise . . . far less emphasis on matrix algebra and routine for computation than is found in most of the books and articles on factor analysis . . . and far more emphasis on underlying philosophy, meanings and interpretation. . . .

" No serious student can afford to remain unfamiliar with this book. . . ."

Review of 3rd Ed.:

Brit. J. Educ. Psychol., 1949, **19**, 65.

" The fact that this standard work has now reached the third edition, is a testimony both to the high standard of the treatment of a difficult subject, and to the increasing interest in statistics as applied to psychology . . . the book is now, more than ever, an essential textbook for the statistical psychologist."

THURSTONE, L. L. *MULTIPLE FACTOR ANALYSIS*
1947. Chicago University Press, xix+535 pp.

Chapter	Contents
	Mathematical Introduction
1	The Factor Problem
2	Fundamental Equations
3	Geometrical Models
4	A Factor Problem in Two Dimensions
5	The Grouping Method of Factoring
6	Factors as Explanatory Concepts
7	The Spherical Model
8	The Centroid Method of Factoring
9	Configurations and Factor Patterns
10	Rotation of Axes
11	The Method of Extended Vectors
12	The Special Case of Unit Rank
13	The Unknown Communalities
14	The Simple Structure Concept
15	Oblique Structure
16	Factorial Invariance
17	Alternative Methods of Rotation
18	Second-Order Factors
19	The Effects of Selection
20	The Principal Axes
21	The Appraisal of Individual Abilities

J. Amer. Statist. Ass., 1947, **42**, 651.

" While the factor problem originated in connection with psychological data, almost no psychology will be found discussed . . . regards multiple factor analysis to be a general scientific tool which may be appropriate in many different sciences apart from psychology . . . exploration by the techniques of multiple-factor analysis may show how to construct a meaningful frame of reference for the variables. . . .

" . . . It would be unfortunate, however, if certain algebraic routines became a substitute for thinking. It would be a setback for psychology—or any other discipline if students were so drilled that, on being confronted with a table of correlations, they would automatically ' multiple-factor ' it. Thurstone has contributed perhaps more than anyone else to the opening of the eyes of psychologists and other social scientists to the world of multivariate analysis. It is a subtle world, and perhaps not tractable to any single approach for examining its structure in different situations."

TIPPETT, L. H. C. *TECHNOLOGICAL APPLICATIONS OF STATISTICS*
1952. Williams and Norgate, ix + 189 pp.

Chapter	Contents
1	The Measurement of Quality
2	Theory of the Control Chart
3	Practical Application of the Control Chart Procedure
4	Statistical and Technical Details in Applying the Control Chart Procedure
5	Control of the Fraction Defective
6	Special Applications and Adaptations of the Control Chart
7	Acceptance Sampling
8	Experimentation and the Statistical Theory of Errors
9	Practial Application of the Statistical Theory of Errors
10	Applications of the Analysis of Variance: Basic Forms
11	Applications of the Analysis of Variance: Composite Forms
12	Applications of Correlation Analysis
13	Planning an Investigation

Appl. Statist., 1952, **1**, 148.

" In a book of this sort it is important that the basic principles are fully explained, and this is one of the strong points of Mr. Tippett's book. Particularly well presented are the chapters on significance testing and the precision of estimates and confidence limits, although the reviewer would have liked a greater shift of emphasis to the use of confidence limits at the expense of tests of significance. Mr. Tippett intends this book as an introduction and companion to a systematic text-book or course of study in applied statistics. In this he has been successful. The book is well suited for a first reading of statistical methods for industrial technicians and students."

J. R. Statist. Soc. A, 1953, **116**, 88.

" This book is based on a series of lectures given by Mr. Tippett early in 1948 at the Massachusetts Institute of Technology. It makes no pretence of standing on its own, and is intended ' as an introduction and companion to a systematic text-book or course of study in applied statistics '. In this lies its chief value to students of all kinds, for although it makes constant use of many aspects of the theory, it does not attempt to give an outline of the theory and the reader is frequently advised to refer to appropriate text-books. While the book is obviously of great value to a technician in industry starting to study and to apply statistical methods, its value to the student of theory is equally important. Although the book makes no new approach to the development of theory it puts theory in the correct perspective. . . . The only complaint to be made about this book is that it does not deal with all those aspects of the subject on which the author's opinion would be of interest. . . . These defects are, however, slight, particularly when compared with the great merits of the book, and it will be surprising if the book did not take a permanent place in statistical literature and become a classic in its own field."

VANCE, L. L. AND NETER, J. *STATISTICAL SAMPLING FOR AUDITORS AND ACCOUNTANTS*
    1956. Wiley, x+310 pp.

Chapter   *Contents*
   1   Need for Statistical Sampling Techniques in Auditing
   2   Some Basic Sampling Concepts
   3   Introduction to Statistical Decision Making
   4   Important Aspects of Acceptance Sampling Plans
   5   Choosing an Acceptance Sampling Plan from Published Tables
   6   Calculation of Acceptance Sampling Plans and Related Considerations

7	Problems in Applying Statistical Acceptance Sampling Methods in Auditing
8	Controlling the Accuracy of Clerical Work
9	Introduction to Statistical Estimation
10	Simple Random Sampling
11	Stratified Random Sampling and other Sampling Procedures
12	Special Topics in Estimation
13	Sampling Accounting Records and Physical Property: Case Illustrations
14	Organization in the Auditor's Office for Utilization of Statistical Sampling Techniques

Inc. Statist., 1957, **8**, 47.

" The background of the book is essentially American, with examples drawn mainly from large scale enterprises. Nevertheless, the book should commend itself to a wide circle of accountants in this country as some of the applications of sampling techniques may well be of value in smaller businesses, when sufficient experience has been gained. . . . The book is well written and will repay careful study. The examples are numerous and clearly set out and there are a number of excerpts from published tables."

J. Amer. Statist. Ass., 1957, **52**, 268.

" The treatment of the subject is largely from the point of view of the external auditor. From this viewpoint, the choice of topics for presentation, and the relative amount of space devoted to each topic, seems very good on the whole. The use of illustrations from the auditing field will doubtless make the discussion more intelligible to accountants than the usual presentation in statistical literature. . . . The principal defect in the book is the poor English composition in many places. . . . Most accountants who read this book from cover to cover will learn a good deal about sampling theory and its application to accounting problems. There now appears to be no other single volume where they can find nearly all the essentials on how to apply this theory in their own accounting work."

J. Inst. Actuar., 1957, **83**, 67.

" An American professor of accounting and a professor of

statistics have collaborated to produce an excellent practical textbook on sampling. Not only is it thoroughly practical and technically sound but also, once the American statistical jargon is mastered, easy to read, and one that should be read. . . . The major part of the work deals with simple and multiple sampling from a binomial population of accounting entries or calculations that are either correct or incorrect. The remainder concerns itself with the estimation, by sampling from a normal population, of a variable such as the average cost per item for the calculation of stock values."

J. R. Statist. Soc. A, 1957, **120**, 225.

" This book consists largely of an attempt to present to auditors the modern statistical techniques for sampling which might be used in situations, such as test checks, where sampling of a rather more rough and ready kind is already in use; it does, however, also attempt to suggest that sampling methods might be used in other accounting situations where they have not so far been extensively used. Apart from various discussions of actual or possible applications of the methods in auditing practice, the book's main contents are expositions first of the techniques of acceptance sampling and then of statistical estimation. . . . The authors leave an impression of meticulous care in their presentation of the statistical techniques. When the methods given in the text are not exact, attention is frequently drawn to the fact in a footnote—although the reader for whom the book is intended will often be unable to understand the footnote. . . . Despite the book's lack of statistical theory, the authors have succeeded admirably in presenting the methods of statistical sampling, and their book may well become a standard work on the application of such methods in auditing."

YOUDEN, W. J. *STATISTICAL METHODS FOR CHEMISTS*
    1951. Wiley, x+126 pp.

Chapter	Contents
1	Precision and Accuracy
2	The Measurement of Precision
3	The Comparison of Averages
4	The Resolution of Errors

5   Statistics of the Straight Line
6   The Analysis of Variance
7   Interaction Between Factors
8   Requirements for Data
9   Arrangements for Improving Precision
10 Experiments with Several Factors

Appl. Statist., 1952, **1**, 148.

" This book represents an attempt to give the analytical chemist of some maturity an idea of the application to his work of significance testing and experimental design. The style is discursive rather than systematic; formulae are very infrequent, and techniques are presented mainly through examples. . . . In the reviewer's opinion, the book will be most useful when studied with a standard introductory text-book, when it may help chemists a good deal in applying statistics. It does not speak sufficiently clearly about principles to stand alone as an introduction, nor is it comprehensive or systematic enough to serve as a general reference book."

J. R. Statist. Soc. A, 1952, **115**, 437.

" The book is unashamedly of the ' cook-book ' type, theory and proofs being completely omitted. Dr. Youden realizes the dangers of this approach, but balances them against the ease with which the non-mathematician can find his way about. One result is that the various methods are justified by examples of their use in a way which should convince the practical worker better than pages of mathematics. It is a pity, however, that there are very few references from which the worker with a liking for mathematics could trace out the theory underlying the mathematics. A great deal of dead wood which encumbers the usual course of statistics has been cut out. . . . The style of writing is informal. . . . The discussion of basic principles is excellent, with a continual insistence on the link between the analysis and the method of collecting the data. . . . On the whole, Dr. Youden's book can be recommended to any laboratory worker who wants to know what statistics is for and how it can help him in his work, though he may not find it altogether convenient for day to day use."

Nature, 1952, **170**, 219.

" In this short book, chemists are shown not only how to use statistical analysis but also why to use it and how to plan investigations so that numerical observations will be made to the best advantage. Dr. W. J. Youden writes as one of the few chemists who have studied and practised modern techniques of statistics: his book is full of the wisdom that comes from long experience of his subject-matter. The book is elementary and well suited for a reader without previous knowledge of statistics. . . the emphasis is on general principles rather than details of interpretation and the chemist concerned with elaborate experiments would probably need further guidance from another book. . . . Perhaps the most surprising point is the complete absence of discussion of discrete variation: neither χ^2 nor the binomial distribution is mentioned. . . . Such flaws are inevitable in so short a book."

JOURNALS CONSULTED FOR REVIEWS

CONTRACTED TITLES	FULL TITLES
Ann. Eugen.	Annals of Eugenics
Ann. Hum. Genet.	Annals of Human Genetics (London)
Appl. Statist.	Applied Statistics
Biometrika	Biometrika
Brit. J. Educ. Psychol.	British Journal of Educational Psychology
Brit. J. Psychol.	British Journal of Psychology
Econ. J.	Economics Journal
Economica	Economica
Econometrica	Econometrica
Eugen. Rev.	Eugenics Review
Inc. Statist.	Incorporated Statistician
J. Amer. Statist. Ass.	Journal, American Statistical Association
J. Inst. Actuar.	Journal of the Institute of Actuaries
J. R. Statist. Soc. A	Journal of the Royal Statistical Society Series A
Nature	Nature
Occupational Psychology	Occupational Psychology
Operat. Res.	Operations Research Society of America, Journal
Operat. Res. Quarterly	Operational Research Quarterly
Rev. Int. Statist. Inst.	Review International Statistical Institute
Sankhyā	Sankhyā
Social Forces	Social Forces
Sociological Review	Sociological Review

LIST OF PUBLISHING HOUSES

Academic Press
    111 5th Avenue, New York 3, USA
    Berkeley House, Berkeley Square, London, w. 1

Allen & Unwin, Ltd.
    40 Museum Street, London, w.c. 1

Almqvist & Wicksell
    26 Gamla Brogatan, Stockholm, Sweden

Bailey Bros. & Swinfen
    Hyde House, West Central Street, London, w.c. 1
    ALSO: Scarecrow Press, 257 Park Avenue S., New York 10, USA

Bokforlaget Borum, AB
    Stockholm, Sweden

Butterworth & Co. (Publishers) Ltd.
    88 Kingsway, London, w.c. 1

Cambridge University Press
    200 Euston Road, London, N.W. 1

Cassell & Co. Ltd.
    35 Red Lion Square, London, w.c. 1

Chelsea Publishing Co.
    50 E. Fordham Road, New York 68, USA

Chicago University Press
    Chicago 37, Illinois, USA

Columbia University Press
    2960 Broadway, New York 27, USA
    6A Bedford Square, London, w.c. 1

Dover Publications Inc.
    180 Varick Street, New York 14, USA

English Universities Press
    102 Newgate Square, London, E.C. 1
    Warwick Square, London, E.C. 4

Free Press
    Glencoe, Illinois, USA

Ginn & Co. Ltd.
    72, 5th Avenue, New York 11, USA
    18 Bedford Row, London, w. c. 1

Griffin & Co. Ltd.
    42 Drury Lane, London, w.c. 2

LIST OF PUBLISHING HOUSES

Handbook Publishers Inc.
    Sandusky, Ohio, USA
        ALSO: McGraw-Hill Publishing Co. Ltd.
        95 Farringdon Street, London, E.C. 4

William Heinemann Ltd.
    15 Queen Street, London, W. 1

Harper & Co. Ltd.
    8 Lloyds Avenue, London, E.C. 3

Home University Library (Oxford University Press)
    Amen House, Warwick Square, London, E.C. 4

Holt, Rinehart & Winston Inc.
    383 Madison Avenue, New York 17, USA

Hutchinson's University Library
Hutchinson's University Co. (Publishers) Ltd.
    178 Great Portland Street, London, W. 1

Iowa State University Press
    Press Building, Ames, Iowa, USA

Irwin
    1818 Ridge Road, Homewood, Illinois, USA

E. & S. Livingstone Ltd.
    48 Bloomsbury Street, London, W.C. 1

Macmillan & Co. Ltd.
    St. Martin's Street, London, W.C. 2

The Macmillan Co. New York
    10 South Audley Street, London, W. 1

Macdonald & Evans
    8 John Street, London, W.C. 1

McGraw-Hill Publishing Co. Ltd.
    95 Farringdon Street, London, E.C. 4

Melbourne University Press
    c/o Cambridge University Press, 200 Euston Road, London, N.W. 1

Methuen & Co. Ltd.
    36 Essex Street, London, W.C. 2

Einar Munksgaard, Copenhagen
    c/o Oliver & Boyd Ltd., 39A Welbeck Street, London, W. 1

North Holland Publishing Co.
    PO Box 103 Amsterdam, Netherlands

Oliver & Boyd Ltd.
    Tweeddale Court, 14 High Street, Edinburgh 1

Oxford University Press
    Amen House, Warwick Square, London, E.C. 4

LIST OF PUBLISHING HOUSES

Penguin Books Ltd.
    Harmondsworth, Middlesex
    303 High Holborn, London, w.c. 1

Pergamon Press Ltd.
    Headington Hill Hall, Oxford
    4 and 5 Fitzroy Square, London, w. 1

Pitman Publishers (Sir Isaac Pitman & Sons)
    39 Parker Street, London, w.c. 2

Prentice Hall International Inc.
    28 Welbeck Street, London, w. 1.

Princeton University Press
    Princeton, NJ, USA

Principia Press Inc.
    Bloomington, Indiana, USA

Reinhold Publishing Corporation
    c/o Chapman & Hall, 37 Essex Street, London, w.c. 2

Routledge & Kegan Paul Ltd.
    68 Carter Lane, London, E.C. 4

Row Peterson & Co.—now Harper & Row Publishers
    49E 33 Street, New York 16, USA

Stanford University Press
    Stanford, California, USA

Scarecrow Press Inc.
    257 Park Avenue S., New York 10, USA
        ALSO: Bailey Bros. & Swinfen, Hyde House, West Central Street, w.c. 1

Simon & Schuster Inc.
    630, 5th Avenue, New York 20, USA

Staples Press
    29 Portland Street, London, w. 1
        ALSO: Dryden Press Inc., New York, USA

University College, Department of Statistics
    Gower Street, London, w.c. 1

D. Van Nostrand Co. Inc.
    120 Alexander Street, Princeton, NJ, USA
    358 Kensington High Street, London, w. 14

John Wiley
    440 Park Avenue South, New York 16, USA
    Gordon House, Greencoat Place, London, s.w. 1
        ALSO: Technology Press, Mass. Inst. Technology

Williams & Norgate Ltd.
    Bouverie House, Fleet Street, London, E.C. 4

SUPPLEMENTARY LIST OF BOOK TITLES 1960-62

GENERAL INTRODUCTORY TEXTS
ELEMENTARY

GRIFFIN, J. I. *Statistics: Methods and Applications*
   1962   Holt, Rinehart and Winston Inc.   533 pp.
HAMMOND, K. R. and HOUSEHOLDER, J. E.   *Introduction to the Statistical Method*
   1962   Alfred A. Knopf Inc.
REICHMANN, W. J.   *Use and Abuse of Statistics*
   1961   Methuen   336 pp.
SMITH, G. M.   *A Simplified Guide to Statistics for Psychology and Education*
   1962   Holt, Rinehart and Winston Inc.   3rd Ed.
VESSELO, I. R.   *How to Read Statistics*
   1962   Harrap   208 pp.

INTERMEDIATE

CROW, E. L., DAVIS, F. A. and MAXFIELD, M. W.   *Statistics Manual with Examples taken from Ordnance Development*
   1960   Dover Publications Inc.   xvii+288 pp.
FREUND, J. E.   *Modern Elementary Statistics*
   1960   Prentice-Hall Inc.   x+413 pp.   2nd Ed.
MERRETT, A. J. and BANNOCK, G.   *Business Economics and Statistics*
   1962   Hutchinson   271 pp.
MUELLER, J. H. and SCHUESSLER, K. F.   *Statistical Reasoning in Sociology*
   1961   Houghton Mifflin Co.   xv+442 pp.
SPURR, W. A., KELLOG, L. S. and SMITH, J. H.   *Business and Economic Statistics*
   1961   Richard D. Irwin Inc.   xii+560 pp.   Rev. Ed.
WEINBERG, G. H. and SCHUMAKER, J. A.   *Statistics: an Intuitive Approach*
   1962   Wadsworth Publishing Co.   xii+338 pp.

ADVANCED

BOWKER, A. H. and LIEBERMAN, G. H.   *Engineering Statistics*
   1959   Prentice-Hall Inc.   xiv+585 pp.
EKEBLAD, F. A.   *The Statistical Method in Business*
   1962   Wiley   xii+791 pp.
MCNEMAR, Q.   *Psychological Statistics*
   1962   J. Wiley and Sons Inc.   3rd Ed.

MATHEMATICAL STATISTICS

GENERAL TEXTS

ALDER, H. L. and ROESSLER, E. B. *Introduction to Probability and Statistics*
  1962 W. H. Freeman and Co. xii+289 pp. 2nd Ed.
ALEXANDER, H. W. *Elements of Mathematical Statistics*
  1961 J. Wiley and Sons, Inc. xii+367 pp.
BAKER, G. A. *Statistical Techniques Based on Probabilistic Models*
  1962 University of California
BIRNBAUM, Z. W. *Introduction to Probability and Mathematical Statistics*
  1962 Harper and Brothers viii+325 pp.
FREUND, J. E. *Mathematical Statistics*
  1962 Prentice-Hall Inc. xiii+390 pp.
KEEPING, E. S. *Introduction to Statistical Inference*
  1962 D. Van Nostrand Co. Inc. xi+451 pp.
KENDALL, M. G. and STUART, A. *The Advanced Theory of Statistics: Vol. 2 Inference and Relationship*
  1961 Griffin ix+676 pp.
KOZELKA, R. M. *Elements of Statistical Inference*
  1961 Addison-Wesley Publishing Co. x+150 pp.
TUCKER, H. G. *An Introduction to Probability and Mathematical Statistics*
  1962 Academic Press xii+228 pp.
WADSWORTH, G. P. and BRYAN, J. G. *Introduction to Probability and Random Variables*
  1960 McGraw-Hill Book Co. Inc. vii+292 pp.
WILKS, S. S. *Mathematical Statistics*
  1962 J. Wiley and Sons Inc. xvi+644 pp.

SPECIAL TOPICS

GRAYBILL, F. A. *An Introduction to Linear Statistical Models Vol. 1*
  1961 McGraw-Hill Book Co. Inc. xiv+463 pp.
KULLDORFF, G. *Contributions to the Theory of Estimation from Grouped and Partially Grouped Samples*
  1961 Almqvist and Wiksell 144 pp.
LINNIK, YU. V. *Method of Least Squares and Principles of the Theory of Observations*
  1961 Pergamon Press Ltd. xii+360 pp.
MAXWELL, A. E. *Analysing Qualitative Data*
  1961 J. Wiley and Sons Inc. 163 pp.
MORAN, P. A. P. *The Statistical Processes of Evolutionary Theory*
  1962 Oxford University Press
SARHAN, A. E. and GREENBERG, B. G. *Contributions to Order Statistics*
  1962 J. Wiley and Sons Inc. xxv+482 pp.
SARNDAL, C. *Information from Censored Samples*
  1962 Almqvist and Wiksell 120 pp.

WAGNER, H. M. *Statistical Management of Inventory Systems*
  1962   J. Wiley and Sons Inc.   xiv+235 pp.
WALSH, J. E. *Handbook of Nonparametric Statistics*
  1962   D. Van Nostrand Co. Inc.   xxvi+549 pp.
ZACKRISSON, U. *A Study of Truncation and Censoring with Economic Subsidiary Conditions*
  1962   University of Goteborg   117 pp.

PROBABILITY AND STOCHASTIC PROCESSES

BARTLETT, M. S. *Stochastic Population Models in Ecology and Epidemiology*
  1960   J. Wiley and Sons Inc.   x+84 pp.
CHUNG, K. L. *Markov Chains with Stationary Transition Probabilities*
  1960   Springer-Verlag   ix+278 pp.
COX, D. R. *Renewal Theory*
  1962   J. Wiley and Sons Inc.   ix+142 pp.
COX, D. R. and SMITH, W. L. *Queues*
  1961   J. Wiley and Sons Inc.   xii+180 pp.
COX, R. T. *The Algebra of Probable Inference*
  1961   Johns Hopkins Press   xii+114 pp.
DAVID, F. N. and BARTON, D. E. *Combinatorial Chance*
  1962   Hafner Publishing Co.   x+356 pp.
GNEDENKO, B. V. *The Theory of Probability*
  1962   Chelsea Publishing Co.   459 pp.
GNEDENKO, B. V. and KHINCHIN, A. Y. *An Elementary Introduction to the Theory of Probability*
  1961   W. H. Freeman and Co.   139 pp.
GOLDBERG, S. *Probability: An Introduction*
  1960   Prentice-Hall Inc.   xiv+322 pp.
JEFFREYS, H. *Theory of Probability*
  1961   Oxford University Press   x+447 pp. 3rd Ed.
KHINTCHINE, A. Y. *Mathematical Methods in the Theory of Queueing*
  1960   Hafner Publishing Co.   120 pp.
MOSTELLER, F., ROURKE, E. K. and THOMAS, G. B. Jn. *Probability : A First Course*
  1961   Addison-Wesley Publishing Co.   xvi+319 pp.
MOSTELLER, F., ROURKE, E. K. and THOMAS, G. B. Jn. *Probability with Statistical Applications*
  1961   Addison-Wesley Publishing Co.   xvi+478 pp.
PARZEN, E. *Stochastic Processes*
  1962   Holden-Day Inc.
RIORDAN, J. *Stochastic Service Systems*
  1962   J. Wiley and Sons Inc.   x+139 pp.
ROBINSON, E. A. *Random Wavelets and Cybernetic Systems*
  1962   Charles Griffin and Co. Ltd.   x+125 pp.
ROSENBLATT, M. *Random Processes*
  1962   Oxford University Press   x+208 pp.

RUNNENBURG, J. T. *On the Use of Markov Processes in One-server Waiting-Time Problems and Renewal Theory*
    1960   University of Amsterdam   139 pp.

SAATY, T. L. *Elements of Queueing Theory: with Applications*
    1961   McGraw-Hill Book Co. Inc.   xv+423 pp.

SYSKI, R. *Introduction to Conjestion Theory in Telephone Systems*
    1960   Oliver and Boyd   xvi+742 pp.

TAKACS, L. *Introduction to the Theory of Queues*
    1962   Oxford University Press   x+268 pp.

WOLF, F. L. *Elements of Probability and Statistics*
    1962   McGraw-Hill Book Co. Inc.   xv+332 pp.

SAMPLE SURVEYS: THEORY AND PRACTICE

MANALANOBIS, P. G. *Experiments in Statistical Sampling in the Indian Statistical Institute*
    1961   Asia Publishing House   viii+70 pp.

MARK, M. L. *Statistics in the Marking: A Primer in Statistical Survey Method*
    1958   The Ohio State University   xxvi+436 pp.

SAMPFORD, M. R. *An Introduction to Sampling Theory with Applications to Agriculture*
    1962   Oliver and Boyd   xxiv+292 pp.

STUART, A. *Basic Ideas of Scientific Sampling*
    1962   Charles Griffin and Co. Ltd.   99 pp.

U.N. STATISTICAL OFFICE. *A Short Manual on Sampling. Vol. 1: Elements of Sample Survey Theory*
    1960   Statistical Office of the United Nations   vi+214 pp.

WEIBULL, C. *Some Aspects of Statistical Inference with Applications to Sample Survey Theory*
    1960   Statistical Institute of the University of Gothenburg.   87 pp.

ZARKOVICH, S. S. *Sampling Methods and Censuses: Vol. 1 Collecting Data and Tabulation*
    1961   Food and Agricultural Organization of the United Nations   iii+157 pp.

DESIGN OF EXPERIMENTS

KLEPIKOV, N. P. and SOKOLOV, S. N. *Analysis and Planning of Experiments by the Method of Maximum Likelihood*
    1962   Pergamon Press Ltd.   x+127 pp.

WINER, B. J. *Statistical Principles in Experimental Design*
    1962   McGraw-Hill Book Co. Inc.

QUALITY CONTROL AND INSPECTION

FEIGENBAUM, A. V. *Total Quality Control: Engineering and Management*
    1961   McGraw-Hill Book Co. Inc.   xii+627 pp.

WALLIS, P. N. *Quality Control in the Office*
    1961   Current Affairs Ltd.   190 pp.

ECONOMETRICS, TIME SERIES AND INDEX NUMBERS

SPENCER, M. H., CLARK, C. G. and HOGUET, P. W. *Business and Economic Forecasting*
    1961   Richard D. Irwin Inc. xii+412 pp.
THEIL, H. *Contributions to Economic Analysis: Economic Forecasts and Policy*
    1961   North Holland Publishing Co. xxxii+567 pp. 2nd Ed.

STATISTICAL DECISION AND INFORMATION THEORY

CHURCHMAN, C. W. *Prediction and Optimal Decision*
    1961   Prentice-Hall Inc. xiv+394 pp.
FANO, R. M. *Transmission of Information: A Statistical Theory of Communications*
    1961   J. Wiley and Sons Inc. x+389 pp.
LEE, Y. W. *Statistical Theory of Communication*
    1960   J. Wiley and Sons Inc. xvii+509 pp.
RAIFFA, H. and SCHLAIFER, R. *Applied Statistical Decision Theory*
    1961   Harvard Business School xxviii+356 pp.
SCHLAIFER, R. *Introduction to Statistics for Business Decisions*
    1961   McGraw-Hill Book Co. Inc. x+382 pp.
SHACKLE, G. L. S. *Decision Order and Time in Human Affairs*
    1961   Cambridge University Press xiv+302 pp.
WEISS, L. *Statistical Decision Theory*
    1961   McGraw-Hill Book Co. Inc. viii+195 pp.
WOLFOWITZ, J. *Coding Theorems of Information Theory*
    1961   Springer-Verlag x+125 pp.

DEMOGRAPHY, BIOMETRY AND MEDICAL STATISTICS

ARMITAGE, P. *Sequential Medical Trials*
    1960   Blackwell Scientific Publications 105 pp.
GERSHENSON, H. *Measurement of Mortality*
    1961   Society of Actuaries xii+340 pp.
HILL, A. B. *Principles of Medical Statistics*
    1961   The Lancet x+367 pp. 7th Ed.
HILL, A. B. *Statistical Methods in Clinical and Preventive Medicine*
    1962   Livingstone 610 pp.
MCARTHUR, N. *Introducing Population Statistics*
    1961   Oxford University Press xiv+137 pp.
PETERSEN, W. *Population*
    1961   Macmillan Co. xx+652 pp.

MISCELLANEOUS APPLICATION OF STATISTICAL METHODS

BAZOVSKY, I. *Reliability Theory and Practice*
   1962   Prentice-Hall Inc.   xii+292 pp.

CALABRO, S. R. *Reliability Principles and Practices*
   1962   McGraw-Hill Book Co. Inc.   xii+371 pp.

CYERT, R. M. and DAVIDSON, H. J. *Statistical Sampling for Accounting Information*
   1962   Prentice-Hall Inc.   224 pp.

DUNCAN, O. D., CUZZORT, R. P. and DUNCAN, B. *Statistical Geography: Problems in Analysing Areal Data*
   1961   Free Press of Glencoe Inc.   vii+191 pp.

FINNEY, D. J. *An Introduction to Statistical Science in Agriculture*
   1962   Ejnar Munksgaard   216 pp.   2nd Ed.

HERDAN, G. *Small Particle Statistics*
   1960   Butterworths   xxiii+418 pp.   2nd Ed.

LLOYD, D. K. and LIPOW, M. *Reliability: Management, Methods and Mathematics*
   1962   Prentice-Hall Inc.   528 pp.

MURPHY, T., NORRIS, K. P. and TIPPETT, L. H. C. *Statistical Methods for Textile Technologists*
   1960   The Textile Institute   107 pp.

PETERSON, E. L. *Statistical Analysis and Optimization of Systems*
   1961   J. Wiley and Sons Inc.   xii+190 pp.

TALBOT, P. A. and MULHALL, H. *A Physical Anthropology of Southern Nigeria: A Biometric Study in Statistical Method*
   1962   Cambridge University Press   xvi+127 pp.

WEIBULL, W. *Fatigue Testing and Analysis of Results*
   1961   Pergamon Press   xiii+305 pp.

INDEX OF AUTHORS
FOR BOOKS IN TEXT

Ackoff, R. L. 163
Acton, F. S. 92
Adcock, C. J. 268
Aitchison, J. 94
Aitken, A. C. 61
Allen, R. G. D. 1
Anderson, R. L. 62
Anderson, R. W. 96
Arley, N. 130

Bailey, N. T. J. 27
Bancroft, T. A. 62, 248
Barnes, R. M. 269
Bartlett, N. S. 131
Benjamin, B. 250
Bennett, C. A. 64
Bernstein, L. 29
Bharucha-Reid, A. T. 133
Bizley, M. T. C. 134
Blackwell, D. 236
Bliss, C. I. 251, 252
Bowley, A. L. 2
Brookes, B. C. 3
Brooks, C. E. P. 270
Bross, I. D. J. 238
Brown, J. A. C. 94
Brownlee, K. A. 65
Brunk, H. D. 66
Bryant, E. C. 41
Buch, K. R. 130
Burrington, R. S. 30

Calhoun, D. W. 252
Cantril, H. 164
Carruthers, N. 270
Cattell, R. B. 272
Chernoff, H. 239
Chew, V. 190
Cochran, W. G. 166, 192
Columbia Research Group 210
Connor, L. R. 5
Cowden, D. J. 7, 32, 211
Cox, D. R. 194

Cox, G. M. 192
Cox, P. R. 254
Craig, A. T. 75
Cramér, H. 67, 136
Croxton, F. E. 7, 32

Dalenius, T. 167
David, F. N. 9, 137
Davidson, D. 240
Davies, O. L. 42, 196
Davis, H. T. 223
Deming, W. E. 98, 169, 170
Derman, C. 33
Dick, W. F. L. 3
Dixon, W. J. 44
Dodge, H. F. 214
Doob, J. L. 139
Dubois, P. H. 99
Duncan, A. J. 215
Dynkin, E. B. 141

Edwards, F. 172
Emmens, C. W. 255
Ezekiel, M. 100

Federer, W. T. 197
Feller, W. 142
Ferguson, G. A. 45
Festinger, L. 174
Finney, D. J. 102, 199, 256, 273
Fisher, R. A. 47, 68, 201
Fox, K. A. 100
Franklin, N. L. 64
Fraser, D. A. S. 70, 104
Freund, J. E. 10
Fryer, H. C. 12

Girschick, M. 236
Goodman, R. 48
Goulden, C. H. 49
Grant, E. L. 218
Grenander, U. 144
Guilford, J. P. 258
Gumbel, E. J. 105

INDEX OF AUTHORS

Hald, A. 72
Hannan, E. J. 145
Hansen, M. H. 176
Hendricks, W. A. 177
Hill, A. B. 259
Hirsch, W. Z. 13
Hoel, P. G. 34, 74
Hogg, R. V. 75
Houthakker, H. S. 226
Hurwitz, W. N. 176
Hyman, H. H. 178, 179

Johnson, N. L. 76, 78
Johnston, J. 224
Juréen, L. 233

Karmel, P. H. 35
Katz, D. 174
Keeping, E. S. 83, 84
Kemeny, J. G. 146
Kempthorne, O. 202, 261
Kendall, M. G. 59, 79, 80, 81, 106, 107
Kenney, J. F. 83, 84
Kerrich, J. E. 147
Klein, L. R. 225
Klein, M. 33
Kolmogorov, A. N. 148
Kullback, S. 241

Lehmann, E. L. 109
Lev, J. 24, 57
Lindgren, B. W. 149
Loeve, M. 150
Lukacs, E. 111
Lyle, P. 274

Madow, W. G. 176
Mann, H. B. 204
Massey, F. J. 44
Mather, K. 263
May, D. C. 30
McCarthy, P. J. 15
McElrath, G. W. 149
McNemar, Q. 51
Mills, F. C. 36
Mood, A. M. 85
Moore, P. G. 16
Moran, P. A. P. 151

Moroney, M. J. 37
Morrell, A. J. M. 5
Morse, P. M. 152
Moser, C. A. 180
Moses, L. E. 239
Mounsey, J. 18

Neiswanger, W. A. 19
Neter, J. 280
Neyman, J. 154

Paradine, C. G. 86
Parzen, E. 155
Parten, M. 182
Payne, S. I. 183
Plackett, R. L. 113
Prais, S. J. 226

Quenouille, M. H. 21, 40, 52, 114, 116, 206

Rao, C. R. 87
Rhodes, E. C. 22
Riordan, J. 157
Rivett, B. H. P. 86
Roberts, H. V. 25
Robinson, E. A. 117
Romig, H. G. 214
Rosenblatt, M. 144
Roy, S. N. 119

Sanders, H. G. 208
Savage, L. J. 121
Schlaifer, R. 243
Scheffé, H. 124
Schrock, E. M. 219
Shewhart, W. A. 220
Slonin, M. J. 184
Snedecor, G. W. 54
Snell, J. L. 146
Spiegelman, M. 264
Steel, R. G. D. 55
Stuart, A. 81
Sukhatme, P. V. 185
Suppes, P. 240

Takács, L. 159
Tetley, H. 76, 78

INDEX OF AUTHORS

Theil, H. 227
Thomson, G. H. 276
Thurstone, L. L. 278
Tinbergen, J. 228
Tintner, G. 229
Tippett, L. H. C. 23, 89, 279
Torrie, J. H. 55
Tschuprow, A. A. 125

Valvanis, S. 231
Vance, L. L. 280
von Hofsten, E. 232
von Mises, R. 160

Wald, A. 127, 246
Walker, H. M. 24, 57
Wallis, W. A. 25
Weatherall, M. 29
Weatherburn, C. E. 89
Wilks, S. S. 27, 91
Williams, E. J. 128
Williams, F. J. 10
Wishart, J. 208
Wold, H. 161, 233
Wolfenden, H. H. 265

Yates, F. 187
Youden, W. J. 282
Yule, G. U. 59

Z
7553
M48I55
1963